DEFINING DOCUMENTS
IN WORLD HISTORY

# Pandemics, Plagues
# &
# Public Health

DEFINING DOCUMENTS
IN WORLD HISTORY

# Pandemics, Plagues
# &
# Public Health

**Volume 2**

Editor

Michael Shally-Jensen, PhD

SALEM PRESS
A Division of EBSCO Information Services, Inc.
Ipswich, Massachusetts

**GREY HOUSE PUBLISHING**

Publisher's Cataloging-In-Publication Data
(Prepared by The Donohue Group, Inc.)

Names: Shally-Jensen, Michael, editor.
Title: Pandemics, plagues & public health / editor, Michael Shally-Jensen, PhD.
Other Titles: Pandemics, plagues and public health | Defining documents in world history.
Description: Ipswich, Massachusetts : Salem Press, a division of EBSCO Information Services ; Amenia, NY : Grey House Publishing, [2020] | Includes bibliographical references and index.
Identifiers: ISBN 9781642657333 (set) | ISBN 9781642657357 (v. 1) | ISBN 9781642657364 (v. 2)
Subjects: LCSH: Epidemics--History--Sources. | Public health--History--Sources. | Substance abuse--History--Sources.
Classification: LCC RA649 .P36 2020 | DDC 614.49--dc23

FIRST PRINTING
PRINTED IN THE UNITED STATES OF AMERICA

# Table of Contents

## Volume 1

### SICKNESS UNTO DEATH IN EARLY TIMES

### DISEASE IN THE INDUSTRIAL ERA

# Volume 2

## DISEASE IN THE MODERN ERA

## SCOURGES OF WAR

## Substance Abuse and Public Health

## Appendixes

# DISEASE IN THE MODERN ERA

The HIV/AIDS epidemic of the 1980s produced a new kind of crises in the United States, with victims and activists pleading with federal and state governments to launch an all-out public health response, while conservative leaders in power, including members of the Reagan administration, were arguing on moral grounds that individual responsibility was the key, given that the disease primarily affected the LGBT community and users of intravenous drugs. Today, HIM/AIDS treatments have advanced and are less controversial than in the past.

The late twentieth century also saw much discussion about the safety of vaccinations, particularly the claim of a link between the measles, mumps and rubella (MMR) vaccine and autism. This has since been disproved and the 1998 research paper making the claim was retracted in 2004. Nonetheless, controversies about the safety of vaccinations continue to swirl and, although parents cannot be forced to vaccinate their children, unvaccinated children are not permitted to attend public or private schools.

The H1N1 swine flu pandemic started in 2009 and lasted nineteen months. It infected nearly 500,000 with nearly 20,000 confirmed deaths. In 2015, the Zika virus spread from Africa to the Americas, and was associated with birth malformations and neurological disorders.

In late 2019, a new coronavirus—COVID-19—quickly spread from China to every country around the globe. A controversy surrounding COVID-19 has erupted, similar to that of the AID/HIV epidemic in the 1980s, where the virus has become politicized in the United States and other countries (e.g. Britain, Brazil), whereas in most European Union (EU) and East Asian countries a coordinated response led to a downturn in the rate of infections and deaths. Early predictions by the Trump administration that the coronavirus would soon "disappear," and that control measures like wearing masks and practicing social distancing were unnecessary, quickly proved overly optimistic. By fall 2020, more than 6.5 million U.S. cases had been confirmed and nearly 200,000 deaths had occurred. The world-wide picture was similarly troubling, with about 29 million confirmed cases and over 925,000 deaths (and rising).

# ■ "1,112 and Counting"

**Date:** March 14, 1983
**Author:** Larry Kramer
**Genre:** Essay; article
**Geographic Region:** United States

## Summary Overview

Larry Kramer was already an accomplished writer; the AIDS epidemic made him an impassioned activist. He wrote the essay reprinted here for the *New York Native* in early 1983, less than two years into the deadly AIDS epidemic. In the piece, Kramer is direct and furious. The early years of the AIDS epidemic were harrowing, filled with chaos and confusion, as well as death and destruction. This arduous atmosphere is clear in Kramer's invective against everything from New York mayor Ed Koch to the National Institutes of Health to closeted gay doctors. The piece was meant to affect Kramer's initial audience, to upset and anger them, and most of all to rouse them to action. Glimpsed in the essay are Kramer's authorial potency and his passion for helping those effected by the AIDS epidemic, as well as his capacity to grate, vex, and push for conflict.

## Defining Moment

Heading into the 1980s, members of the Gay Rights movement had reasons to be cautiously optimistic. Their movement was growing. Ten years after the Stonewall riots, the National March on Washington for Lesbian and Gay Rights catapulted the movement onto the national stage. There was hope that the 1980s would see more progress towards acceptance and equality and away from discrimination, stigmatization, and bigotry. Then the AIDS epidemic tore through the gay community, spreading quickly and killing tens of thousands of Americans per year by the end of the decade. Beyond the death toll, the virus suffocated the Gay Rights movement's fragile progress and created an atmosphere of fear and distrust that reinvigorated stigmatization of the gay community.

On June 5th, 1981, the U.S. Centers for Disease Control and Prevention published the cases of five young men with rare infections and what looked to be immune deficiencies. Within days of the publication, a plethora of additional cases were reported to CDC, as were a sharp increase in cases of Kaposi's Sarcoma, an aggressive cancer. The majority of reported cases were concerning homosexual men clustered in Los Angeles, San Francisco, and New York. In the months and years that followed, the cases—and deaths—accumulated. This early period was filled with fear and confusion. It was not until February, 1983, that a doctor from the National Institutes of Health (NIH) suggested that the retrovirus HIV was responsible for AIDS; it was not until March of that year that CDC released a report suggesting that HIV/AIDS is communicable via sexual contact and blood. Before and even after this report, rumors and misinformation ran rampant. People were led to believe that you could contract the virus from hugging or kissing those with the virus or from using public toilets. Since the majority of cases were found in homosexual men, particularly in those early years, the virus sparked a wave of fear and bigotry against the gay community.

With people dying, misinformation and fear widespread, and healthcare and government officials struggling to keep up, AIDS organizations rose up to fill the void and help those in need. In 1982, Cleve Jones, Marcus Conant, Frank Jacobson, and Richard Keller founded the organization that would come to be known as the San Francisco AIDS Foundation. That same year, Larry Kramer brought together eighty men in his New York City apartment. This meeting led to the founding of Gay Men's Health Crisis. Other organizations, such as AIDS action, the American Foundation for AIDS Research, and ACT UP, followed in their wake. These organizations fought for, among other things, the allocation of resources and the spreading of reliable, lifesaving information.

Decades later, the virus persists. However, treatments have advanced to the point where a diagnosis is no longer seen as a death sentence. Moreover, as ignorance gives way to knowledge and fear dissipates, the stigma that the virus brought upon the gay community is being combatted and wiped away. This would not have been fathomable without the tireless work of AIDS activists such as Larry Kramer.

## Author Biography

Larry Kramer is a prolific writer and tireless activist. Born on June 25, 1935 in Bridgeport, Connecticut, Kramer graduated from Yale in 1957 and first made his mark writing screenplays. His adaptation of D. H. Lawrence's novel *Women in Love* earned him an Academy Award nomination. Openly gay himself, his depiction of homosexual promiscuity and drug use in his 1978 novel *Faggots* earned him pushback from both the gay and the straight communities, yet the work resonated with enough people to make it instantly popular and, over time, influential. Kramer found himself on the frontlines of the AIDS epidemic as many of his friends contracted the virus when it first broke out in the early 1980s. He helped form Gay Men's Health Crisis (GMHC) as a response to the deadly outbreak and resultant stigma it brought upon the gay community. Kramer's manner was outspoken and confrontational, as witnessed in this 1983 article. Leaders of the GMHC, grated by his methods and pension for conflict, ousted him later that same year. He processed this tumultuous part of his life in the play *the Normal Heart*, which became an instant success. Still called to activism, he was influential in the founding of AIDS Coalition to Unleash Power (ACT UP), whose aggressive style suited his own better than GMHC had. In 1988, Kramer was diagnosed with HIV, the virus he had already been fighting for the better half of a decade. The diagnosis only intensified Kramer's writing and activism. *The Destiny of Me*, Kramer's sequel to *the Normal Heart*, became a finalist for the Pulitzer Prize for Drama. Kramer lives in New York and Connecticut with Daniel Webster. The two had a relationship in the 1970s, got back together in 1991, and married in 2013.

## HISTORICAL DOCUMENT: 1,112 and Counting

If this article doesn't scare the s*** out of you, we're in real trouble. If this article doesn't rouse you to anger, fury, rage, and action, gay men may have no future on this earth. Our continued existence depends on just how angry you can get.

I am writing this as Larry Kramer, and I am speaking for myself, and my views are not to be attributed to Gay Men's Health Crisis.

I repeat: Our continued existence as gay men upon the face of this earth is at stake. Unless we fight for our lives, we shall die. In all the history of homosexuality we have never before been so close to death and extinction. Many of us are dying or already dead.

Before I tell you what we must do, let me tell you what is happening to us.

There are now 1,112 cases of serious Acquired Immune Deficiency Syndrome. When we first became worried, there were only 41. In only twenty-eight days, from January 13th to February 9th [1983], there were 164 new cases - and 73 more dead. The total death tally is now 418. Twenty percent of all cases were registered this January alone. There have been 195 dead in New York City from among 526 victims. Of all serious AIDS cases, 47.3 percent are in the New York metropolitan area.

These are the serious cases of AIDS, which means Kaposi's sarcoma, Pneumocystis carinii pneumonia, and other deadly infections. These numbers do not include the thousands of us walking around with what is also being called AIDS: various forms of swollen lymph glands and fatigues that doctors don't know what to label or what they might portend.

The rise in these numbers is terrifying. Whatever is spreading is now spreading faster as more and more people come down with AIDS.

And, for the first time in this epidemic, leading doctors and researchers are finally admitting they don't know what's going on. I find this terrifying too - as terrifying as the alarming rise in numbers. For the first time, doctors are saying out loud and up front, "I don't know."

For two years they weren't talking like this. For two years we've heard a different theory every few weeks. We grasped at the straws of possible cause: promiscuity, poppers, back rooms, the baths, … anal intercourse, urine, semen, … saliva, sweat, blood, blacks, a single virus, a new virus, repeated exposure to a virus, amoebas carrying a virus, drugs, Haiti, voodoo, Flagyl [Metronidazole], constant bouts of amebiasis, hepatitis A and B, syphilis, gonorrhea.

I have talked with the leading doctors treating us. One said to me, "If I knew in 1981 what I know now, I would never have become involved with this disease." Another said, "The thing that upsets me the most in all of this is that at any given moment one of my patients is in the hospital and something is going on with him that I don't understand. And it's destroying me because there's some craziness going on in him that's destroying him." A third said to me, "I'm very depressed. A doctor's job is to make patients well. And I can't. Too many of my patients die."

After almost two years of an epidemic, there still are no answers. After almost two years of an epidemic, the cause of AIDS remains unknown. After almost two years of an epidemic, there is no cure.

Hospitals are now so filled with AIDS patients that there is often a waiting period of up to a month before admission, no matter how sick you are. And, once in, patients are now more and more being treated like lepers as hospital staffs become increasingly worried that AIDS is infectious.

Suicides are now being reported of men who would rather die than face such medical uncertainty, such uncertain therapies, such hospital treatment, and the appalling statistic that 86 percent of all serious AIDS cases die after three years' time.

If all of this had been happening to any other community for two long years, there would have been, long ago, such an outcry from that community and all its members that the government of this city and this country would not know what had hit them.

Why isn't every gay man in this city so scared ... that he is screaming for action? Does every gay man in New York want to die?

Let's talk about a few things specifically.

Let's talk about which gay men get AIDS.

No matter what you've heard, there is no single profile for all AIDS victims. There are drug users and non-drug users. There are the truly promiscuous and the almost monogamous. There are reported cases of single-contact infection.

All it seems to take is the one wrong f\*ck. That's not promiscuity - that's bad luck. Let's talk about AIDS happening in straight people.

We have been hearing from the beginning of this epidemic that it was only a question of time before the straight community came down with AIDS, and that when that happened AIDS would suddenly be high on all agendas for funding and research and then we would finally be looked after and all would then be well.

I myself thought, when AIDS occurred in the first baby, that would be the breakthrough point. It was. For one day the media paid an enormous amount of attention. And that was it, kids.

There have been no confirmed cases of AIDS in straight, white, non-intravenous-drug-using, middle-class Americans. The only confirmed straights struck down by AIDS are members of groups just as disenfranchised as gay men: intravenous drug users, Haitians, eleven hemophiliacs (up from eight), black and Hispanic babies, and wives or partners of IV drug users and bisexual men.

# RARE CANCER SEEN IN 41 HOMOSEXUALS

## Outbreak Occurs Among Men in New York and California —8 Died Inside 2 Years

By LAWRENCE K. ALTMAN

Doctors in New York and California have diagnosed among homosexual men 41 cases of a rare and often rapidly fatal form of cancer. Eight of the victims died less than 24 months after the diagnosis was made.

The cause of the outbreak is unknown, and there is as yet no evidence of contagion. But the doctors who have made the diagnoses, mostly in New York City and the San Francisco Bay area, are alerting other physicians who treat large numbers of homosexual men to the problem in an effort to help identify more cases and to reduce the delay in offering chemotherapy treatment.

The sudden appearance of the cancer, called Kaposi's Sarcoma, has prompted a medical investigation that experts say could have as much scientific as public health importance because of what it may teach about determining the causes of more common types of cancer.

### First Appears in Spots

Doctors have been taught in the past that the cancer usually appeared first in spots on the legs and that the disease took a slow course of up to 10 years. But these recent cases have shown that it appears in one or more violet-colored spots anywhere on the body. The spots generally do not itch or cause other symptoms, often can be mistaken for bruises, sometimes appear as lumps and can turn brown after a period of time. The cancer often causes swollen lymph glands, and then kills by spreading throughout the body.

If there have been - and there may have been - any cases in straight, white, non-intravenous-drug-using, middle-class Americans, the Centers for Disease Control isn't telling anyone about them. When pressed, the CDC says there are "a number of cases that don't fall into any of the other categories." The CDC says it's impossible to fully investigate most of these "other category" cases; most of them are dead. The CDC also tends not to believe living, white, middle-class male victims when they say they're straight, or female victims when they say their husbands are straight and don't take drugs.

Why isn't AIDS happening to more straights? Maybe it's because gay men don't have sex with them.

Of all serious AIDS cases, 72.4 percent are in gay and bisexual men.

Let's talk about "surveillance."

The Centers for Disease Control is charged by our government to fully monitor all epidemics and unusual diseases.

To learn something from an epidemic, you have to keep records and statistics. Statistics come from interviewing victims and getting as much information from them as you can. Before they die. To get the best information, you have to ask the right questions.

There have been so many AIDS victims that the CDC is no longer able to get to them fast enough. It has given up. (The CDC also had been using a questionnaire that was fairly insensitive to the lives of gay men, and thus the data collected from its early study of us have been disputed by gay epidemiologists. The National Institutes of Health is also fielding a very naive questionnaire.)

Important, vital case histories are now being lost because of this cessation of CDC interviewing. This is a woeful waste with as terrifying implications for us as the alarming rise in case numbers and doctors finally admitting they don't know what's going on. As each man dies, as one or both sets of men who had interacted with each other come down with AIDS, yet more information that might reveal patterns of transmissibility is not being monitored and collected and studied. We are being denied perhaps the easiest and fastest research tool available at this moment.

It will require at least $200,000 to prepare a new questionnaire to study the next important question that must be answered: How is AIDS being transmitted? (In which bodily fluids, by which sexual behaviors, in what social environments?)

For months the CDC has been asked to begin such preparations for continued surveillance. The CDC is stretched to its limits and is dreadfully underfunded for what it's being asked, in all areas, to do.

Let's talk about various forms of treatment.

It is very difficult for a patient to find out which hospital to go to or which doctor to go to or which mode of treatment to attempt.

Hospitals and doctors are reluctant to reveal how well they're doing with each type of treatment. They may, if you press them, give you a general idea. Most will not show you their precise numbers of how many patients are doing well on what and how many failed to respond adequately.

Because of the ludicrous requirements of the medical journals, doctors are prohibited from revealing publicly the specific data they are gathering from their treatments of our bodies. Doctors and hospitals need money for research, and this money (from the National Institutes of Health, from cancer research funding organizations, from rich patrons) comes based on the performance of

> **W**hy isn't every gay man in this city so scared … that he is screaming for action?

their work (i.e., their tabulations of their results of their treatment of our bodies); this performance is written up as "papers" that must be submitted to and accepted by such "distinguished" medical publications as the New England Journal of Medicine. Most of these "distinguished" publications, however, will not publish anything that has been spoken of, leaked, announced, or intimated publicly in advance. Even after acceptance, the doctors must hold their tongues until the article is actually published. Dr. Bijan Safai of Sloan-Kettering has been waiting over six months for the New England Journal, which has accepted his interferon study, to publish it. Until that happens, he is only permitted to speak in the most general terms of how interferon is or is not working.

Priorities in this area appear to be peculiarly out of kilter at this moment of life or death.

Let's talk about hospitals.

Everybody's full up, fellows. No room in the inn.
Part of this is simply overcrowding. Part of this is cruel.
Sloan-Kettering still enforces a regulation from pre-AIDS days that only one dermatology patient per week can be admitted to that hospital. (Kaposi's sarcoma falls under dermatology at Sloan-Kettering.) But Sloan-Kettering is also the second-largest treatment center for AIDS patients in New York. You can be near death and still not get into Sloan-Kettering.

Additionally, Sloan-Kettering (and the Food and Drug Administration) requires patients to receive their initial shots of interferon while they are hospitalized. A lot of men want to try interferon at Sloan-Kettering before they try chemotherapy elsewhere.

It's not hard to see why there's such a waiting list to get into Sloan-Kettering.

Most hospital staffs are still so badly educated about AIDS that they don't know much about it, except that they've heard it's infectious. (There still have been no cases in hospital staff or among the very doctors who have been treating AIDS victims for two years.) Hence, as I said earlier, AIDS patients are often treated like lepers.

For various reasons, I would not like to be a patient at the Veterans Administration Hospital on East 24th Street or at New York Hospital. (Incidents involving AIDS patients at these two hospitals have been reported in news stories in the Native.)

I believe it falls to this city's Department of Health, under Commissioner David Sencer, and the Health and Hospitals Corporation, under Commissioner Stanley Brezenoff, to educate this city, its citizens, and its hospital workers about all areas of a public health emergency. Well, they have done an appalling job of educating our citizens, our hospital workers, and even, in some instances, our doctors. Almost everything this city knows about AIDS has come to it, in one way or another, through Gay Men's Health Crisis. And that includes television programs, magazine articles, radio commercials, newsletters, health-recommendation brochures, open forums, and sending speakers everywhere, including - when asked - into hospitals. If three out of four AIDS cases were occurring in straights instead of in gay men, you can bet all hospitals and their staffs would know what was happening. And it would be this city's Health Department and Health and Hospitals Corporation that would be telling them.

Let's talk about what gay tax dollars are buying for gay men.

Now we're arriving at the truly scandalous. For over a year and a half the National Institutes of Health has been "reviewing" which from among some $55 million worth of grant applications for AIDS research money it will eventually fund.

It's not even a question of NIH having to ask Congress for money. It's already there. Waiting. NIH has almost $8 million already appropriated that it has yet to release into usefulness.

There is no question that if this epidemic was happening to the straight, white, non-intravenous-drug-using middle class, it that money would have been put into use almost two years ago, when the first alarming signs of this epidemic were noticed by Dr. Alvin Friedman-Kien and Dr. Linda Laubenstein at New York University Hospital.

During the first two weeks of the Tylenol scare, the United States Government spent $10 million to find out what was happening.

Every hospital in New York that's involved in AIDS research has used up every bit of the money it could find for researching AIDS while waiting for NIH grants to come through. These hospitals have been working on AIDS for up to two years and are now desperate for replenishing funds. Important studies that began last year, such as Dr. Michael Lange's at St. Luke's-Roosevelt, are now going under for lack of money. Important leads that were and are developing cannot be pursued. (For instance, few hospitals can afford plasmapheresis machines, and few patients can afford this experimental treatment either, since few insurance policies will cover the $16,600 bill.) New York University Hospital, the largest treatment center for AIDS patients in the world, has had its grant application pending at NIH for a year and a half. Even if the application is successful, the earliest time that NYU could receive any money would be late summer.

The NIH would probably reply that it's foolish just to throw money away, that that hasn't worked before. And, NIH would say, if nobody knows what's happening, what's to study?

Any good administrator with half a brain could survey the entire AIDS mess and come up with twenty leads that merit further investigation. I could do so myself. In any research, in any investigation, you have to start somewhere. You can't just not start anywhere at all.

But then, AIDS is happening mostly to gay men, isn't it?

All of this is indeed ironic. For within AIDS, as most researchers have been trying to convey to the NIH, perhaps may reside the answer to the question of what it is that causes cancer itself. If straights had more brains, or were less bigoted against gays, they would see that, as with hepatitis B, gay men are again doing their suffering for them, revealing this disease to them. They can use us as guinea pigs to discover the cure for AIDS before it hits them, which most medical authorities are still convinced will be happening shortly in increasing numbers.

(As if it had not been malevolent enough, the NIH is now, for unspecified reasons, also turning away AIDS patients from its hospital in Bethesda, Maryland. The hospital, which had been treating anyone and everyone with AIDS free of charge, now will only take AIDS patients if they fit into their current investigating protocol. Whatever that is. The NIH publishes "papers," too.)

Gay men pay taxes just like everyone else. NIH money should be paying for our research just like everyone else's. We desperately need something from our government to save our lives, and we're not getting it.

Let's talk about health insurance and welfare problems.

Many of the ways of treating AIDS are experimental, and many health insurance policies do not cover most of them. Blue Cross is particularly bad about accepting anything unusual.

Many serious victims of AIDS have been unable to qualify for welfare or disability or social security benefits. There are increasing numbers of men unable to work and unable to claim welfare because AIDS is not on the list of qualifying disability illnesses. (Immune deficiency is an acceptable determining factor for welfare among children, but not adults. Figure that one out.) There are also increasing numbers of men unable to pay their rent, men thrown out on the street with nowhere to live and no money to live with, and men who have been asked by roommates to leave because of their illnesses. And men with serious AIDS are being fired from certain jobs.

The horror stories in this area, of those suddenly found destitute, of those facing this illness with insufficient insurance, continue to mount. (One man who'd had no success on other therapies was forced to beg from his friends the $16,600 he needed to try, as a last resort, plasmapheresis.)....

\* \* \*

I am sick of our electing officials who in no way represent us. I am sick of our stupidity in believing candidates who promise us everything for our support and promptly forget us and insult us after we have given them our votes. Koch is the prime example, but not the only one. Daniel Patrick Moynihan isn't looking very good at this moment, either. Moynihan was requested by gay leaders to publicly ask Margaret Heckler at her confirmation hearing for Secretary of Health and Human Services if she could be fair to gays in view of her voting record of definite anti-gay bias. (Among other horrors, she voted to retain the sodomy law in Washington, D.C., at Jerry Falwell's request.) Moynihan refused to ask this question, as he has refused to meet with us about AIDS, despite our repeated requests. Margaret Heckler will have important jurisdiction over the CDC, over the NIH, over the Public Health Service, over the Food and Drug Administration - indeed, over all areas of AIDS concerns. Thank you, Daniel Patrick Moynihan. I am sick of our not realizing we have enough votes to defeat these people, and I am sick of our not electing our own openly gay officials in the first place. Moynihan doesn't even have an openly gay person on his staff, and he represents the city with the largest gay population in America.

I am sick of closeted gay doctors who won't come out to help us fight to rectify any of what I'm writing about. Doctors - the very letters "M.D." - have enormous clout, particularly when they fight in groups. Can you imagine what gay doctors could accomplish, banded together in a network, petitioning local and federal governments, straight colleagues, and the American Medical Association? I am sick of the passivity or nonparticipation or halfhearted protestation of all the gay medical associations (American Physicians for Human Rights, Bay Area Physicians for Human Rights, Gay Psychiatrists of New York, etc., etc.), and particularly our own New York Physicians for Human Rights, a group of 175 of our gay doctors who have, as a group, done nothing. You can count on one hand the number of our doctors who have really worked for us.

I am sick of the *Advocate*, one of this country's largest gay publications, which has yet to quite acknowledge that there's anything going on. That newspaper's recent AIDS issue was so innocuous you'd have thought all we were going through was little

Memorandum

ate JUL 3 0 1981

rom Director
Centers for Disease Control

Subject Kaposi's Sarcoma and Opportunistic Infections

To Vincent T. DeVita, Jr., M.D.
Director, National Cancer Institute
Through: Director, National Institutes of Health 7/3/61

A recently discovered outbreak of serious illnesses presents an opportunity
for the National Cancer Institute and the CDC to collaborate to address a
problem of significant public health concern and scientific importance. The
attached copies of the MMWR contain reports of 15 cases of *Pneumocystis carinii*
pneumonia and 26 cases of Kaposi's sarcoma (KS) among homosexual men in New York
City and California. All patients tested had evidence of previous or current
cytomegalovirus infection, while some were reported to be severely immuno-
suppressed. To date, we have received case reports from 105 patients with KS
and/or serious opportunistic infections without known underlying disorders.
Forty-eight of 51 men with histopathologically diagnosed KS were less than
50 years of age and 50 were homosexual. Ten of those 51 men have died. Due
to the unusual presentation and distribution of these KS cases, it is not
surprising that misdiagnoses, delays in diagnosis, and uncertainties about
therapy have been frequently reported.

Currently, surveillance and epidemiologic studies are needed to define the
scope of the KS problem. Studies designed to define possible microbiologic,
immunologic, and/or toxic roles in oncogenesis are also needed. These investigations could be coordinated with therapy trials.

The CDC has formed a multidisciplinary task force and has begun active
surveillance and case investigation. Dr. James Curran, coordinator of the
task force, and others at CDC, have already been in communication with
investigators in several NCI units. They have quickly learned of the depth
of experience and expertise NCI has to offer—specific to KS as well as all
areas of cancer investigation.

In order to encourage collaboration in current investigative efforts, we would
appreciate it if you would name an NCI contact person to coordinate interagency
communication with Dr. Curran (FTS 236-3935).

William H. Foege, M.D.
Assistant Surgeon General

Attachments

worse than a rage of the latest designer flu. And their own associate editor, Brent Harris, died from AIDS. Figure that one out.

With the exception of the New York Native and a few, very few, other gay publications, the gay press has been useless. If we can't get our own papers and magazines to tell us what's really happening to us, and this negligence is added to the negligent non-interest of the straight press (The New York Times took a leisurely year and a half between its major pieces, and the Village Voice took a year and a half to write anything at all), how are we going to get the word around that we're dying? Gay men in smaller towns and cities everywhere must be educated, too. Has the Times or the Advocate told you that twenty-nine cases have been reported from Paris?

I am sick of gay men who won't support gay charities. Go give your bucks to straight charities, fellows, while we die. Gay Men's Health Crisis is going crazy trying to accomplish everything it does - printing and distributing hundreds of thousands of educational items, taking care of several hundred AIDS victims (some of them straight) in and out of hospitals, arranging community forums and speakers all over this country, getting media attention, fighting bad hospital care, on and on and on, fighting for you and us in two thousand ways, and trying to sell 17,600 Circus tickets, too. Is the Red Cross doing this for you? Is the American Cancer Society? Your college alumni fund? The United Jewish Appeal? Catholic Charities? The United Way? ....

\* \* \*

I don't want to die. I can only assume you don't want to die. Can we fight together?

For the past few weeks, about fifty community leaders and organization representatives have been meeting at Beth Simchat Torah, the gay synagogue, to prepare action. We call ourselves the AIDS Network. We come from all areas of health concern: doctors, social workers, psychologists, psychiatrists, nurses; we come from Gay Men's Health Crisis, from the National Gay Health Education Foundation, from New York Physicians for Human Rights, the St. Mark's Clinic, the Gay Men's Health Project; we come from the gay synagogue, the Gay Men's Chorus, from the Greater Gotham Business Council, SAGE, Lambda Legal Defense, Gay Fathers, the Christopher Street Festival Committee, Dignity, Integrity; we are lawyers, actors, dancers, architects, writers, citizens; we come from many component organizations of the Gay and Lesbian Community Council.

We have a leader. Indeed, for the first time our community appears to have a true leader. Her name is Virginia Apuzzo, she is head of the National Gay Task Force, and, as I have said, so far she has proved to be magnificent.

The AIDS Network has sent a letter to Mayor Koch. It "contains twelve points that are urged for his consideration and action."....

\* \* \*

Volunteers Needed for Civil Disobedience

It is necessary that we have a pool of at least three thousand people who are prepared to participate in demonstrations of civil disobedience. Such demonstrations might include sit-ins or traffic tie-ups. All participants must be prepared to be arrested. I am asking every gay person and every gay organization to canvass all friends and members and make a count of the total number of people you can provide toward this pool of three thousand.

Let me know how many people you can be counted on providing. Just include the number of people; you don't have to send actual names - you keep that list yourself. And include your own phone numbers. Start these lists now.

L.K.

## GLOSSARY

**Koch:** Ed Koch, mayor of New York City from 1978 to 1989

## Document Analysis

Larry Kramer penned this essay in early 1983, at the height of the chaos and confusion of the early AIDS epidemic. That chaos and confusion comes through in the piece as the status quo against which Kramer pushes back. His essay is an eloquent and stirring call-to-action, addressed specifically to the American gay community and its allies; it calls them to rise up and fight against the spreading epidemic as well as the inertia of American society and the stigmatization of the gay community. The document allows us to see both the chaotic atmosphere of 1983 and Kramer's resilient response.

The context in which this document was written—the early years of the AIDS epidemic—is hard to imagine in retrospect. Decades later, the virus continues to plague our society, and we are generally aware that is has left a destructive wake. Yet the form and intensity of that history is often lost on those who did not experience it firsthand. This document captures the sheer confusion that marked those early years. People were getting sick and dying, but no one knew where the disease came from or how it was spreading. Kramer explains, "We grasped at the straws of possible cause: promiscuity, poppers, back rooms, the baths, … anal intercourse, urine, semen, … saliva, sweat, blood, blacks, a single virus, a new virus, repeated exposure to a virus, amoebas carrying a virus, drugs, Haiti, voodoo, Flagyl [Metronidazole], constant bouts of amebiasis, hepatitis A and B, syphilis, gonorrhea." The long list of potential causes and its overwhelmingly varied nature depict the desperation in the chaotic quest for understanding. Yet, as he explains, the quest had thus far been fruitless: "After almost two years of an epidemic, there still are no answers. After almost two years of an epidemic, the cause of AIDS remains unknown. After almost two years of an epidemic, there is no cure." The continued lack of answers only fueled more desperation.

Beyond desperation, Kramer showcases another key feature of the atmosphere of 1983, bigotry. The first victims of the AIDS epidemic were male homosexuals and other vulnerable members of society. This fact coupled with entrenched American prejudices caused the reaction to the outbreak to be one of othering and stigmatization as opposed to one of camaraderie and compassion. Kramer describes how he believed that America at large would begin to pay closer attention to the disease once the first baby, an innocent bystander if there ever were one, was diagnosed; he then relays his disappointment when the response to this event was short-lived. He details the groups of people that have been diagnosed so far: "The only confirmed straights struck down by AIDS are members of groups just as disenfranchised as gay men: intravenous drug users, Haitians, eleven hemophiliacs (up from eight), black and Hispanic babies, and wives or partners of IV drug users and bisexual men." As Kramer says, these groups all represent disenfranchised peoples in one form or another. In contrast to them, Kramer describes the privileged echelons of American society. These latter categories had not been affected by the epidemic: "There have been no confirmed cases of AIDS in straight, white, non-intravenous-drug-using, middle-class Americans." When he writes "middle-class," he means middle-class or higher. There has, since the writing of this essay, been confirmed cases of AIDS within this group he defines. However, given the identification of the earliest victims and the majority of victims till this day, AIDS remains in the eyes of many Americans an epidemic of homosexuals, minorities, and IV drug users. It was not through the spreading of the virus to more privileged groups that diminished the stigma associated with the virus but through the tireless work of advocates such as Kramer.

His voice throughout this piece is urgent, pressing his audience and rousing them to action. His background as a writer is evident in the piece's eloquence, but it's primary feature is its directness. Kramer immediately grabs his readers' attention: "If this article doesn't scare the s*** out of you, we're in real trouble." (The original publication did not censor out the curse word.) Kramer's directness expands well beyond the opening. He is not afraid to call out by name those individuals and organizations he considers to be falling short in their response to the epidemic. The Centers for Disease Control (CDC) is "stretched to its limits and is dreadfully underfunded for what it's being asked, in all areas, to do." He calls the New England Journal of Medicine a ""distinguished" publication," questioning its reputation with scare quotes. Most hospital staffs? "Still so badly educated about AIDS that they don't know much about it, except that they've heard it's infectious." Commissioner David Sencer, and the Health and Hospitals Corporation, under Commissioner Stanley Brezenoff? "They have done an appalling job of educating our citizens, our hospital workers, and even, in some instances, our doctors." Health Insurance companies are bad, but "Blue Cross is particularly bad." Our elected officials? "In no way represent us." Closeted gay doctors? "Won't come out to help us fight to rectify any of what I'm writing about." "The Advocate, one of this country's largest gay publications,… has yet to quite acknowledge that there's anything going on." Moreover, aside from a few exceptions, "the gay press has been useless." The sheer number of individuals and organizations that Kramer calls out is truly impressive, as is their wide range of fields. Kramer believes that by evoking these individuals and organizations by name he can either get their attention himself or provide targets whose attention his readers can attain. His directness, in this essay and elsewhere, sometimes landed Kramer in trouble; in fact, soon after the publication of this article, Gay Men's Health Crisis and Kramer parted ways, primarily over his confrontational tactics. However, those same tactics are what breath such vivacity into this document and how Kramer, throughout his life, garnered such support to combat this epidemic.

## Essential Themes

The theme of urgency courses throughout this entire document. It begins with the first sentence, "If this article doesn't scare the s*** out of you, we're in real trouble." If the promise of terror and the curse word do not grab your attention, Kramer continues, "If this article doesn't rouse you to anger, fury, rage, and action, gay men may have no future on this earth. Our continued existence depends on just how angry you can get…I repeat: Our continued existence as gay men upon the face of this earth is at stake. Unless we fight for our lives, we shall die. In all the history of homosexuality we have never before been so close to death and extinction." Such thoughts as death and extinction may seem like hyperbole in retrospect, but for those living through the first years of the AIDS epidemic, they properly captured the desperation of their circumstance. The premonition of extinction in the opening introduces the urgency behind Kramer's direct tone, examined in the Document Analysis section above. The urgency throughout the entire essay sets the stage for Kramer's plea at the closing of the document. "I don't want to die," he begins, "I can only assume you don't want to die. Can we fight together?" He then focuses on what he specifically wants from his audience: "Volunteers Needed for Civil Disobedience." He even details the first step he wants his readers to take, contacting him with the number of people (willing to be arrested) that each reader can provide for sit-ins and traffic tie-ups. At its core, the essay is a call-to-arms, the theme of urgency acts as a necessary catalyst in the spur to action.

—*Anthony Vivian, PhD*

## Bibliography and Additional Reading

France, David. *How to Survive a Plague: The Story of How Activists and Scientists Tamed AIDS*. New York: Vintage, 2017. Print.

# ◼ ACT UP Founding Document and Speech

**Dates:** March 1987; May 8, 1988
**Author:** AIDS Network, Vito Russo
**Genre:** broadside; speech

## Summary Overview

This document outlines the now infamous Don't Ask, Don't Tell policy concerning homosexuality in the military. (Note that we employ the term homosexuality here to describe those who engage in homosexual activity, bisexuality, etc.) This policy represented a stepping stone between the prohibition of homosexuals from the armed forces that was codified during World War II and the inclusive policy in place today. It reaffirmed the armed forces' long-standing ban on homosexuality, as the majority of the document is devoted to confirming and justifying this ban. However, the practice of questioning recruits about their sexual orientation was put to an end, allowing homosexuals to serve in the military, provided that they did not vocalize their sexual orientation. The policy remained in place for less than two decades before it was repealed alongside the restrictions of homosexuals in the United States military.

## Defining Moment

Discrimination against and discharges of homosexuals form the United States military range back to the eighteenth century. Homosexuals were regularly charged with sodomy and dishonorably discharged from the armed forces up through the First World War. In the Second World War, the ban on homosexuals was first codified within individual branches of the military. In 1949, the Department of Defense standardized the policy across all military branches, and this policy would remain in place until 1993.

All of the candidates in the Democratic primary of 1992 advocated for an end to the ban on homosexuals in the military, and the official party platform of that year included language outlining the same position. With his victory in both the Democratic primary and the general election, Bill Clinton assumed the responsibility to follow through on this campaign promise. Although the Democrats wielded a majority in both houses of Congress, they did not hold the

supermajorities necessary for Clinton to enact his agenda at will, and the president met strong resistance from Republicans regarding homosexuality in the military. He therefore sought this policy as a compromise that would appease hardline Republicans yet still allow him to say that he followed through on his campaign promise to allow individuals to serve in the military regardless of their sexual orientation. The compromise helped assure passage of the National Defense Authorization Act in which the policy appeared, despite the majority of Democrats' opposition. The policy was implemented upon passage, and anything regarding sexual orientation was removed from the questions asked of new recruits.

The policy remained in place for less than two decades until the election of Barack Obama in 2008 and a new push to remove the ban altogether. Congress enacted and President Obama signed a bill to repeal this policy in 2010, preceded and succeeded by extensive studies to ensure that any changes would not hinder the efficacy of the military. On September 20, 2011, the policy was officially repealed and homosexuals were finally allowed to serve openly in the military. In the debate to repeal Don't Ask, Don't Tell, the policy was vilified for discriminatorily forcing homosexuals to hide their sexual orientation. True as this may be, we should not forget that this policy, too, was originally implemented to increase the civil rights for homosexuals in the military. The speed with which views of this policy have shifted reflect the speed with which public opinion on homosexuality in general has changed in the early twenty-first century.

## Author Biography

The 103rd United States Congress, which served throughout 1993 and 1994, showcased majorities for the Democrats in both the Senate and the House of Representatives. This congress was solidified in the same 1992 elections in which Bill Clinton defeated incumbent George H.W. Bush for the presidency. President Clinton, who signed this Act into law, served as president throughout the entire 103rd Congress. The National Defense Authorization Act for Fiscal Year 1994, in which this policy first appeared, relied heavily on across-the-aisle Republican support for passage; the vast majority of Republicans in both houses voted for the Act, while a majority of Democrats in both houses voted against it. The 103rd United States Congress is also notable for ratifying the North American Free Trade Agreement and passing two pieces of gun control legislation, a Federal Assault Weapons Ban and the Brady Bill, which required federal background checks and a five-day waiting period for gun purchasers.

## HISTORICAL DOCUMENT: ACT UP Founding Document and Speech

Passed in Senate (63 to 33) on *September 9, 1993*
Passed in House (301 to 134) on *September 28, 1993*
1993 S. 1337; *SEPTEMBER 16, 1993*

SEC. 546.
Policy concerning homosexuality in the armed forces.
    (a) Codification.
    1.    Chapter 37 of Title 10, United States Code, is amended by adding at the end the following new section: 654. Policy concerning homosexuality in the armed forces

    (A) Findings. Congress makes the following findings:
    1.    Section 8 of Article I of the Constitution of the United States commits exclusively to Congress the powers to raise and support armies, provide and maintain and a navy, and make rules for the government and regulation of the land and naval forces.
    2.    There is no constitutional right to serve in the armed forces.
    3.    Pursuant to the powers conferred by Section 8 of Article I of the Constitution of the United States, it lies within the discretion of the Congress to establish qualifications for and conditions of service in the armed forces.
    4.    The primary purpose of the armed forces is to prepare for and to prevail in combat should the need arise.

5.    The conduct of military operations requires members of the armed forces to make extraordinary sacrifices, including the ultimate sacrifice, in order to provide for the common defense.

6.    Success in combat requires military units that are characterized by high morale, good order and discipline, and unit cohesion.

7.    One of the most critical elements in combat capability is unit cohesion, that is, the bonds of trust among individual service members that make the combact effectiveness of a military unit greater than the sum of the combat effectiveness of the individual unit members.

8.    Military life is fundamentally different from civilian life in that

(A) The extraordinary responsibilities of the armed forces, the unique conditions of military service, and the critical role of unit cohesion, require that the military community, while subject to civilian control, exist as a specialized society; and

(B) The military society is characterized by its own laws, rules, customs, and traditions, including numerous restrictions on personal behavior, that would not be acceptable in civilian society.

9.    The standards of conduct for members of the armed forces regulate a member's life for 24 hours each day beginning at the moment the member enters military status and not ending until that person is discharged or otherwise separated from the armed forces.

10.   Those standards of conduct, including the uniform code of military justice, apply to a member of the armed forces at all times that the member has a military status, whether the member is on base or off base, and whether the member is on duty or off duty.

11.   The pervasive application of the standards of conduct is necessary because members of the armed forces must be ready at all times for worldwide deployment to a combat environment.

12.   The worldwide deployment of United States military forces, the international responsibilities of the United States, and the potential for involvement of the armed forces in actual combat routinely make it necessary for members of the armed forces involuntarily to accept living conditions and working conditions that are often spartan, primitive, and characterized by forced intimacy with little or no privacy.

13.   The prohibition against homosexual conduct is a longstanding element of military law that continues to be necessary in the unique circumstances of military service.

14.   The armed forces must maintain personnel policies that exclude persons whose presence in the armed forces would create an unacceptable risk to the armed forces' high standards of morale, good order and discipline, and unit cohesion that are the essence of military capability.

15.   The presence in the armed forces of persons who demostrate a propensity or intent to engage in homosexual acts would reate an unacceptable risk to the high

standards of morale, good order and discipline, and unit cohesion that are the essence of military capability.

(B) Policy. A member of the armed forces shall be separated from the armed forces under regulations prescribed by the secretary of defense if one or more of the following findings is made and approved in accordance with prodecures set forth in such regulations:

16. That the member has engaged in, attempted to engage in, or solicited another to engage in a homosexual act or acts unless there are further findings, made and approved in accordance with procedures set forth in such regulations, that the member has demonstrated that-

(A) Such donduct is a departure from the member's usual and customary behavior;

(B) Such conduct, under all the circumstances, is unlikely to recur;

(C) Such condict was not accomplished by use of force, coercion, or intimidation;

(D) Under the particular circumstances of the case, the member's continued presence in the armed forces is consistent with the interests of the armed forces in proper discipline, good order, and morale; and

(E) The member does not have a propensity or intent to engage in homosexual acts.

17. That the member has stated that he or she is a homosexual or bisexual, or words to that effect, unless there is a further finding, made and approved in accordance with procedures set forth in the regulations that the member has demonstrated that he or she is not a person who engages in, has a propensity to engage in, or intends to engage in homosexual acts.

18. That the member has married or attempted to marry a person known to be of the same biological sex.

(C) Entry Standards and Documents.

19. The secretary of defense shall ensure that the standards for enlistment and appointment of members of the armed forces reflect the policies set forth in Subsection (B).

20. The documents used to effectuate the enlistment or appointment of a person as a member of the armed forces shall set forth the provisions of Subsection (B).

(D) Required Briefings.

The briefings that members of the armed forces receive upon entry in to the armed forces and periodically thereafter under Section 937 of this Title (Article 137 of the Uniform Code of Military Justice) shall include a detailed explanation of the applicable laws and regulations governing sexual conduct by members of the armed forces, including the policies prescribed under Subsection (B).

(E) Rule of Construction.

> **T**he prohibition against homosexual conduct is a longstanding element of military law that continues to be necessary.

Nothing in Subsection (B) shall be construed to require that a member of the armed forces be processed for separation from the armed forces when a determination is made in accordance with regulations prescribed by the secretary of defense that

21. The member engaged in conduct or made statements for the purpose of avoiding or terminating military service; and

22. Separation of the member would not be in the best interest of the armed forces.

(F) Definitions.

In this Section:

23. The term 'homosexual' means a person, regardless of sex, who engages in, attempts to engage in, has a propensity to engage in, or intends to engage in homosexual acts, and includes the terms 'gay' and 'lesbian'.

24. The term 'bisexual' means a person who engages in, attemps to engage in, has a propensity to engage in, or intends to engage in homosexual and heterosexual acts.

25. The term 'homosexual act' means

(A) Any bodily contact, actively undertaken or passively permitted, between members of the same sex for the purpose of satisfying sexual desires; and

(B) Any bodily contact which a reasonable person would understand to demonstrate a propensity or intent to engage in an act described in Subparagraph (A).

2. The Table of Sections at the beginning of such chapter is amended by adding at the end the following: 654. Policy concerning homosexuality in the armed forces.

(A) Reulations. Not later than 90 days after the date of enactment of this act, the secretary of defense shall revise Department of Defense regulations, and issue such new regulations as may be necessary to implement Section 654 of title 10, United States Code, as added by Subsection (A).

(B) Savings Provision. Nothing in this Section or Section 654 of Title 10, United States Code, as added by Subsection (A) may be construed to invalidate any inquiry, investigation, administrative action or proceeding, court-martial, or judicial proceeding conducted before the effective date of regulations issued by the secretary of defense to implement such Section 654.

(D) Sense of Congress. It is the sense of Congress that

1. The suspension of questioning concerning the processing of individuals for accession in to the armed forces under the interim policy of January 29, 1993, should be continued, but the secretary of defense may reinstate that questioning with such questions or such revised questions as he considers appropriate if the secretary determines that it is necessary to do so in order to effectuate the policy set forth in Section 654 of Title 10, United States Code, as added by Subsection (A); and the secretary of defense should consider issuing guidance governing the circumstances under which

members of the armed forces questioned about homosexuality for administrative purpose should be afforded warnings similar to the warnings under Section 831(B) of Title 10, United States Code, (Article 31(B) of the Uniform Code of Military Justice).

## Document Analysis

In the decades that followed the implementation of Don't Ask, Don't Tell, the accelerating shift in public opinion exposed the discrimination inherent in the policy. However, at the time it was enacted, President Bill Clinton presented Don't Ask, Don't Tell as an expansion of civil rights, and compared to the policy that proceeded it, it was. Despite this fact, the document reads like anything but a progressive broadening of rights for homosexuals. The majority of the document is devoted to reaffirming the existing, discriminatory exclusion policy; not until the very end does the document present a positive, albeit imperfect, step forward for civil rights. This analysis will examine these two sections in turn.

Not only does the progressive part not appear until the very end of the document, but one also has to sift through a good deal of material before any mention of homosexuality is made in the body of the text. Two headers do key the reader into the fact that this section will be about homosexuality in the armed forces. However, it is not until bullet point thirteen of section a.1.A that homosexuality is brought up again. The first twelve points set the stage for the reinforcement of the discriminatory status quo outlined in the points thereafter. For example, points one and three affirm that the Constitution grants Congress the right to raise an army and set its qualifications and conditions. These points buttress bullet point two which reads, "There is no constitutional right to serve in the armed forces." In

this way, the authors contrast their (Congress's) right to limit enrollment with the fact that the Constitution does not affirm a right for citizens to serve. The next points detail the differences between civilian and military life; for more on this section, consult the "Essential Themes" section below. When homosexuality does get mentioned again, in bullet point thirteen, the authors point to precedent: "The prohibition against homosexual conduct is a longstanding element of military law." The authors cite the established tradition of prohibiting homosexuals from the military to bolster their clause. In addition, they cite perceived security dangers, claiming this ban would "Create an unacceptable risk to the high standards of morale, good order and discipline, and unit cohesion that are the essence of military capability." The lifting of this ban in 2011 and the fact that there were no negative consequences disprove this point. However, the fact that it is so adamantly expressed in this document showcases its efficacy as an argument at the time, despite its falseness.

The policy which came to be known as Don't Ask, Don't Tell doesn't appear until the final paragraph of the document. When it finally does come, it is a far cry from a proud assertion of civil rights. The authors anticlimactically say "The suspension of questioning concerning homosexuality…should be continued." Similar to above, when the authors used the longstanding tradition of the ban on homosexuals in the military to justify its continuance, the authors again point to a precedent. Here they continue

President Clinton's interim policy from earlier that year and by citing it, avoid taking responsibility for the shift. They thereby put the onus for this change completely on the shoulders of the president, revealing their own skepticism. The next phrase likewise deflects responsibility, granting the secretary of defense the right to overturn this suspension of questioning if he should see fit. The framing of this shift in policy and the language used to describe it expose the authors' own reluctance on this issue.

## Essential Themes

While reaffirming the ban on homosexuals in the military, the authors take large strides to reinforce their assertion that military life is significantly different from civilian life. This theme is developed throughout the first half of the document. It is most clearly stated in bullet point eight, when the authors state that the military's extraordinary responsibilities and unique conditions, "Require that the military community, while subject to civilian control, exist as a specialized society." The authors go on to explain how this is particularly relevant: "The military society is characterized by its own laws, rules, customs, and traditions, including numerous restrictions on personal behavior, that would not be acceptable in civilian society." By showing the military as divorced from civilian life, the authors attempt to prepare their audience for the continuation of prohibitions that many would find unacceptable in civilian life. As this theme is further developed, there is a hint of unintentional irony in bullet point twelve. Continuing to depict the uniqueness and difficult conditions, the authors employ the adjective, "spartan," which means "austere" or "bare." The adjective stems from the reputation of the ancient Spartans who were famous for their austerity. They were also renowned fighters, so the adjective might seem particularly suited for the authors' purposes. However, the Spartans, like other ancient Greeks, were known to commonly engage in homoerotic behavior, an undertone less suited for the authors' purposes.

—*Anthony Vivian, PhD*

## Bibliography and Additional Reading

Brooks, Adrian. *The Right Side of History: 100 Years of LGBTQ Activism.* Berkeley, CA: Cleis P, 2015. Print.

Faderman, Lillian. *The Gay Revolution: The Story of the Struggle.* New York: Simon & Schuster, 2015. Print.

McGowan, Jeffrey. *Major Conflict: One Gay Man's Life in the Don't-Ask-Don't-Tell Military.* New York: Broadway Books, 2007. Print.

Rimmerman, Craig A. *Gay Rights, Military Wrongs: Political Perspectives on Lesbians and Gays in the Military.* New York: Routledge, 2013. Print.

# ■ Retraction of *Lancet* Paper on MMR Vaccine and Autism

**Date:** March 6, 2004
**Authors:** Simon H. Murch, and others
**Genre:** Retraction; statement

## Summary Overview

In 1998, the *Lancet*, a respected British peer-reviewed general medical journal, published a paper titled "Ileal-lymphoid-nodular hyperplasia, non-specific colitis, and pervasive developmental disorder in children." Authored by Andrew Wakefield and eleven coauthors, the paper claimed to have found a link between the measles, mumps, and rubella (MMR) vaccine and autism. The result was the birth of the antivaccination movement, as parents, fearful that their children might develop autism, chose to skip lifesaving vaccinations. However, a subsequent investigation found that Wakefield had not disclosed numerous conflicts of interest, had manipulated results, and generally acted unethically. As a result, the paper was partially retracted in 2004, and formally retracted in 2010. Despite the controversy, Wakefield's subsequent disgrace, and the paper's retraction, the fraudulent findings became the chief evidence used by antivaccination activists. In fact, as of 2020, mention of Wakefield's research can still be found in antivaccination books and literature.

The *Lancet* is one of the world's oldest and most respected peer-reviewed medical journals, second only in circulation to the *New England Journal of Medicine*. The audience of the journal is comprised mainly of medical professionals, medical researchers, and academics. However, given the publication's prestige, breakthroughs and controversies publicized in the journal's pages often have a wider scope. When Wakefield's paper was published, it created a firestorm among medical professionals and parents. While some parents cited the paper as a reason not to vaccinate their children, medical researchers heavily criticized the paper's findings along with the *Lancet* for publishing it.

## Defining Moment

Although inoculation to disease had been common throughout human history, the first successful vaccines were not developed until 1796, when British surgeon Edward Jenner was able to "vaccinate" subjects against smallpox by first infecting them with cowpox, a virus that had a mild effect in human beings but was closely linked to smallpox. In 1880, French doctor Louis Pasteur developed vaccines for chicken cholera and anthrax, and was declared a national hero as a result. As vaccines became more and more prevalent and commonplace, nation-states began to adopt laws demanding compulsory vaccination. It was reasoned that vaccines should be compulsory not only to curtail the sort of viral outbreaks that had devastated national populations throughout human history, but as a means to also protect those members of society, who, for whatever reason could not be vaccinated.

The twentieth century was witness to the development of a whole host of vaccines, including those against diphtheria, measles, mumps, rubella, and polio. At the same time that vaccines were becoming an essential and established necessity of life, researchers, including Hans Asperger of the Vienna University Hospital, began to shine the light on a never before classified and diagnosed form of developmental disorder that they called autism. As the disorder gradually became more known and medical professionals became better trained on recognizing the signs of autism, which were not always easy to detect, the rates of autism diagnosis began to climb. As time went on, and millions of children across the globe were found to have autism, parents, desperate for answers, began searching for the root causes of the disorder. As autism is usually imperceptible until after fourteen months, and often cannot be identified until ages three or four, some began to link autism to vaccinations, which start as early as early as two months. These antivaccination proponents, also known as *anti-vaxxers*, began to claim that chemical additives within vaccines, or possibly a combination of vaccines, caused damage in the brain, therefore leading to autism.

At first, anti-vaxxers were a small and largely ignored community, but that changed with the publication of Andrew Wakefield's 1998 paper in the *Lancet*. Wakefield was a British physician and medical researcher who had made his name studying the small intestine and first gained attention when in 1993 he published papers claiming to have found a link between the measles virus and Crohn's disease. Two years later, after having been approached by an advocate claiming that autism was the cause of severe allergies, Wakefield shifted his research, and eventually landed on the theory that the MMR vaccine (for measles, mumps, and rubella) might in fact be the actual cause of autism. This new line of study resulted in the infamous paper published in the *Lancet* in 1998.

Immediately, the claim that the MMR vaccine was linked to autism, caused controversy. The *Lancet* was heavily criticized by researchers

in the field, a special panel of the UK's Medical Research Council was quickly convened to study the claims of the paper, and the media began publishing wild reports about the possibility that vaccines, one of the most important discoveries in human history, were actually harmful to human health. Wakefield doubled down on his assertions, despite the fact that his paper made no such overt connections, and called for the suspension of the MMR vaccine. Then in February 2004, the *Sunday Times* revealed that some of the parents of the children featured in Wakefield's study were recruited by a lawyer who was preparing a lawsuit against MMR manufacturers. Moreover, the investigation revealed that the Royal Free Hospital, where Wakefield had worked at the time of the research, received generous cash payments from an antivaccination legal group, with Wakefield himself receiving as much as £400,000. Meanwhile, the *Lancet* had conducted its own investigation, claiming that Wakefield's research was fatally flawed, and accusations began to swirl that Wakefield had forged his results.

## About the Author

Simon H. Murch is an eminent professor of pediatrics and child health at Warwick Medical School in Coventry, England. Prior to this, Murch was a senior lecturer in Paediatric Gastroenterology at the Royal Free and University College School of Medicine in London. His research background is in mucosal immunology and his clinical interests include paediatric inflammatory bowel disease, coeliac disease, food allergy, and complex inherited enteropathies. He has published numerous papers and academic articles, and was a coauthor on Andrew Wakefield's infamous *Lancet* paper linking the MMR vaccine to autism. In 2004 he led the charge to retract the paper's main assertions.

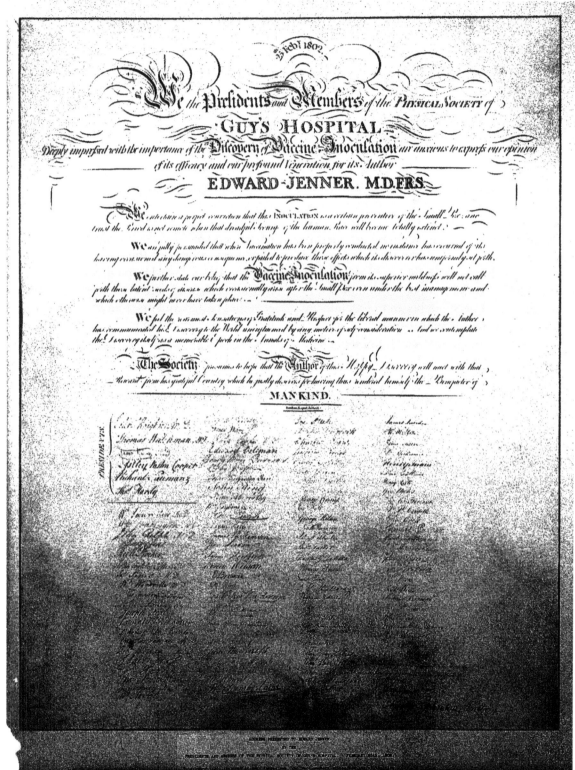

*Edward Jenner, testimonial to the efficacy of vaccination, signed by 112 members of the Physical Society, London, 1802. (Wellcome Images)*

## HISTORICAL DOCUMENT: Retraction of *Lancet* Paper on MMR Vaccine

"Retraction of an Interpretation"

By Simon H. Murch, et al.

This statement refers to the Early Report "Ileal-lymphoid-nodular hyperplasia, non-specific colitis, and pervasive developmental disorder in children", published in *The Lancet* in 1998. It is made by 10 of the 12 original authors who could be contacted. It should be noted that this statement does not necessarily reflect the views of the other co-authors.

The main thrust of this paper was the first description of an unexpected intestinal lesion in the children reported. Further evidence has been forthcoming in studies from the Royal Free Centre for Paediatric Gastroenterology and other groups to support and extend these findings.

While much uncertainty remains about the nature of these changes, we believe it important that such work continues, as autistic children can potentially be helped by recognition and treatment of gastrointestinal problems.

We wish to make it clear that in this paper no causal link was established between MMR vaccine and autism as the data were insufficient. However, the possibility of such a link was raised and consequent events have had major implications for public health. In view of this, we consider now is the appropriate time that we should together formally retract the interpretation placed upon these findings in the paper, according to precedent.

### References

Wakefield AJ, et al. "Ileal-lymphoid-nodular hyperplasia, non-specific colitis, and pervasive developmental disorder in children." Lancet. 1998; 351: 637–641.
[Source: Lancet 363: 750, 6 March 2004]

## GLOSSARY

**autism:** a broad range of conditions characterized by challenges with social skills, repetitive behaviors, speech and nonverbal communication

**gastrointestinal:** relating to the stomach and the intestines

**causal link:** the connection between a cause and an effect

**lesion:** an area in an organ or tissue which has suffered damage through injury or disease

**MMR vaccine:** a vaccine against measles, mumps, and rubella

*Sixteenth century Aztec drawing of a measles victim. (From (2009) Viruses, Plagues, and History: Past, Present and Future, Oxford University Press, USA, p. 144)*

## Document Analysis

The carefully worded statement of retraction by Simon H. Murch and nine of the original authors of Andrew Wakefield's now infamous paper, "Ileal-lymphoid-nodular hyperplasia, non-specific colitis, and pervasive developmental disorder in children," is short and to the point. Murch makes it clear that the two authors not listed, including Wakefield himself, do not necessarily agree with the retraction. Murch then goes on to explain the central thesis of the original paper, namely, that children given the MMR vaccine appeared to develop unexpected intestinal lesions. While further research has backed up these primary findings, the conclusions and assertions made in the original paper, namely that these developments are evidence of a link between the MMR vaccine and autism have not been proven. Murch writes: "the possibility of such a link was raised and consequent events have had major implications for public health." By this understatement, Murch means that the article created an uproar among medical researchers and parents, galvanizing the modern antivaccination movement, and therefore, he reasons, the paper's interpretations should be retracted. It should be noted that Murch did not call for a full retraction of the paper as he believed some of the findings were correct and required further publication and study. Murch simply called for Wakefield's assertion that vaccination is linked to autism to be struck from the publication.

## Essential Themes

As a result of the controversy and widespread accusations of fraud, Andrew Wakefield was discredited as a serious researcher. Subsequent investigations also discredited most if not all of Wakefield's work done prior to and after the *Lancet* paper, and he was eventually stripped of all research grants and his medical degree, and was barred from ever practicing medicine in the United Kingdom again. Following the partial

*The Cow-Pock—or—the Wonderful Effects of the New Inoculation!—the Publications of ye Anti-Vaccine Society. Color engraving) published June 12, 1802 . In this cartoon, the British satirist James Gillray caricatured a scene at the Smallpox and Inoculation Hospital at St. Pancras, showing cowpox vaccine being administered to frightened young women, and cows emerging from different parts of people's bodies. The cartoon was inspired by the controversy over inoculating against the dreaded disease, smallpox. Opponents of vaccination had depicted cases of vaccines developing bovine features.*

retraction of Wakefield's paper by his coauthors, the *Lancet* formally fully retracted it in 2010. By that point, however, the damage had been done.

Following the initial publication of Wakefield's research in 1998, vaccination rates in the United Kingdom, Ireland, and the United States began to fall. The antivaccination movement, which had been a small collection of parent groups, largely ignored by the general public and the mainstream media, became a major and vocal movement, claiming that vaccines were the true cause of autism. Wakefield, whose discredited research became the cornerstone of the antivaccination movement, became a celebrity among anti-vaxxers. It is unclear how many children have died or suffered as a result of Wakefield's fraud, but news of disease outbreaks, thought unthinkable just twenty years ago, have become commonplace. As of 2020, Andrew Wakefield continues to deny that he perpetrated fraud, and has not suffered any legal consequences for his actions.

—*K.P. Dawes, MA*

## Bibliography and Additional Reading

Allen, Arthur. *Vaccine: The Controversial Story of Medicine's Greatest Lifesaver*. New York: W.W. Norton, 2007.

Myers, Martin G., and Pineda, Diego. *Do Vaccines Cause That?!: A Guide for Evaluating Vaccine Safety Concerns*. Galveston, TX: i4ph, 2008.

Mnookin, Seth. *The Panic Virus: The True Story Behind the Vaccine-Autism Controversy*. New York: Simon & Schuster, 2011.

Murch, Simon H. "Retraction of *Lancet* Paper on MMR Vaccine and Autism." *The Lancet* 363 (2004): 750.

Offit, Paul A. *Deadly Choices: How the Anti-Vaccine Movement Threatens Us All*. New York: Basic Books, 2011.

Wadman, Meredith. *The Vaccine Race: Science, Politics, and the Human Costs of Defeating Disease*. New York: Penguin, 2017

# ■ Reports Concerning the H1N1 Swine Flu Pandemic

**Date:** April 26, 2009; August 5, 2010
**Authors:** Reuters; World Health Organization
**Genre:** news reporting; report from nongovernmental organization (NGO)

## Summary Overview

As the international community has grown increasingly more highly connected during the twentieth and twenty-first centuries, so has the impact and consequences of widespread disease and pandemics. The 2009–2010 H1N1 pandemic—often referred to colloquially as the swine flu pandemic—lasted nineteen months and was confirmed to have infected almost half a million people worldwide with nearly 20,000 confirmed deaths. The total number of infections and deaths from the disease, however, may have been much higher (as discussed in the "Defining Moment," below). The two selections presented here provide valuable insights into the impact of the pandemic. The first, consisting of a report from the Reuters news wire service, details the steps taken throughout East Asia to limit the spread of the disease. The second selection is a weekly update from the World Health Organization (WHO) from July 18 through July 25, 2010. This update gives us a snapshot of the manner in which WHO collects, organizes, analyzes, and shares vital information about infectious disease.

## Defining Moment

In the spring of 2009, health authorities detected a new (or "novel") strain of influenza A. Although the WHO officially designated it (H1N1)pdm09, the disease was commonly referred as the Swine Flu. Epidemiologists suspected that the disease may have initially been transferred from pigs in central Mexico to humans as early as the autumn of the previous year. Outbreaks of the disease in Mexico triggered a closing-down of public facilities in an effort to limit the spread of the virus, but by April the disease was present throughout North America. WHO declared H1N1 to be a "Public Health Emergency of International Concern." WHO had developed this designation in 2005 to describe disease outbreaks that had "implications for public health beyond the affected state's national border" and called for "immediate international action." The 2009 H1N1 outbreak was the first time that WHO had used this designation. Agencies around the world, including the Centers for Disease Control and Prevention (CDC) in the United States, began investigating a vaccine. By June 2009, WHO reported that there were 30,000 confirmed cases across 74 countries and declared H1N1 to be a pandemic.

The 2009 H1N1 virus was particularly challenging to medical personnel and researchers because of the differences between it and other influenza strains. Existing vaccines had little to no effect on (H1N1)pdm09. Additionally, although some people over the age of 60 had some immunity, younger people did not have such protection. Thus, this pandemic disproportionately affected younger people. According to the CDC, people under the age of 65 accounted for 80 percent of deaths from the (H1N1)pdm09 pandemic. By late 2009, however, a vaccine was developed and approved for use, and in August 2010 WHO declared that conditions had moved into a "post-pandemic" phase.

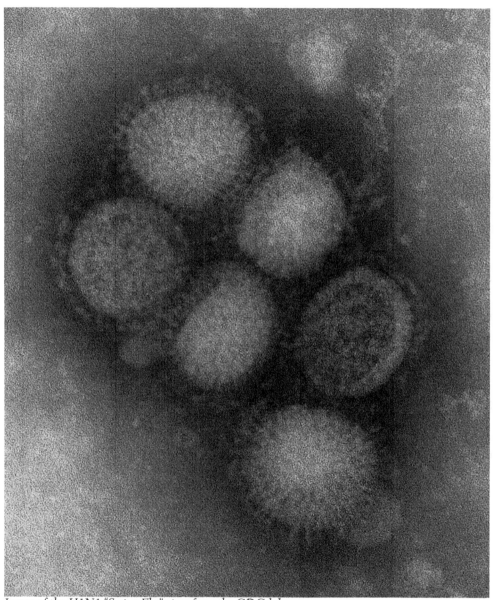

*Image of the H1N1 "Swine Flu" virus from the CDC laboratory.*

Ultimately, this pandemic resulted in nearly half a million "lab-confirmed" cases. However, experts estimate that many times that number may have been infected. Similarly, although there were 18,449 (H1N1)pdm09 deaths that were confirmed by laboratory findings, the CDC estimated that 284,000 deaths occurred, with the number of deaths being disproportionally high in Africa and Southeast Asia.

## Author Biography

In 1850, in the city of Aachen—part of the German Confederation under the control of Prussia—Paul Reuter developed a system of delivering news using homing pigeons and, later, telegraphs. This telegraph-based messaging service between Aachen and Brussels, Belgium was the origin of the Reuters news service. Reuters moved his operation to London in 1851 and established a wire service that provided business news to newspapers around Europe. Incorporated as Reuter's Telegram Company, by the end of the nineteenth century, Reuters operations had expanded into East Asia and South America. While undergoing several restructurings and changes of ownership during the last two centuries, Reuters continues to be a major news outlet throughout the world.

While there had been a number of international efforts to coordinate researching treatment of disease going back to the mid-nineteenth century, WHO had its immediate origins in the League of Nations. The League of Nations was established in 1920 following the First World War to work for collective security and international cooperation. The League of Nations formed a Health Organization with the goal of "endeavour[ing] to take steps in matters of international concern for the prevention and control of disease." There was, however, another international public health organization—the Paris-based Office international d'Hygiène publique—which had existed since 1907. The United States belonged to this organization, but not to the League of Nations. Thus, the League's desire to merge all international health efforts into the new Health Organization went unfulfilled and both organizations existed side-by-side.

Following the Second World War and the establishment of the United Nations (UN) in 1945, there were initiatives to establish a new organization to direct and manage multinational disease control efforts. A constitution was drafted in 1946 that designated the new World Health Organization an agency of the UN. Although its constitution was in place in 1946, it did not go into effect until 26 UN member nations ratified it, which happened on April 7, 1948. Following a brief transition period, WHO began its work toward (in the words of its constitution), "the attainment by all peoples of the highest possible level of health."

Part of WHO's work that is particularly significant to the story of the (H1N1)pdm09 pandemic is its role in classifying diseases, establishing "a common standard for reporting diseases." These common standards for designating and reporting diseases make possible the broad International understanding of a pandemic's behavior that we see in these reports.

## HISTORICAL DOCUMENT: Reports Concerning the H1N1 Swine Flu Pandemic

### FACTBOX—Asia Moves to Ward off New Flu Virus (2009)

April 26 (Reuters)—Asia, a continent that has battled deadly viruses such as the H5N1 bird flu and SARS in recent years, began taking steps over the weekend to ward off a new flu virus. The swine flu virus has killed up to 81 people in Mexico and infected 11 others in the United States. More than 1,300 are believed to be infected in Mexico. Following are some details of how Asian countries are responding to the crisis and how markets are expected to react:

### ASIAN MARKETS

Analysts did not think the epidemic would have a dramatic impact on markets on Monday morning, but warned that if the epidemic worsens that could change.

"It's still too early to say how far and wide this may spread but investors will be cautious," said Ben Kwong, chief operating officer with KGI Asia.

Patrick Shum, strategist at Karl Thomson Securities, agreed that investors would be keeping a close eye on developments in the coming days.

"There won't be an immediate significant impact on the market but if it is anything like SARS, especially coming at a time when most global economies are in a recession, then markets will take a hit," he said.

### CHINA

China's quarantine authority issued an emergency notice on Saturday night requiring people to report flu-like symptoms at ports of entry when coming from swine flu-affected places. The ministries of health and agriculture say they are closely monitoring the situation.

### SINGAPORE

Singapore's ministry of health says it is monitoring the situation closely and has urged medical staff to be on the alert for any suspected human cases.

It advised the public to seek immediate medical attention if they develop symptoms of swine flu within seven days of travel to California, Texas or Mexico. It urged them to maintain good hygiene

> *Asia... began taking steps over the weekend to ward off a new flu virus.*

and wash hands frequently, especially after contact with respiratory secretions. Those who are sick with respiratory illnesses should avoid crowded areas and wear masks.

Health Minister Khaw Boon Wan urged citizens to limit their travel to affected areas such as Mexico and the United States, state-run FM 938 radio reported on Sunday.

"Another worrisome sign is that many of the patients have not come in contact with any farms or pigs before. So that means the human-to-human transmission is quite efficient. And of course, it has now crossed borders into the southern part of the U.S.," Khaw said.

## VIETNAM

Vietnam has launched its disease surveillance system to detect suspected cases and was seeking more information from the World Health Organisation on the disease and ways of prevention.

Nguyen Huy Nga, head of the health ministry's Preventive Medicine Department, was quoted by the state-run Tuoi Tre (Youth) newspaper on Sunday as saying the country needed to watch developments closely as the virus may be spreading in U.S. states where many people of Vietnamese origin live.

## SOUTH KOREA

The government has stepped up quarantine and safety checks on travellers arriving from the United States and Mexico, as well as pork imports from those countries.

An emergency quarantine system is in place, with simple tests conducted on people arriving with flu symptoms at airports.

## HONG KONG

Hong Kong has stepped up surveillance at border control points and travellers found with swine flu symptoms will be taken to hospitals for further checks.

Samples taken from people with flu-like symptoms and who had travelled in the affected places within seven days before the onset of symptoms will be tested in laboratories.

## JAPAN

Japan's Narita airport, east of Tokyo, ramped up temperature checks for travellers from Mexico using thermographic imaging equipment, which was previously in place at the airport.

Japan's foreign ministry issued an advisory asking those who were going to Mexico to consider if such trips were necessary.

According to Japan's Kyodo news agency, Prime Minister Taro Aso has ordered the cabinet's crisis management officer to come up with measures to block swine flu from entering Japan, closely cooperate with other countries and provide information to the public. The cabinet will meet on Monday to discuss the issue.

Kyodo said Japan's farm ministry had instructed animal quarantine officers to examine imported live pigs to make sure they were not infected.

The ministry did not ask for checks on imported pork as it says cooking kills the virus. It regarded the possibility of the virus turning up in pork to be low, Kyodo reported.

## THE PHILIPPINES

Agriculture Secretary Arthur Yap ordered more monitoring of ports of entry to stop the entry of pigs or pork from Mexico and the United States.

Yap said there was no outbreak of swine flu in the Philippines but ordered government agencies to encourage regular vaccination of hogs.

## MALAYSIA

Malaysia's health ministry has begun screening passengers travelling to and from Mexico at all border points.

The veterinary department will meet the Pig Farmers Association on Monday and brief the health minister on the matter, the Veterinary Services Department's Director General, Abd Aziz Jamaluddin, told Reuters by phone on Sunday.

## BANGLADESH

Sheikh Altaf Ali, secretary of the ministry of health and family planning, said the government was aware of the flu outbreak and was monitoring it. (Reporting by Asian bureaux; Writing by Tan Ee Lyn in Hong Kong; Editing by Alex Richardson and Dean Yates)

= = =

## World Health Organization—Weekly Virological Update, 05 August 2010

Virological Surveillance, week 18 July to 24 July 2010

Summary on week 29

- Overall influenza activity has remained at low levels in most parts of the world.
- Co-circulation of pandemic A(H1N1), A(H3N2) and influenza B viruses has been reported from some countries,
- Influenza type B virus detections have decreased.

## Global Virological Surveillance

Overall influenza activity has remained low. Globally 51.1% of the subtyped influenza A viruses were pandemic influenza A(H1N1) with circulation reported from Australia, China, Chile, Ghana, India, New Zealand and Thailand. Co-circulation of pandemic A(H1N1), A(H3N2) and influenza B viruses was reported from China, Chile and Thailand. Sporadic influenza B activity has been observed in some countries with decreased level of detections in China (34.9% of all influenza detections).

### FluNet Report (For the week 18 July to 24 July 2010)

The total number of specimens reportedly positive for influenza viruses by National Influenza Centres (NICs) from 23 countries was 572. Of these, 389 (68%) were typed as influenza A and 183 (32%) as influenza B.

From the start of the pandemic in 19 April 2009 to 24 July 2010, the total number of specimens reported positive for influenza by NIC laboratories was 651,449*. Of these, 491,382 (75.4%) were pandemic A(H1N1), 8,960 (1.4%) were seasonal A(H1N1), 345,069 (5.4%) were A(H3N2), 81,070 (12.4%) were A (not subtyped) and 34,841 (5.3%) were influenza B.

### Pandemic virus characterization

19 April 2009 to 1st August 2010—cumulatively 155 countries shared a total of 26,543 specimens (20,177 clinical and 6,366 isolates) with WHO CCs.

The majority of pandemic A(H1N1) 2009 influenza viruses analyzed to date are antigenically and genetically closely related to the recommended vaccine virus A/California/7/2009.

So far, 302 cases associated with oseltamivir resistant pandemic A(H1N1) viruses have been reported by GISN and other partners. All of these viruses showed the H275Y substitution and all remain sensitive to zanamivir.

## GLOSSARY

**"respiratory secretions:"** saliva, mucus, or water droplets expressed through the nose and mouth

**SARS:** Severe Acute Respiratory Syndrome, a 2002–04 epidemic that was particularly damaging in East Asia

**Thermographic imaging equipment:** temperature sensing devices that use infrared sensors rather than a thermometer to detect heat

## Document Analysis

The April 26, 2009, report from *Reuters* provides a summary of efforts taken to limit the spread of the H1N1 swine flu throughout Asia as well as the pandemic's impact on economic markets in the region. The report, in its opening sentence, reminds readers of two previous disease crises in the twenty-first century, the H5N1 Bird (or Avian) flu and the 2002-04 outbreak of Severe Acute Respiratory syndrome (SARS), which originated in the People's Republic of China and was particularly widespread throughout Asia. Following an update on the state of the H1N1 outbreak in Mexico and the United States, the *Reuters* report begins with a summary of expert opinions on the effects of the epidemic (it was not yet designated a pandemic). At this point, in April 2009, analysts seemed unwilling to commit to predictions, beyond a warning that a downturn in economic activity was likely if the disease worsened.

The report then moves to a nation-by-nation summary of actions taken by various East Asian States in response to the spread of H1N1. Despite the People's Republic of China being by far the most dominant power in the region, their update was among the briefest. China required reporting of symptoms but, otherwise, at that point, was simply "closely monitoring the situation." Singapore, in contrast, having understood that human-to-human infection is "quite efficient" encouraged careful personal hygiene and the use of face coverings as well as avoiding crowds and limiting travel to affected areas. Much like China, public health officials in Vietnam were "watch[ing] developments closely." Nguyen Huy Nga, notably, connects the nation's concern about the outbreak to the significant number of Vietnamese-born residents of the United States, where the virus was spreading. While all the nations discussed were taking basic precautions such as screening people who had travelled to affected areas like the United States or Mexico, some nations were also investigating possible concerns from meat processing and food sourcing. South Korea, Japan, the Philippines, and Malaysia all reported measures aimed at ensuring that live pigs as well as processed pork did not pose a danger to public health.

One consistent feature in these reports is that government officials in the region were not taking restrictive measures. This was early in the development of the Swine Flu pandemic and greater numbers of infections were still to come.

In contrast, the WHO's Weekly Virological Update for July 18–24, 2010 dates from the tail-end of the pandemic period. The organization is reporting that influenza has remained "at low levels." This assessment, note, includes not only H1N1 but other strains of the virus as well. While activity is low, over 50 percent of the type A influenzas were of the H1N1 variety.

There is also a report from FluNet. Established in 1997, FluNet is "a global web-based tool for influenza virological surveillance." This, along with the final section on "pandemic virus characterization" demonstrates the importance of international cooperation. The hundreds of nations contributing data to WHO provide the means to have the fullest understanding not only of the H1N1 pandemic but of other diseases as well. The also, in this report, provide information on vaccine effectiveness as well, speaking to the organization's role not only in studying and tracking disease but working toward prevention as well.

## Essential Themes

There are a number of important strands that these selections consistently demonstrate. The broadest and, perhaps, most significant is the degree of interconnection between different regions of the world and the role that recognizing these connections plays in limiting the spread and severity of global pandemics. This recognition extends not only to the need to limit or outright restrict travel form heavily infected areas but also to the acknowledgement of the effect of the H1N1 pandemic on agriculture and other sectors of the global economy. The materials from WHO illustrate the importance of coordinating information from around the world in order to determine the spread and severity of the disease. As the research from this specific week's report shows, such information gathering also allows organizations like WHO to also determine when the levels of a pandemic have lessened which, in turn, can help inform policymaking in nations around the world. Although increased global interconnections can be a factor in the rapid spread of disease, this interconnectedness can also lead to the level of cooperation necessary to combat pandemics.

—*Aaron John Gulyas, MA*

## Bibliography and Additional Reading

"2009 H1N1 Pandemic (H1N1pdm09 virus)." *US Centers for Disease Control and Prevention*, www.cdc.gov/flu/pandemic-resources/2009-h1n1-pandemic.html. Accessed 18 Aug. 2020.

Gholipour, Bahar. "2009 Swine-Flu Death Toll 10 Times Higher Than Thought." *LiveScience*, 26 Nov. 2013, www.livescience.com/41539-2009-swine-flu-death-toll-higher.html. Accessed 18 Aug. 2020.

Mena, Ignacio, et al. "Origins of the 2009 H1N1 Influenza Pandemic in Swine in Mexico." *eLife*, vol. 5 e16777, 28 June 2016, www.ncbi.nlm.nih.gov/pmc/articles/PMC4957980/. Accessed 18 Aug. 2020.

"Pandemic (H1N1) 2009." *World Health Organization.* www.who.int/csr/disease/swineflu/en/. Accessed 18 Aug. 2020.

"Seasonal Influenza and Influenza A(H1N1)," *World Health Organization.* www.who.int/ith/diseases/si_iAh1n1/en/. Accessed 18 Aug. 2020.

# ■ On the Spread of the Zika virus to the Americas

**Date:** January 28, 2016
**Author:** Dr. Margaret Chan, Director-General of the World Health Organization
**Genre:** briefing; report

## Summary Overview

The briefing examined here, delivered by Dr. Margaret Chan, Director-General of the World Health Organization (WHO), explained the history of the Zika virus and its spread from Africa to the Americas. Previously, the virus had infected few humans. However, it was now found in twenty-three countries in the Americas with increasing numbers of humans sickened. Dr. Chan expressed alarm that the virus was associated with Guillain-Barré syndrome and birth defects, both potentially serious conditions. She identified three main areas of concern: birth malformations and neurological disorders; international spread of the virus; and lack of immunity and the absence of vaccines. She proposed an Emergency Committee to identify an appropriate level of international concern, or readiness, and recommend measures to be undertaken in the affected countries. Dr. Chan ended with a call to prioritize research in areas of urgent need.

## Defining Moment

The World Health Organization (WHO) became concerned over the spread of the Zika virus throughout the Americas in 2015 and its association with microcephaly (babies born with abnormally small heads) and Guillain-Barré syndrome, a rare nerve disorder. Although first reported in the Zika Forest of Uganda in 1947 in a rhesus monkey and in the Aedes africanus mosquito in 1948, the virus did not appear in humans until 1952 in East Africa. From the 1950s to the 1980s the virus was detected in monkeys and mosquitoes in equatorial African countries and then in parts of equatorial Asia including India, Pakistan, Malaysia, and Indonesia. Human infection was not common and hard to identify as many cases were asymptomatic. Those with symptoms reported fatigue, rash, headache, fever, and conjunctivitis.

The Zika virus appeared to be contained in those African and Asian countries until 2007 when there was an outbreak in Yap, an island in the western Pacific between the Philippines and Guam. Spread by mosquitoes, the virus infected as much as 75 percent of the island's 7,391 inhabitants. In 2013 and 2014 the virus reached New Caledonia, east of Australia, the Cook Islands, and Rapa Nui (Easter Island). The largest outbreak occurred between 2013 and 2014 in French Polynesia, with 20,000 cases reported on the island of Tahiti. Although suspected and confirmed cases of Zika virus were thought to have arrived with travelers, there were also autochthonous cases among the local population.

The identification in 2014 of the Zika virus on Easter Island, a special territory of Chile, marked the first time the virus had appeared to the Americas. In early 2015, reports of patients with skin rashes in northeastern Brazil led to testing that confirmed the presence of the Zika virus. In May 2015, the Pan American Health Organization (PAHO) issued an Epidemiological Alert that described the Zika virus and gave recommendations for detecting infections. Throughout 2015 the number of cases continued to climb and spread to more states in Brazil. Colombian authorities also reported the first Zika infections in that nation. By the end of 2015 there were outbreaks of Zika in El Salvador, Guatemala, Panama, Honduras, and in the Caribbean.

Although symptoms in those infected were not severe, there was an alarming increase in birth defects, as pregnant mothers gave birth to babies with microcephaly and several fatalities were reported. There were also reports of Guillain-Barré syndrome in various countries. In January 2016, PAHO published an update with the title "Neurological Syndrome, Congenital Malformations and Zika Virus Infection." The update alerted health authorities in affected countries to these associated defects and ways to enhance surveillance. In February 2016 Dr. Margaret Chan, Director-General of WHO, called a meeting of the Emergency Committee and, with input from Brazil, France, the United States, and El Salvador, declared a Public Health Emergency of International Concern (PHEIC). Among the recommendations provided were travel advisories for pregnant women that cautioned against travel to affected countries in South and Central America and the Caribbean.

## Author Biography

Dr. Margaret Chan was born in Hong Kong in 1947 and received her bachelor's degree at Bres-

cia University College in London, Ontario, in 1973 and her medical degree from the University of Western Ontario in 1977. She also received a Masters in Public Health at the National University of Singapore in 1985. She worked in the Department of Public Health in Hong Kong from 1978 until 1994 when she became the first woman to be named its director, serving until 2003. Dr. Chan's focus was on communicable diseases, and she received praise for her work during the H5N1 bird flu epidemic in 1997. She authorized the elimination of Hong Kong's 1.5 million poultry stock and was credited with averting a major pandemic. Her response to the 2003 severe acute respiratory syndrome (SARS) outbreak was initially criticized as slow, although her actions helped to end the threat in Hong Kong by May of that year.

Dr. Chan joined WHO in 2003 where she was the Director of the Department of Protection of the Human Environment. From 2005 until 2007 she was the Representative of the Director-General for Pandemic Influenza and the Assistant Director-General for Communicable Diseases. Dr. Chan was chosen as the Director General of WHO in 2007 and was reelected in 2012, serving until 2017.

## HISTORICAL DOCUMENT: WHO Director-General Briefs Executive Board on Zika Situation

Dr Margaret Chan
World Health Organization
Geneva, Switzerland
28 January 2016

Distinguished members of the Board, representatives of Member States, ladies and gentlemen,

Welcome to this briefing on the Zika situation. I will give you a brief history of this disease and explain why WHO is so deeply concerned.

The Zika virus was first isolated in 1947 from a monkey in the Zika forest of Uganda. Its historical home has been in a narrow equatorial belt stretching across Africa and into equatorial Asia.

For decades, the disease, transmitted by the Aedes genus of mosquito, slumbered, affecting mainly monkeys. In humans, Zika occasionally caused a mild disease of low concern.

In 2007, Zika expanded its geographical range to cause the first documented outbreak in the Pacific islands, in the Federated States of Micronesia. From 2013–2014, 4 additional Pacific island nations documented large Zika outbreaks.

In French Polynesia, the Zika outbreak was associated with neurological complications at a time when the virus was co-circulating with dengue. That was a unique feature, but difficult to interpret.

The situation today is dramatically different. Last year, the virus was detected in the Americas, where it is now spreading explosively. As of today, cases have been reported in 23 countries and territories in the region.

The level of alarm is extremely high.

Arrival of the virus in some places has been associated with a steep increase in the birth of babies with abnormally small heads and in cases of Guillain-Barré syndrome.

> *The level of concern is high, as is the level of uncertainty. Questions abound. We need to get some answers quickly.*

A causal relationship between Zika virus infection and birth malformations and neurological syndromes has not yet been established but is strongly suspected.

The possible links, only recently suspected, have rapidly changed the risk profile of Zika, from a mild threat to one of alarming proportions. The increased incidence of microcephaly is particularly alarming, as it places a heart-breaking burden on families and communities.

WHO is deeply concerned about this rapidly evolving situation for 4 main reasons:

- the possible association of infection with birth malformations and neurological syndromes
- the potential for further international spread given the wide geographical distribution of the mosquito vector
- the lack of population immunity in newly affected areas
- and the absence of vaccines, specific treatments, and rapid diagnostic tests.

Moreover, conditions associated with this year's El Nino weather pattern are expected to increase mosquito populations greatly in many areas.

The level of concern is high, as is the level of uncertainty. Questions abound. We need to get some answers quickly.

For all these reasons, I have decided to convene an Emergency Committee under the International Health Regulations. The Committee will meet in Geneva on Monday, 1 February.

I am asking the Committee for advice on the appropriate level of international concern and for recommended measures that should be undertaken in affected countries and elsewhere. I will also ask the Committee to prioritize areas where research is most urgently needed.

Decisions concerning the Committee's advice to me will be made public on our web site.

Thank you.

## Document Analysis

The briefing by Chan occurred at a moment of increasing concern regarding the transmission of the Zika virus throughout the Americas. She describes the history of the Zika virus from its discovery in eastern Africa in 1947 and its spread into other African and Asian countries during the last half of the twentieth century. At that time there were few human cases and no deaths associated with the virus. In 2007, however, the Zika virus was detected in humans in Yap, a small island in the western Pacific.

Dr. Chan describes the trajectory of the virus across the Pacific, eventually reaching French Polynesia in 2013 and Chile's Easter Island in 2014. By 2015 the Zika virus appeared in northeastern Brazil, with patients reporting fever and rashes. At first, the Zika virus was thought to be a form of Dengue fever and infected persons were tested for that virus. However, Dr. Chan notes that this new virus is different, although also spread by mosquitoes. She also fears that the current El Niño weather patterns may increase the mosquito population, adding to the transmission of the virus. She reports that babies born with abnormally small heads (microcephaly) in French Polynesia cause alarm and additional cases of birth defects as well as Guillain-Barré syndrome in Brazil mean the WHO must take an active role.

In January 2016, Dr. Chan organized an emergency meeting of the Executive Board to give a briefing on the Zika virus and call for action because of the international transmission due to mosquitoes. She remarks in the briefing that the association of the virus with birth malformations and neurological disorders creates

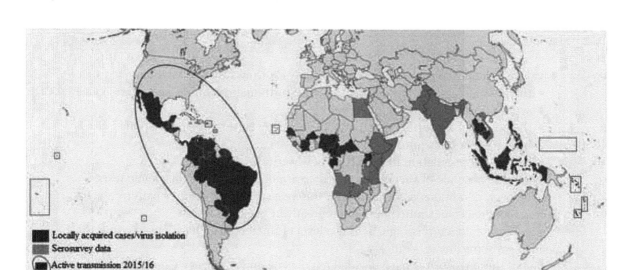

*The spread of Zika virus caused great concern in 2016, in part because of its relationship to birth defects*

heart-breaking burdens on families. Dr. Chan states that there is a lack of immunity among the population of the affected countries and no current vaccines, treatments or diagnostic tests. She calls for a meeting of the Emergency Committee of WHO. The Committee is comprised of a chair and thirteen public health experts from around the world. Dr. Chan tasks the Committee with publishing an appropriate measure of concern to the international community and actions to be taken in countries affected by the virus.

In response, the Committee made the following recommendations regarding Zika transmission, travel measures, and data sharing. Specifically, the Committee recommended enhanced surveillance measures and to prioritize new diagnostics for the Zika virus infection. The Committee also highlighted the need for personal protective measures and the need to warn pregnant women about the incidence of birth defects associated with the virus. Restrictions on trade and travel to the affected areas were not necessary, said the Committee, but every effort should be made to warn travelers of the risks involved when traveling to these countries. Finally, the Committee called for the rapid sharing by WHO of data regarding Zika virus transmission and associated rates of microcephaly and Guillain-Barré syndrome.

A PHEIC was published by WHO in February 2016. In response, PAHO initiated cooperation missions to Guatemala and Honduras in Central America and affected countries in the Caribbean and South America. There were meetings on health system organization, clinical surveillance, and pregnancy management along with training initiatives and published technical guidelines. Laboratory reagents were distributed for the detection of the Zika virus, and a dedicated portal for disseminating information was created.

**Essential Themes**

The briefing Dr. Chan gave in January 2016 showed her concern for the tragedy of birth defects associated with the Zika virus and her determination to act quickly and decisively to stop the spread of the virus, especially in the Americas. Although there was no immediate threat to Europe or to North America other than that posed by travelers returning from infected regions, Dr. Chan wanted to make the resources of WHO and its regional organization, PAHO, available to those countries suffering from the virus and its associated issues.

The intervention by Dr. Chan in calling a meeting of the Emergency Committee and the dissemination of information by WHO and PAHO helped stem the spread of the Zika virus in the Americas. The public health emergency was lifted in November 2016.

The swiftness of Dr. Chan's actions was due, in part, to contradictory criticisms leveled against her in previous pandemics. In 2009, Dr. Chan's early warnings over-emphasized the seriousness of the swine flu virus. Although wide-spread and killing about 250,000 individuals, the swine flu virus was no more deadly than the seasonal flu, which typically causes an equal or greater number of deaths. Then, in 2014 Dr. Chan was criticized for a slow response to the Ebola virus epidemic in west Africa. She appeared to strike the right note of concern and the need for action in her briefing to the Executive Committee of WHO in January 2016 and the release of a PHEIC the following month. As a result, recommendations from the Emergency Committee sparked actions to contain the spread of the virus and mitigate the incidence of birth defects and neurological disorders. Before the end of the year, the emergency was over, although the Zika virus continues to infect individuals in parts of the Americas.

—*James Baer, PhD*

## Bibliography and Additional Reading

Chan, Margaret. "Who Director-General Briefs Executive Board on Zika Situation." WHO, World Health Organization. 28 Jan. 2016, www.who.int/dg/speeches/2016/zika-situation/en/. Accessed 20 Aug. 2020.

Gatherer, Derek, and Alain Kohl, "Zika Virus: A Previously Slow Pandemic Spreads Rapidly through the Americas," *Journal of General Virology*, 2016, vol. 97, no. 2, pp. 269–73, doi.org/10.1099/jgv.0.000381. Accessed 19 Aug. 2020.

Hennessey, Morgan, et al. "Zika Virus Spreads to New Areas—Region of the Americas, May 2015–January 2016," Centers for Disease Control and Prevention, *Morbidity and Mortality Weekly Report*, 29 Jan. 2016, vol. 65, no. 3, pp. 55–58, www.cdc.gov/mmwr/volumes/65/wr/mm6503e1.htm. Accessed 19 Aug. 2020.

"Update on the Zika Virus in the Americas," *Pan American Health Organization*, Provisional Agenda Item 7.6, CE158/INF/6, 20 May 2016, iris.paho.org/handle/10665.2/33749. Accessed 19 Aug. 2020.

"Zika Virus Infection," *Pan American Health Organization*, Epidemiological Alert.7 May 2015, iris.paho.org/handle/10665.2/34232, Accessed 19 Aug. 2020.

# ■ California's Vaccination Law

**Date:** June 20, 2019
**Authors:** Jane Meredith Adams; Diana Lambert, Richard Pan
**Genre:** Article

## Summary Overview

This article summarizes the changes proposed to California's vaccination requirements for schools. These legislative efforts aim to create "herd immunity," that is, vaccination of a sufficient proportion of the population to make the population as a whole safe; individuals who medically cannot receive immunizations would still be protected from contracting diseases. Parents of children entering new schools or entering into certain grade levels must show proof of immunization, or else provide a legitimate reason for lack of vaccination. As this article demonstrates, the California legislature has had to continue to refine its requirements for public health because of anti-vaccine proponents (anti-vaxxers) who had been bypassing these protocols because of their personal beliefs. California had had a loophole to accommodate anti-vaxxers, the "personal belief" exemption, before an outbreak of measles in 2014 at Disneyland changed legislative priorities. A subsequent law in 2015 removed the personal belief exemption and permitted only medical exemptions; but reports showed a sharp increase in doctors granting these exemptions without merit. Yet another law coming afterward, still in discussion at the time that the authors published this piece, entrusts state officials with the ability to affirm or deny medical exemptions and thus protect the general population from easily preventable dangerous diseases.

## Defining Moment

Fear and doubt about vaccines are no recent phenomenon. From the time when Edward Jenner first tested a vaccine for smallpox in 1796, there were people who distrusted the motives of doctors, the ingredients used in the vaccines themselves, or who believed that vaccines counteracted the design of divine or natural forces. Nevertheless, government intervention required children of certain ages to receive vaccinations in an effort to eradicate harmful and preventable diseases like smallpox and measles. In turn, antivaccinationists like William Tebb (1830–1917) rallied supporters to exert pressure on governments to rescind compulsory vaccinations. Citing social liberty and bodily autonomy as reasons to object to government-mandated vaccination, Tebb and his National Anti-Vaccination League were responsible for introducing a "conscientious objection" clause to the United Kingdom's Vaccination Acts.

Although antivaccination sentiment has been a consistent undercurrent to many medical achievements and public health legislation, the twenty-first-century incarnation of antivaccination has its genesis in a paper by a British ex-physician named Andrew Wakefield. In this paper, which was ultimately discredited by the scientific community, Wakefield alleged that the MMR vaccine, which immunizes children against measles, mumps, and rubella (MMR), was linked to autism. Wakefield had his license revoked by medical authorities after his coauthors retracted the paper, but the persistent myth he helped create has contributed to a resurgence in these diseases and a spike in hospitalizations. Around the same time as Wakefield published his discredited article, activists for the "Green Our Vaccines" movement in the United States claimed that thimerosal, a mercury compound used as a preservative in vaccines, was responsible for a number of childhood developmental delays and deaths. Commonly known as anti-vaxxers, these supporters have continued to disseminate erroneous claims about vaccines causing harm.

Scientific evidence has discredited such claims, but the involvement of celebrities like the TV personality Jenny McCarthy and the proliferation of unsourced pseudoscience on the internet continue to harm the health of children and immunocompromised individuals who cannot medically receive vaccines, the research shows.

Populations require a vaccination rate of 95 percent to protect individuals who have valid medical reasons not to receive vaccines, but vaccination rates have been declining across the United States in recent years. In California, for example, vaccination rates for measles declined to 92.3 percent in 2013. As a consequence, the United States saw outbreaks of diseases once thought to have been eliminated, including measles.

## Author Biography

Jane Meredith Adams and Diana Lambert are both reporters who have written on topics related to education and teaching for EdSource, the publisher of this article, and other news outlets. EdSource is a nonprofit news website that provides reporting on education issues in California. Founded in 1977, EdSource has chronicled a variety of reforms in Californian education.

State Senator Richard Pan, a Democrat representing Sacramento, is one of the primary authors of the vaccination law discussed in this article. Pan's background as a pediatrician has influenced his dedication to healthcare as a politician; he continues his medical practice while serving in the California State Senate. After an outbreak of measles in 2014 at Disneyland, Pan helped author a bill to prevent parents from being able to use "personal belief" as a valid excuse not to vaccinate their children. Some doctors began improperly to grant medical exemptions, nonetheless, and Pan proposed Senate Bill 276 to create state standards for medical exemptions that doctors and antivaccine parents could not circumvent. Pan, it should be noted, has received threatening and violent pushback from the anti-vax community in response to his efforts.

## HISTORICAL DOCUMENT: California's Vaccination Law

Changes to California's current vaccination law being considered in Sacramento would make it more difficult for parents to use medical exemptions to avoid immunizing their children before enrolling them in school. A bill is making its way through the Legislature and is expected to be signed by Gov. Gavin Newsom.

Senate Bill 276 is meant to close loopholes in the 2015 vaccination law that eliminated so-called "personal belief" exemptions allowing parents to opt out of immunizing their children based solely on their personal beliefs.

Hearings on the proposed changes have brought large crowds of opponents to the state Capitol over the past several months. This week Newsom negotiated amendments to the bill with its authors, easing proposed restrictions on medical exemptions.

Sen. Richard Pan, D-Sacramento, who authored the 2015 vaccination law, proposed changes to the law after a series of recent measles outbreaks in California and across the country. In his original proposal, doctors would be required to submit all medical exemption requests to the California Department of Public Health, which would have had to approve them.

His bill would require doctors to certify they examined the child and include in the request their name, their medical license number and the reason for the exemption. The public health department would be required to keep a database of the exemptions and it would have the authority to revoke exemptions if they're later found to be fraudulent.

After discussions with the governor's office, the newly amended version of the bill retains many of the same requirements, but would only require review of medical exemptions by the Dept. of Public Health if a child's school has an immunization rate of less than 95 percent, or if the doctor who signed the request has written five or more medical exemptions during the year.

With the passage of the 2015 vaccination law (SB277), which amended the California Health and Safety Code and took effect July 1, 2016, the era of granting "personal belief exemptions" to vaccinations ended in California. Parents who once declined to vaccinate their children attending school are making their choices: vaccinate, enroll in home-school/independent study, seek a medical exemption or qualify their children for special education services regardless of vaccination status.

To recap: Parents do not have to immunize their children. But under the law, children must be immunized against 10 serious communicable diseases if they want to attend public or private schools and child care centers. Studies have linked clusters of unimmunized children to outbreaks of measles, pertussis and varicella.

Students are affected by the immunization law only at certain grade-levels or other checkpoints: upon entering child care, transitional kindergarten/kindergarten or 7th grade, or when transferring into schools or child care from out of state or out of the country. Otherwise, the immunization status of students is not an issue.

Here's what is known about the 2015 vaccination law currently in place in California:

**What does the current law say?**
Private or public child care centers, preschools, elementary schools and secondary schools cannot admit children unless they are immunized against 10 diseases: diphtheria, Haemophilus influenzae Type B (bacterial meningitis), measles, mumps, pertussis (whooping cough), polio, rubella, tetanus, hepatitis B and chicken pox.

## How is the current law different from the previous law?

The law eliminated the personal belief exemption for required vaccinations. This exemption allowed parents to opt out of vaccinating their children by completing a form, signed by a health care practitioner, attesting that vaccinations were counter to their personal beliefs.

The law also overrode an allowance for religious exemptions to vaccinations that was not explicitly in state law.

## Can some children get exemptions from vaccinations?

Yes.

*Medical*: If SB276 is signed into law medical exemptions will still be allowed, but will have added restrictions. Beginning Jan. 1, 2021 licensed physicians or surgeons will be required to write up medical exemption requests on a standardized electronic form that will be filed with the California Immunization Registry. The State Department of Public Health will monitor immunization levels at schools, as well as whether individual doctors have submitted unusually high numbers of exemptions.

The new bill states that children who may have been exposed to one of the 10 diseases and who don't have proof they have been immunized for that illness may be temporarily excluded from school. They would remain out of school until the local health officer determines they are no longer at risk of developing the disease or transmitting it.

*Homeschooling or independent study without classroom instruction*: As of July 1, 2016, students who attend a home-based private school or an independent study program without classroom-based instruction are not subject to immunization requirements for entry. Home schools and independent study programs are obligated to maintain records of students' immunization status. Students in independent study programs that include classroom-based instruction must be vaccinated according to state laws.

Special Education: According to the California Department of Public Health "students who have an individualized education program (IEP) may continue to receive all necessary services identified in their IEP regardless of their immunization status."

## Is there an appeal process if a medical exemption is denied?

Parents or guardians can appeal the denial of a medical exemption to the Secretary of California Health and Human Services. The secretary is required to appoint an independent expert review panel, consisting of three licensed primary care physicians or immunization experts, to evaluate and rule on appeals.

### Are kindergartners allowed to enroll "conditionally" if they have not yet completed all of the required vaccinations?

Yes, if they meet certain requirements. Kindergartners must have a mumps and a rubella vaccination before enrolling—there is no conditional enrollment involving the mumps and rubella vaccinations. Kindergartners also must be as current as possible with other immunizations, given the need to space out certain vaccine doses.

> *Under the law, children must be immunized against 10 serious communicable diseases if they want to attend public or private schools and child care centers.*

Kindergartners may be conditionally admitted with at least one dose of the following vaccines: polio; diphtheria, tetanus and pertussis; measles; hepatitis B and varicella (chicken pox).

School districts already have their own systems for tracking and following up with kindergartners who are not fully immunized. Whatever systems districts are currently using remain in place.

If students are entering the public school system as transitional kindergartners, these conditional immunization rules apply to them as well.

### What about children who currently have personal belief exemptions on file?

Children who before Jan. 1, 2016 held personal belief exemptions to vaccinations are not subject to the new law until they reach their next vaccination checkpoint.

The law defines these checkpoints as "grade spans," as follows:

Birth to preschool;

Kindergarten and grades 1 to 6, inclusive, including transitional kindergarten;

Grades 7 to 12, inclusive.

For example, a 6th grade student with a personal belief exemption in December 2015 will still have to comply with vaccination requirements upon entering 7th grade, which is a vaccination checkpoint.

If a child has been exposed to one of the 10 diseases named in the immunization requirements and does not have proof of immunization, the child temporarily may be kept out of school.

### Do unvaccinated children with personal belief exemptions who move from one California school or district to another have to meet the vaccination requirements of new students?

Not unless the student is entering a vaccination checkpoint grade span: a child care facility or preschool, a transitional kindergarten/kindergarten or 7th grade. Personal belief exemptions can be transferred between child care facilities and schools in

California both within and across school districts, according to the state. Personal belief exemptions from another state or country are not valid.

### What vaccinations are required of unvaccinated students before entering 7th grade?

As of July 1, 2016, all previously unvaccinated students entering 7th grade must provide documentation of the vaccines needed for school entry based on age. These include the polio series, the diphtheria/tetanus/pertussis series, the varicella (chicken pox) vaccine and two doses of MMR, according to the California Department of Public Health.

But while immunization against hepatitis B is required for entry to lower grades, the law states that it is not required for entry to 7th grade.

### What are the options for parents who do not want to have their children vaccinated but want to enroll them in school?

Parents who do not want to vaccinate their children attending school have three options: obtain a medical exemption to vaccinations, enroll in homeschooling or independent study without classroom instruction, or have their children evaluated and enrolled in special education services.

### What is homeschooling and independent study?

According to the California Homeschool Network, parents who wish to homeschool have four options:

Establish their own private home school by filing a private school affidavit. Parents are free to collaborate with other homeschools. Homeschools are required to teach California mandated subject areas, but have latitude as to when and how such subjects are taught.

Join another private home school and become a "satellite" home school.

Enroll in a district or charter public school that offers independent study. The student receives assignments from a teacher but fulfills most of the work independently.

Homeschool a child by hiring a credentialed tutor.

### Are schools required to track immunizations?

Schools are required to document each student's immunization history. The immunization record of each student enrolled conditionally must be reviewed regularly to ensure they receive their immunizations by the required time. Those who fail to get their immunizations by the designated date will be prohibited from attending school.

Each district school board is being asked to file an annual report on the immunization status of all new students to the California Department of Public Health or its local health department. The local health department will have access to the immunization record of every student in school.

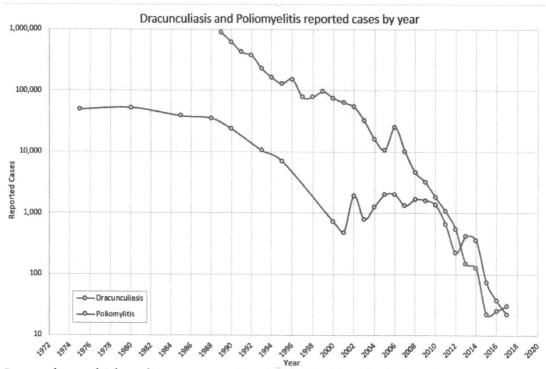

*Dracunculiasis and Poliomyelitis cases per year. Data from WHO. (Graph by Anxietycello)*

## Document Analysis

The authors of this article maintain an objective, nonpartisan tone throughout their summary of the proposed changes to California's vaccination requirements. This rhetorical approach by the authors may be an attempt to counteract the often fear-mongering rhetoric of the anti-vaxxers; at the same time, it serves perhaps to soothe the fears of parents looking for clarity about their children's health. The article uses a question-and-answer format that contributes to the clarity of its discussion; the dearth of quotations from vaccine supporters or from detractors eliminates a personal voice from the article and suggests a consensus view. As a consequence, a reader of the piece can feel confident that the authors have not skewed the information to satisfy any particular political aim, and thus find trust in the facts as written.

## Essential Themes

California Governor Gavin Newsom signed SB 276 on September 9, 2019. This law, which took effect on January 1, 2020, gives the California Department of Public Health the final decision over whether a patient's medical exemption is legitimate or not. The law was not without controversy, however, even among supporters of vaccination. Governor Newsom pushed for the law to stipulate that existing medical exemptions remained valid, while Senator Pan hoped to see many fraudulent exemptions removed. Another law may eventually reverse some of these existing exemptions. An amendment to SB 276, SB 714 requires the renewal of existing exemptions at certain points in a child's schooling, such as kindergarten and seventh grade. Through this change, state authorities could revoke fraudulently granted exemptions. The amendment also would invalidate medical exemptions granted by doctors who have received disciplinary actions by official boards. These changes could result in revoking hundreds of the medical exemptions granted improperly by doctors. Time will prove whether California's efforts to standardize medical exemptions results in decreased outbreaks of the preventable diseases addressed through vaccination.

—*Ashleigh Fata, MA*

## Bibliography and Additional Reading

Conis, Elena. *Vaccine Nation: America's Changing Relationship with Immunization*. Chicago: University of Chicago Press, 2015.

Hoffman, Jan. "How Anti-Vaccine Sentiment Took Hold in the United States." *New York Times*, September 23, 2019.

Krishnakumar, Priya, and Soumya Karlamangla. "How Stricter Vaccine Laws Spared California from a Major Measles Outbreak." *Los Angeles Times*, May 6, 2019.

Reich, Jennifer A. *Calling the Shots: Why Parents Reject Vaccines*. New York: New York University Press, 2018.

*Secretary of State Mike Pompeo speaks about COVID-19 in the Press Briefing Room, January 2020*

# ■ Secretary of State Mike Pompeo Interview Regarding the Coronavirus

**Date:** April 17, 2020; April 30, 2020
**Authors:** Mike Pompeo, Hugh Hewitt
**Genre:** interview

## Summary Overview

On April 17, 2020, US Secretary of State Mike Pompeo gave an interview with conservative commentator Hugh Hewitt in which he focused on China's role in the spread of the novel coronavirus SARS-CoV-2 throughout the world. While his criticisms regarding the Chinese government's early denials and lack of transparency regarding the outbreak were shared by many across the American political spectrum, what made headlines about the interview was Pompeo's claim, which became a theme for President Donald J. Trump and him over the following month, that it was suspected that the virus originated in Wuhan Institute of Virology, raising concerns that the virus might have been engineered by the Chinese government and then either escaped or was deliberately released into the world. Critics of the president and secretary quickly responded by accusing Pompeo and Trump of using their criticisms of China to direct media attention away from the shortcomings in the Trump administration's own response to the crisis.

## Defining Moment

Since at least late January or early February, critics of the Trump administration had begun complaining loudly about what they saw as a lack of effort by the federal government to combat the crisis, which had started with a single case in Seattle in late December and soon was also present in New York, California, and other locations. With the number of cases in the United States growing rapidly in April, President Trump and his allies appeared to be floating numerous theories about the virus's origins and spread in order to deflect those criticisms and focus the attention of the American public on foreign enemies, such as China.

## Author Biography

Michael Richard Pompeo was born on December 30, 1963 in Orange, California. Pompeo attended the US Military Academy at West Point, obtaining a bachelor's degree in engineering management. He received a JD degree from Harvard Law School in 1974. He was Director of the Central Intelligence Agency (CIA) from January 2017 until April 2018. The appointment of Mike Pompeo as the US Secretary of State on April 26, 2018, was widely seen by administration critics as an effort by President Trump to find a secretary who would not doubt his actions and ideas, but would implement them without question, coming on the heels of Trump's first Secretary of State, Rex Tillerson, whose criticisms of Trump had begun as rumors, but were later confirmed.

## HISTORICAL DOCUMENT: Secretary Pompeo Interview with Hugh Hewitt of the Hugh Hewitt Show

**Hugh Hewitt:** Let me turn to the CCP [Communist Party of China]. On a personal level, Mr. Secretary, not as Secretary of State, do you believe that the Communist Chinese Party has told us the truth on any significant issue in the last three months?

**SECRETARY POMPEO:** Well, I'm sure there have been things they've accurately described to us, but it's pretty clear at this point that the Chinese Communist Party's—one of its central challenges in any institution that is authoritarian is the absence of the ability for information to flow freely. You saw this, Hugh, in the weeks before this. They decided to kick out US journalists, journalists from *The Wall Street Journal*, *The New York Times*, *The Washington Post*. You saw what happened when doctors raised their hand and said hey, I think we have a problem, I think we potentially have a human-to-human virus and it's spread, and they suppressed that by coercion and worse.

Those are the kind of things that authoritarian regimes do. It's the nature of those regimes. And as a result of that, the information didn't get to the right places, and so for days and weeks, the world didn't know what was confronting it, and in a virus like this, those first hours and days and weeks are the most critical in stopping the spread. And the Chinese Communist Party failed to do that properly.

I'll say this too, Hugh: We still need transparency today. We need openness today. We are still in the middle of this. We still don't know the precise source and origin spot of the virus. That will turn out to be important for epidemiologists and experts to help us get to the back side of this. We still need that kind of openness, and we urge every country that has information about the virus and data sets and is working on a vaccine or therapeutics to share that information broadly in the scientific community so the world can stop this pandemic from continuing to spread. We're getting on top of this here in the United States, but the world is still at enormous risk and we need to have every piece of information, including from the Chinese Communist Party, available for scientists and researchers.

> *I*n a virus like this, those first hours and days and weeks are the most critical in stopping the spread. And the Chinese Communist Party failed to do that properly.

**H.H.:** Yesterday, there was a long press conference in Beijing. The foreign ministry spokesperson, their senior spokesperson, rejected American journalism's stories that the virus originated in a Wuhan lab—and they rejected the story that a underground nuclear test, in violation of the nuclear test ban, had occurred. Do you reject the Chinese spokesperson's rejection of both charges?

**POMPEO:** I don't want to comment on the second one, but with respect to the first one, we don't know the answer to the question about the precise origination point. But we do know this: We know that the first sightings of this occurred within miles of the Wuhan Institute of Virology [WIV]. We know that this—the history of the facility, the first BSL-4 lab where there's high-end virus research being conducted, took place at that site. We know that the Chinese Communist Party, when it began to evaluate what to do inside of Wuhan, considered whether the WIV was, in fact, the place where this came from.

And most importantly, we know they've not permitted the world's scientists to go into that laboratory to evaluate what took place there, what's happening there, what's happening there even as we speak, Hugh. Even as we're on the show this morning, we still have not had Western access to that facility so that we can properly evaluate what really has taken off all across the world and how that began.

Those are facts, those are important facts, and the Chinese Communist Party and the World Health Organization have a responsibility to the world to take those facts and take them to their logical conclusion and find out these answers, these important answers. These aren't political. This is about science and health, and we need to get to the bottom of it.

## Document Analysis

US Secretary of State Mike Pompeo, in an April 17, 2020, interview with conservative commentator Hugh Hewitt, discussed what he saw as the possible roles of the Chinese government in the growing global crisis caused by the spread of the novel coronavirus, which by that time had produced over 2.25 million cases of COVID-19 (the illness caused by the virus) and nearly 150,000 deaths worldwide. Much of what Pompeo stated about the Chinese government's role in, first, denying the existence and scope of the early spread of the virus in Wuhan, was not controversial. However, Pompeo strayed into the realm of conspiracy theories when he articulated the idea that the virus had been developed at the Wuhan Institute of Virology, a biological research facility in the city where the virus had first been detected.

Pompeo's statements about the virus's origins were not original to him. In late January 2020, the *Washington Times*, a conservative-leaning news source, published a report that the virus may have been a product of China's biowarfare effort. That theory was picked up by Republican Senator Tom Cotton in mid-February, who began to speak widely of the idea that the virus had been engineered in Wuhan. However, neither the *Washington Times* nor Cotton articulated any evidence that this was, indeed, the case. In fact, by mid-to-late February, numerous experts in biology and virology disputed the possibility that the virus could have been engineered as a bioweapon. Cotton began to moderate his comments, mentioning the laboratory origins of the virus only as a theory, and that it was more likely that the virus had originated naturally. By late March, the *Washington Times* had backtracked on its original reporting, stating that the virus had been shown by leading scientists to have originated naturally.

Despite the fact that most reputable scientists, intelligence officials, news sources, and politicians were now acknowledging the far-fetched nature of the lab origin theory, by April 16, the day before Pompeo sat down with Hewitt for the interview, both *CNN* and *Fox News* reported that top Trump administration officials were calling for investigations into the possibility that the virus had either been engineered or had developed and escaped accidentally in the Wuhan laboratory.

During his interview with Hewitt, Pompeo gave his views on the probability of the virus originating in the Wuhan lab, stating that "[w]e know that the first sightings of this occurred within miles of the Wuhan Institute of Virology," and that "high-end virus research" was conducted at the site. He further stated that the Chinese government was not allowing foreign investigators into the facility.

The day after Pompeo's interview, Yuan Zhiming, the director of the Wuhan Institute of Virology, denied that the lab had any role in the origins of the virus. Meanwhile, Trump repeated Pompeo's baseless assertions in a White House briefing, stating that it "made sense," while during the same briefing Anthony Fauci of the National Institute of Allergy and Infectious Diseases (NIAID) disagreed with the president, citing scientific studies that demonstrated that the virus had, indeed, occurred naturally and jumped from an animal to a human, as most all reputable scientists had concluded.

## Essential Themes

The lack of evidence for and mounting evidence against the theory did not stop Trump, Pompeo, and lawmakers like Cotton from continuing to talk about the conspiracy theory, nor did it stop critics of the administration from arguing that the theory was simply an attempt to divert public opinion from what they saw as the administration's anemic response to the crisis. Cotton even went so far as to write an op-ed in *The Wall Street Journal* about it. But on April 30, the Inspector General of the Intelligence Community issued a statement that the American intelligence agencies "concur with the scientific consensus that the COVID-19 virus was not man-made or genetically modified." Though Trump and Pompeo continued to play up the theory in late March and early April, by May 6, Pompeo, himself a former director of the Central Intelligence Agency (CIA), had begun to walk back his comments.

—*Steven L. Danver, PhD*

## Bibliography and Additional Reading

Basu, Zachary. "Pompeo Says There's 'Enormous Evidence' Coronavirus Originated in Wuhan Lab." *Axios*, May, 2020, www.axios.com/pompeo-coronavirus-wuhan-lab-5f305526-9ceb-49af-943a-fd8291a6d5d9.html. Accessed 18 Aug. 2020.

Brewster, Jack. "A Timeline of the COVID-19 Wuhan Lab Origin Theory." *Forbes*, 24 May 2020, www.forbes.com/sites/jackbrewster/2020/05/10/a-timeline-of-the-covid-19-wuhan-lab-origin-theory/. Accessed 18 Aug. 2020.

Ecarma, Caleb. "Trump's China Coronavirus Conspiracy Is Infiltrating Intelligence Agencies." *Vanity Fair*, 30 Apr. 2020, www.vanityfair.com/news/2020/04/donald-trump-china-coronavirus-lab-conspiracy. Accessed 18 Aug. 2020.

Hansler, Jennifer, and Nicole Gaouette. "Pompeo Admits the US Can't Be Certain Coronavirus Outbreak Originated in Wuhan Lab." *CNN*, 6 May 2020, www.cnn.com/2020/05/06/politics/pompeo-wuhan-lab/index.html. Accessed 18 Aug. 2020.

Holland, Steve, and David Brunnstrom. "Trump Says U.S. Investigating Whether Virus Came from Wuhan Lab." *U.S. News and World Report*, 15 Apr. 2020, www.usnews.com/news/world/articles/2020-04-15/trump-says-us-investigating-whether-virus-came-from-wuhan-lab. Accessed 18 Aug. 2020.

Pompeo, Michael. "Secretary Pompeo Interview with Hugh Hewitt of the Hugh Hewitt Show." Interview by Hugh Hewitt. U.S. Dept. of State, 18 Apr. 2020, china.usembassy-china.org.cn/secretary-pompeo-interview-with-hugh-hewitt-of-the-hugh-hewitt-show/. Accessed 20 Aug. 2020

Sanger, David E. "Pompeo Ties Coronavirus to China Lab, Despite Spy Agencies' Uncertainty." *The New York Times*, 3 May 2020, www.nytimes.com/2020/05/03/us/politics/coronavirus-pompeo-wuhan-china-lab.html. Accessed 18 Aug. 2020.

# ■ Remarks by President Trump and Vice President Pence on the Formation of the Coronavirus Task Force

**Date:** February 26, 2020
**Authors:** Donald J. Trump; Mike Pence
**Genre:** speech

## Summary Overview

In late 2019, a novel coronavirus was detected in Wuhan, China, and quickly spread around the world during early 2020. In January 2020, the first carrier was identified in the United States, and the disease resulting from the virus, COVID-19, began to spread. US President Donald Trump had by then already downplayed the virus on a number of occasions, stating at various times that it was a "hoax" and that it would quickly vanish in the United States. By late February, the disease had slowly begun to spread in the United States, though epidemiologists were warning of an impending disaster because the virus would spread exponentially. On February 26, 2020, Trump announced the formation of a Coronavirus Task Force, to be headed by Vice President Mike Pence. But even as he announced the formation of the Task Force, Trump continued to downplay the seriousness of the situation.

## Defining Moment

Since early January and the growth of the COVID crisis in Wuhan, China, many had expected that the virus would eventually make its way to the United States. With the first cases coming about in the area in and around Seattle, Washington, fears of a pandemic spread quickly, and many looked to President Trump for guidance and a coordinated federal response to the crisis.

## Author Biographies

Donald J. Trump was born on June 14, 1946 in New York. He attended Fordham University in 1964 and received a bachelor's degree in economics from the University of Pennsylvania in 1966. After a career in business, he was elected president of the United States in 2016. President Trump and Vice President Mike Pence coordinated the federal response to the coronavirus crisis in early 2020. Though medical leaders such as Dr. Anthony Fauci and Dr. Deborah Birx were the public faces of the administration's efforts against the virus, the rhetoric used by Trump and Pence, who many accused of being guided more by politics than by science, often seemed to contradict the medical expertise of Fauci and Birx.

**HISTORICAL DOCUMENT: Remarks by President Trump, Vice President Pence, and Members of the Coronavirus Task Force in Press Conference: James S. Brady Briefing Room, Feb. 26, 2020**

President Trump: I have just received another briefing from a great group of talented people on the virus that is going around to various parts of the world. We have, through some very good early decisions—decisions that were actually ridiculed at the beginning—we closed up our borders to flights coming in from certain areas, areas that were hit by the coronavirus and hit pretty hard. And we did it very early. A lot of people thought we shouldn't have done it that early, and we did, and it turned out to be a very good thing.

And the number one priority from our standpoint is the health and safety of the American people. And that's the way I viewed it when I made that decision. Because of all we've done, the risk to the American people remains very low. We have the greatest experts in the world—really, in the world, right here—people that are called upon by other countries when things like this happen.

We—we're ready to adapt and we're ready to do whatever we have to as the disease spreads, if it spreads. As most of you know, the—the level that we've had in our country is very low, and those people are getting better, or we think that in almost all cases they're better, or getting. We have a total of 15. We took in some from Japan—you heard about that—because they are American citizens, and they're in quarantine. And they're getting better too.

But we felt we had an obligation to do that. It could have been as many as 42. And we found that we were—it was just an obligation we felt that we had. We could have left them, and that would have been very bad—very bad, I think—of American people. And they're recovering.

Of the 15 people—the "original 15," as I call them—8 of them have returned to their homes, to stay in their homes until fully recovered. One is in the hospital and five have fully recovered. And one is, we think, in pretty good shape and it's in between hospital and going home.

So we have a total of—but we have a total of 15 people, and they're in a process of recovering, with some already having fully recovered.

We started out by looking at certain things. We've been working with the Hill very, very carefully, very strongly. And I think we have very good bipartisan spirit for money.

We were asking for two and a half billion, and we think that's a lot, but the Democrats, and, I guess, Senator Schumer wants us to have much more than that. And normally, in life, I'd say, "We'll take it. We'll take it."

If they want to give more, we'll do more. We're going to spend whatever is appropriate. Hopefully, we're not going to have to spend so much because we really think we've done a great job in keeping it down to a minimum. And again, we've had tremendous success—tremendous success—beyond what people would have thought.

Now, at the same time, you do have some outbreaks in some countries. Italy and various countries are having some difficulty. China, you know about it, where it started.

I spoke with President Xi. We had a great talk. He's working very hard, I have to say. He's working very, very hard. And if you can count on the reports coming out of China, that spread has gone down quite a bit. The infection seems to have gone down over the last two days. As opposed to getting larger, it's actually gotten smaller. In one instance where we think we can be—it's somewhat reliable, it seems to have gotten quite a bit smaller.

With respect to the money that's being negotiated, they can do whatever they want. I mean, again, we'll do the two and a half. We're requesting two and a half. Some Republicans would like us to get four, and some Democrats would like us to get eight and a half. And we'll be satisfied whatever—whatever it is.

We're bringing in a specialist—a very highly regarded specialist—tomorrow, who works, actually, at the State Department. Very, very tremendously talented in doing this.

I want you to understand something that shocked me when I saw it that—and I spoke with Dr. Fauci on this, and I was really amazed, and I think most people are amazed to hear it: The flu, in our country, kills from 25,000 people to 69,000 people a year. That was shocking to me.

And, so far, if you look at what we have with the 15 people and their recovery, one is—one is pretty sick but hopefully will recover, but the others are in great shape. But think of that: 25,000 to 69,000.

Over the last 10 years, we've lost 360,000. These are people that have died from the flu—from what we call the flu. "Hey, did you get your flu shot?" And that's something.

Now, what we've done is we've stopped non-U.S. citizens from coming into America from China. That was done very early on. We're screening people, and we have been, at a very high level—screening people coming into the country from infected areas.

We have in quarantine those infected and those at risk. We have a lot of great quarantine facilities. We're rapidly developing a vaccine, and they can speak to you—the professionals can speak to you about that. The vaccine is coming along well. And in speaking to the doctors, we think this is something that we can develop fairly rapidly, a vaccine for the future, and coordinate with the support of our partners. We have great relationships with all of the countries that we're talking about. Some fairly large number of countries. Some it's one person, and many countries have no problem whatsoever. And we'll see what happens.

> *So we're at the low level. As they get better, we take them off the list, so that we're going to be pretty soon at only five people. ... So we've had very good luck.*

But we're very, very ready for this, for anything—whether it's going to be a breakout of larger proportions or whether or not we're—you know, we're at that very low level, and we want to keep it that way.

So we're at the low level. As they get better, we take them off the list, so that we're going to be pretty soon at only five people. And we could be at just one or two people over the next short period of time. So we've had very good luck.

The Johns Hopkins, I guess—is a highly respected, great place—they did a study, comprehensive: "The Countries Best and Worst Prepared for an Epidemic." And the United States is now—we're rated number one. We're rated number one for being prepared. This is a list of different countries.

I don't want to get in your way, especially since you do such a good job.

This is a list of the different countries. The United States is rated number one most prepared. United Kingdom, Netherlands, Australia, Canada, Thailand, Sweden, Denmark, South Korea, Finland. These—this is a list of the best-rated countries in the world by Johns Hopkins.

We're doing something else that's important to me, because he's been terrific in many ways, but he's also very good on healthcare. And we really followed him very closely—a lot of states do—when Mike was governor—Mike Pence—of Indiana. They've established great healthcare. They have a great system there. It's a system that a lot of—a lot of the other states have really looked to and changed their systems. They wanted to base it on the Indiana system. It's very good. And I think—and he's, really, very expert at the field.

And what I've done is I'm going to be announcing, exactly right now, that I'm going to be putting our Vice President, Mike Pence, in charge. And Mike will be working with the professionals, doctors, and everybody else that's working. The team is brilliant. I spent a lot of time with the team over the last couple of weeks, but they're totally brilliant, and we're doing really well. And Mike is going to be in charge, and Mike will report back to me. But he's got a certain talent for this.

And I'm going to ask Mike Pence to say a few words. Please. Thank you. Mike?

Vice President Pence: Thank you, Mr. President. President Trump has made clear from the first days of this administration: We have no higher priority than the safety, security, health, and wellbeing of the American people.

And from the first word of a outbreak of the coronavirus, the President took unprecedented steps to protect the American people from the spread of this disease. He recounted those briefly, but the establishment of travel restrictions, aggressive quarantine effort of Americans that are returning, the declaration of a public health emergency, and establishing the White House Corona[virus] Task Force are all reflective of the urgency that the President has brought to a whole-of-government approach.

As a former governor from the state where the first MERS case emerged in 2014, I know full well the importance of presidential leadership, the importance of administration leadership, and the vital role of partnerships of state and local governments and health authorities in responding to the potential threat of dangerous infectious diseases.

And I—I look forward, Mr. President, to serving in this role. I'm bringing together all the members of the Corona Task Force that you've established: HHS, CDC, DHS, the Department of Transportation, and State. This team has been, at your direction, Mr. President, meeting every day since it was established.

My role will be to continue to bring that team together; to bring to the President the best options for action; to see to the safety and wellbeing and health of the American people.

We'll also be continuing to reach out to governors, state and local officials. In fact, in recent days, the White House met with over 40 state, county, and city health officials from over 30 states and territories to discuss how to respond to this—to the potential threat of the coronavirus. We'll be working with them in renewed ways to make sure they have the resources to be able to respond.

And as the President said, we'll be adding additional personnel here at the White House to support our efforts on the President's behalf.

We'll also be working with members of Congress to ensure that the resources are available for this whole-of-government response, and we'll be working very closely with Secretary Azar and his team that have done an outstanding job communicating to the public to ensure the American people have the best information on ways to protect themselves and their families, and also that the public has the most timely information on the potential threat to the American people.

Mr. President, as we've been briefed, while the threat to the American public remains low of a spread of the coronavirus, you have directed this team to take all steps necessary to continue to ensure the health and wellbeing of the American people.

And the people of this country can be confident that, under your leadership, we will continue to bring the full resources of the federal government, in coordination with our state and local partners, to see to the health and wellbeing and to the effective response to the coronavirus here in the United States of America.

## GLOSSARY

**COVID-19:** the disease caused by the novel coronavirus (SARS-CoV-2), which spread rapidly around the world during early 2020

**National Institutes of Health (NIH):** the main agency in the United States government responsible for public health and responding to health-related crises; a part of the NIH, the National Institute of Allergy and Infectious Diseases (NIAID), helps to formulate federal policy in the face of pandemics such as that caused by the coronavirus

*President Donald Trump meets with the Coronavirus Task Force, March 2020.*

## Document Analysis

US President Trump held a press conference on February 26, 2020, during which he announced the formation of the Coronavirus Task Force, to be headed by Vice President Mike Pence, while at the same time downplaying the severity of the virus. Trump began by taking credit for a number of actions he claimed would result in the risk to Americans remaining very low, such as discontinuing flights coming into the United States from affected areas like Wuhan, China. Claiming that only 15 Americans had contracted the virus, some of them returning from a cruise ship off the coast of Japan, Trump continued to try to quell Americans' fears of a virus that had already infected tens of thousands in China.

While stating that the risk remained low, Trump stated that his administration was "ready to adapt and ready to do whatever we have to as the disease spreads, if it spreads." To that end, Trump announced that Vice President Mike Pence would head a Coronavirus Task Force, which Pence stated would "bring the full resources of the federal government . . . to see to the health and well-being and to the effective response to the coronavirus in the United States of America."

But while Trump and Pence downplayed the virus others on the task force, such as Dr. Fauci of the NIAID, saw the outbreak in more stark terms, stating that the United States may have a difficult time controlling the virus until a vaccine could be developed, which he said could take a year to 18 months. Trump, who had already Tweeted numerous times downplaying the severity of the crisis, equivocated a bit after Fauci's comments, responding to a question about whether or not the virus would spread in the United States by stating that "[i]t probably will. It possibly will. It could be at a very small level, or it could be at a larger level. . . Nothing is inevitable."

Trump's comments downplaying the virus were seen by many as contrasting assessments by leaders in the scientific and medical communities, such as Fauci. At various times during February and March 2020, Trump had labeled the disease outbreak a "Democratic hoax" designed by the opposition party to make him look bad and cause panic on Wall Street, and also argued that it would be gone completely in a matter of weeks. However, as the number of those infected grew, Trump's reassurances that the virus was under control came under increased scrutiny.

Critics of the president pointed out the fact that the administration had reduced the budget for the Centers for Disease Control and Prevention (CDC) and the National Institutes of Health (NIH). The pandemic task force that had been in place during the George W. Bush and Barack Obama administrations was eliminated early in the Trump presidency. By the time of the February 26 press conference, the number of infections in the United States was over 60 (as compared to the 15 cited by Trump) and beginning to grow.

## Essential Themes

By the time of Trump's press conference, both the medical and business communities had already begun to see that the outbreak was likely to become a pandemic. Just the day before the press conference, the CDC had issued a warning that stated that the spread of COVID-19 inside the United States was inevitable. Schools and businesses had begun to prepare for disruptions caused by the necessity of students and workers remaining at home. The week of the press conference, the Dow Jones Industrial Average dropped over 2,000 points as the true nature of the crisis was becoming clear.

Trump's claim that "we could be at just one or two people over the next short period of time" seemed unrealistic to many at the time, much more so four months later, with the number of infections passing four million—more than any other nation in the world. The federal response to the crisis has been criticized internationally, from many state and local officials, and caused Trump's approval ratings to fall dramatically.

—*Steven L. Danver, PhD*

## Bibliography and Additional Reading

Choi, Matthew. "Trump Puts Pence in Charge of Coronavirus Response." *Politico*, 26 Feb. 2020, www.politico.com/news/2020/02/26/trump-puts-pence-in-charge-of-coronavirus-response-117790. Accessed 18 Aug. 2020.

Edelman, Adam. "Trump Says Coronavirus Risk to Americans 'Very Low,' Puts Pence in Charge of Gov't Response." *NBC News*, 26 Feb. 2020, www.nbcnews.com/politics/donald-trump/trump-says-coronavirus-risk-americans-very-low-administration-effectively-handling-n1143756. Accessed 18 Aug. 2020.

Lardieri, Alexa. "Trump to Hold Press Conference on Coronavirus." *US News and World Report*. 26 Feb. 2020, www.usnews.com/news/politics/articles/2020-02-26/donald-trump-to-hold-press-conference-on-coronavirus-threat-in-us. Accessed 18 Aug. 2020.

Olorunnipa, Toluse, et al. "Trump Downplays Risk, Places Pence in Charge of Coronavirus Outbreak Response." *The Washington Post*, 26 Feb. 2020, www.washingtonpost.com/politics/trump-downplays-risk-places-pence-in-charge-of-coronavirus-outbreak-response/2020/02/26/ab246e94-58b1-11ea-9000-f3cffee23036_story.html. Accessed 18 Aug. 2020.

Romo, Vanessa. "Trump Appoints Pence to Lead Government's Coronavirus Response." *NPR*, 26 Feb. 2020, www.npr.org/sections/health-shots/2020/02/26/809578063/trump-to-address-response-to-coronavirus. Accessed 18 Aug. 2020.

# ■ COVID-19 Brings Health Disparities Research to the Forefront

**Date:** May 18, 2020
**Author:** Dr. Eliseo Pérez-Stable
**Genre:** Interview

## Summary Overview

On May 18, 2020 Dr. Francis Collins, Director of the National Institutes of Health (NIH), interviewed Dr. Eliseo Pérez-Stable, Director of the National Institute on Minority Health and Health Disparities (NIMHD) about the impact of COVID-19 on racial and ethnic minority communities. Pérez-Stable stated that available studies revealed that racial and ethnic minorities had been disproportionately impacted by COVID-19. Although freely acknowledging that there is still much to learn about COVID-19's impact on minority communities, Pérez-Stable argued that the socio-economic circumstances faced by many minorities made them more susceptible to exposure to the disease. Inequalities in the health-care system have created additional barriers preventing minorities from getting proper diagnosis and care.

## Defining Moment

On January 9, 2020, the World Health Organization (WHO) announced that a mysterious and highly contagious disease had been identified in Wuhan, China. The disease, which resembled pneumonia in its effects, would soon be labelled COVID-19. Although it was unclear whether the disease originated in Wuhan, cases were soon reported in Thailand and Japan. On January 21, the Centers for Disease Control and Prevention (CDC) confirmed the first case in the United States. That same day, Chinese scientists confirmed that the disease could be transmitted from person to person, and a few days later China placed Wuhan under lockdown. By early February, the United States had declared a public health emergency, and restrictions were placed on foreign air travel into the country. On March 11, as the virus continued to spread, the WHO declared COVID-19 a global pandemic.

In reacting to a significant rise in cases, on March 19, California was the first state to issue a stay-at-home order to its residents. Within a few weeks, dozens of other states issued similar orders. On March 27 the Coronavirus Aid, Relief, and Economic Security (CARES) Act was approved by Congress, providing $2 trillion in aid for hospitals, small businesses, and state and local governments, along with direct payments to workers and extensions in unemployment insurance. However, inconsistent and often contradictory messaging from the federal government left many Americans confused and unsure about the nature of the disease or how best to prevent transmission. Throughout April, COVID-19 spread throughout the country. Ignoring this development, the Trump administration at one point proposed reopening the economy in time for Easter in April.

By May 12, the United States reported 80,000 deaths from COVID-19, a number that Anthony Fauci, MD, director of the National Institute of Allergy and Infectious Diseases (NI-

AID), stated was probably an underestimation. A little over two weeks later, the death toll from COVID rose to 100,000. It was in this context that Dr. Collins's interview with Dr. Pérez-Stable took place.

## Author Biography

Dr. Eliseo Pérez-Stable was born in Cuba but grew up in Miami, Florida. He earned a B.A. in chemistry and then an M.D. at the University of Miami. He completed his residency in primary care internal medicine at the University of Cali-fornia, San Francisco. Prior to his appointment as director at NIMHD, Dr. Pérez-Stable was a professor of medicine and chief of the Division of General Internal Medicine at the University of California, San Francisco (UCSF). He was also previously director of the UCSF Center for Aging in Diverse Communities. His research has centered on examining strategies for reducing smoking among minorities, as well as studying health disparities in elderly minority populations. In 2015, he was chosen as director of NIMHD.

## HISTORICAL DOCUMENT: COVID-19 Brings Health Disparities Research to the Forefront

Posted on May 14th, 2020 by Dr. Francis Collins

National Institutes of Health, Director's Blog: directorsblog.nih.gov/2020/05/14/covid-19-brings-health-disparities-research-to-the-forefront/.

The coronavirus 2019 (COVD-19) pandemic has brought into sharp focus many of the troubling things that we already knew about health disparities in the United States but have failed to address. With the bright light now shining on this important issue, it is time to talk about the role research can play in reducing the disproportionate burden of COVID-19, as well as improving the health of *all* people in our great nation.

In recent weeks, we've seen a growing list of disturbing statistics about how blacks, Hispanics, tribal communities, and some other racial, ethnic, and disadvantaged socioeconomic groups are bearing the brunt of COVID-19. One of the latest studies comes from a research team that analyzed county-by-county data gathered about a month ago. Their findings? The 22 percent of U.S. counties that are disproportionately black accounted for 52 percent of our nation's COVID-19 cases and 58 percent of COVID-19 deaths. In a paper awaiting peer review, the team, led by Emory University, Atlanta, and amfAR, the Foundation for AIDS Research, Washington, DC., noted that neither the size of the county nor whether it was urban or rural mattered [1].

Recently, I had an opportunity to discuss the disparate burden of COVID-19 with Dr. Eliseo Pérez-Stable, Director of NIH's National Institute on Minority Health and Health Disparities (NIMHD). Besides leading an institute, Dr. Pérez-Stable is a widely recognized researcher who studies various factors that contribute to health disparities. Our conversation took place via videoconferencing, with him linking in from his home in Washington, D.C., and me from my home in nearby Maryland. Here's a condensed transcript of our chat:

**Collins:** Eliseo, you and I recently had a chance to have a pretty intense discussion with the Congressional Black Caucus about health disparities and the COVID-19 pandemic. So, could you start off with a little bit about what populations are being hit hardest?

**Pérez-Stable:** Collecting data about disease incidence and mortality on the basis of race and ethnicity and other important demographic factors, like socioeconomic status, had really been absent in this pandemic until recently.

Part of that I think is entirely understandable. Hospitals were pressed with a surge of very sick patients, and there was a certain amount of fear and panic in the community. So, people were not completing all these forms that usually get turned in to the health departments and then forwarded to the CDC. If you go back in history, similar things happened in the early 1980s with the HIV epidemic. We weren't collecting data on race and other sociodemographic variables initially. But, with time, we did complete these data and a picture emerged.

With the COVID-19 pandemic, obviously, the outcomes are much faster, with over 60,000 deaths in just a matter of three months. And we started to see reports, initially out of Connecticut, Milwaukee, Chicago, and New Orleans, that African Americans were dying at a disproportionate rate.

Now, the initial—and I think still the most likely—explanation for this higher mortality relates to two factors. The first is a higher rate of co-morbidities. We know that if you have cardiovascular disease, more than mild obesity, or diabetes, you're more likely to get severe COVID-19 and potentially die from it. So, we could have just said, "Aha! It's obvious why this population, and others with higher rates of co-morbidities might be expected to have higher rates of severe disease and higher mortality."

But there is a second factor that relates to getting infected, for which we have much-less clear data. There was recently a map in *The Washington Post* showing the distribution of the rate of COVID-19 infections in Washington, D.C., by ward. The highest rates are in the wards that are east of the Anacostia River, which are about 90 percent African American. So, there is an appearance of a correlation between the proportion of African Americans in the community and the rate of Covid-19 infection. Now why could that be?

**Collins:** Yes, what explains that?

**Pérez-Stable:** Well, I think crowding is part of it, certainly in this neighborhood. A second option would be multiple families living under one roof.

**Collins:** So, you can't exactly practice physical distancing very well in that situation.

**Pérez-Stable:** Absolutely. You and I can go into our respective rooms, probably have our respective bathrooms, and socially and physically isolate from the rest of the household if need be. Many people can't do that. They have three generations in one small apartment, all using one bathroom, maybe two bedrooms for six or eight people.

*Of course, uninsured patients will have even more barriers, although everyone in the healthcare system is trying their best to help patients when they need to be helped, rather than depend on insurance triage.*

So, we do face different conditions by which one casual infection can lead to much more community transmission. But much information still needs to be ascertained and there does seem to be some regional variance. For example, in Chicago, Milwaukee, and Atlanta, the reports, at least initially, are worse than they are in Connecticut or Florida. Also, New York City, which has been the epicenter of the U.S. for this pandemic, has an increased rate of infections and mortality among Latino-Hispanic populations as well. So, it isn't isolated to an African-American issue.

**Collins:** What about access to healthcare?

**Pérez-Stable:** Again, we can postulate based on a little bit of anecdote and a little bit of data. I'm a general internist by background, and I can see the enormous impact this pandemic has had on healthcare settings.

First, elective ambulatory visits and elective admissions to the hospital have been postponed, delayed, or cancelled. About 90 percent of ambulatory care is occurring through telemedicine or telephone connections, so in-person visits are occurring only for really urgent matters or suspected COVID-19.

If you have health insurance and can use systems, you can probably, through telephone triage with a nurse, get either approval or nonapproval for being tested [for COVID-19], drive to a place, get tested by someone wearing protective equipment, and never actually have to visit with anyone. And you'll get your result now back as soon as one day, depending on the system. Now, if you're insured, but don't really know how to use systems, navigating all these things can be a huge challenge. So, that could be a factor.

People are also afraid to come to clinic, they're afraid to show up at the emergency room, because they're afraid to get infected. So, they're worried about going in, unless they get very sick. And when they get very sick, they may be coming in with more advanced cases [of COVID-19].

So, telephone triage, advice from clinicians on the phone, is critical. We are seeing some doctors base their decisions on whether a person is able to breathe okay on the phone, able to say a whole sentence without catching their breath. These kinds of basic things that we learned in clinical medicine training are coming into play in a big way now, because we just cannot provide the kind of care, even in the best of circumstances, that people may need.

Of course, uninsured patients will have even more barriers, although everyone in the healthcare system is trying their best to help patients when they need to be helped, rather than depend on insurance triage.

**Collins:** A big part of trying to keep the disease from spreading has been access to testing so that people, even those with mild symptoms, can find out if they have this virus and, if so, quarantine and enable public health workers to check out their contacts. I'm guessing, from what you said, that testing has been happening a lot less in urban communities that are heavily populated by African Americans and that further propagates the spread of the disease. Am I right?

**Pérez-Stable:** So far, most testing has been conducted on the basis of symptoms. So, if you have enough symptoms that you may potentially need to be hospitalized, then you get tested. Also, if you're a healthcare worker who had contact with a COVID-19 patient, you might be tested, or if there's someone you've been very close to that was infected, you may be tested. So, I don't think so much it's a matter of disproportionate access to testing by one group or another, as much as that the overall triage and selection criteria for testing have been rather narrow. Up until now, it has not been a simple process to get tested for COVID-19. As we scale up and get better point-of-care tests and much easier access to getting tested, I think you'll see dissemination across the board.

**Collins:** It's interesting we're talking about this, because this is an area that Congress recently came to NIH and said, "We want you to do something about the testing by encouraging more technology, particularly technology that can be distributed to the point-of-care, and that is out in the community."

Everyone wants a test that gives you a quick turnaround, an answer within an hour, instead of maybe a day or two. A big part of what NIH is trying to do is to make sure that if we're going to develop these new testing technologies, they get deployed in places that otherwise might not have much access to testing—maybe by working through the community health centers. So, we're hoping we might be able to make a contribution there.

**Pérez-Stable**: The economic factors in this pandemic are also huge. A significant proportion of the population that we're referring to—the disparity population, the minorities, the poor people—work in service jobs where they're on the front line. They were the restaurant servers and people in the kitchen, they're still the bus drivers and the Uber drivers, and those who are working in pharmacies and supermarkets.

On the one hand, they are at higher risk for getting infected because they're in more contact with people. On the other hand, they're really dependent on this income to maintain their household. So, if they test positive or get exposed to COVID-19, we really do have a challenge when we ask them to quarantine and not go to work. They're not in a position where they have sick leave, and they may be putting themselves at risk for being laid off.

**Collins:** Eliseo, you've been studying health disparities pretty much your whole research career. You come from a community where health disparities are a reality, having been born in Cuba and being part of the Latino community. Did you expect that COVID-19 would be this dramatic in the ways in which it has so disproportionately affected certain groups?

**Pérez-Stable**: I can't say that I did. My first thought as a physician was to ask: "Is there any reason to think that an infectious agent like COVID-19 would disproportionally infect or impact any population?" My gut answer was "No." Infectious diseases usually seem to affect all people; sort of equal opportunity invaders. There are some data that would say that influenza and pneumonia are not any worse among African Americans or Latinos than among whites. There are some slight differences in some regions, but not much.

Yet I know this a question that NIH-funded scientists are interested in addressing. We need to make sure that there aren't any particular susceptibility factors, possibly related to genetics or the lung epithelium, that lead to such different COVID-19 outcomes in different individuals. Clearly, something must be going on, but we don't know what that is. Maybe one of those factors tracks through race or ethnicity because of what those social constructs represent.

I recently listened to a presentation by Rob Califf, former FDA Commissioner, who spoke about how the pandemic has created a spotlight on our disparities-creating system. I think much of the time this disparities-creating system is in the background; it doesn't really affect most people's daily lives. Now, we're suddenly hit with a bucket of cold water called COVID-19, and we're saying what is going on and what can we do about it to make a difference. I hope that, once we begin to emerge from this acute crisis, we take the opportunity to address these fundamental issues in our society.

**Collins:** Indeed. Let's talk about what you're doing at NIMHD to support research to try to dig into both the causes of health disparities and the interventions that might help.

**Pérez-Stable:** Prompted by your motivation, we started talking about how minority health and health disparities research could respond to this pandemic. In the short-term, we thought along the lines of how can we communicate mitigation interventions, such as physical distancing, in a more effective way to our communities? We also asked what we could do to enhance access to healthcare for our populations, both to manage chronic conditions and for diagnosis and treatment of acute COVID-19.

We also considered in the mid- and long-term effects of economic disruption—this surge of unemployment, loss of jobs, loss of insurance, loss of income—on people's health. Worries include excess use of alcohol and other substances, and worsening of mental and emotional well-being, particularly due to severe depression and chronic mental disorders not being well controlled. Intimate partner violence has already been noted to increase in some countries, including France, Spain, and the United States, that have gone on physical distancing interventions. Similarly, child abuse can be exacerbated under these circumstances. Just think of 24/7 togetherness as a test of how people can hold it together all the time. I think that that can bring out some fragility. So, interventions to address these, that really activate our community networks and community-based organizations, are real strengths. They build on the resilience of the community to highlight how we can get through this difficult period of time.

I feel optimistic that science will bring answers, in the form of both therapies and vaccines. But in the meantime, we have a way to go and we a lot to do.

**Collins:** You mentioned the promise of vaccines. The NIH is working intensively on this, particularly through a partnership called ACTIV, Accelerating Covid-19 Therapeutic Interventions and Vaccines. We hope that in several more months, we'll be in a position to begin testing these vaccines on a large scale, after having some assurances about their safety and efficacy. From our conversation, it sounds like we should be trying to get early access to those vaccines to people at highest risk, including those in communities with the heaviest burden. But how will that be received? There hasn't always been an easy relationship between researchers, particularly government researchers, and the African-American community.

**Pérez-Stable:** I think we have learned from our historical experiences that mistrust of the system is real. To try to pretend that it isn't there is a big mistake. Address these concerns upfront, obtain support from thought leaders in the community, and really work hard to be inclusive. In addition to vaccines, we need participation in any clinical trials that are coming up for therapeutics.

We also need research on how optimally to communicate this with all the different segments of the population. This includes not just explaining what it means to be eligible for vaccine trials or therapeutic trials, but also discussing the consequences of, say, getting tested, whether it be a viral or antibody test. What does the information mean for them?

Most people just want to know "Am I clear of the virus or not?" That certainly could be part of the answer, but many may require more nuanced responses. Then there's behavior. If I'm infected and I recover, am I safe to go back out and do things that other people shouldn't do? We'd love to be able to inform the population about that. But, as you know, we don't really have the answers to that just yet.

**Collins:** Good points. How do we make sure, when we're trying to reach out to populations that have shouldered such a heavy burden, that we're actually providing information in a fashion that is readily understood?

**Pérez-Stable:** One thing to keep in mind is the issue of language. About 5 to 10 percent of U.S. adults don't speak English well. So, we really have to address the language barrier. I also want to highlight the challenge that some tribal nations are facing. Navajo country has had particular challenges with COVID-19 infections in a setting of minimal medical infrastructure. In fact, there are communities that have to go and get their water for the day at a distant site, so they don't have modern plumbing. How can we recommend frequent hand washing to someone who doesn't even have running water at home? These are just a few examples of the diversity of our country that need to be addressed as we deal with this pandemic.

**Collins:** Eliseo, you've given us a lot to think about in an obviously very serious situation. Anything you'd like to add?

**Pérez-Stable:** In analyzing health outcomes, researchers often think about responses related to a metabolic pathway or to a gene or to a response to a particular drug. But as we use the power of science to understand and contain the COVID-19 pandemic, I'd like to re-emphasize the importance of considering race, ethnicity, socioeconomic status, the built environment, the social environment, and systems. Much of the time these factors may only play secondary roles, but, as in all science related to humans, I think they have to be considered. This experience should be a lesson for us to learn more about that.

**Collins:** Thank you for those wonderful, inspiring words. It was good to have this conversation, Eliseo, because we are the National Institutes of Health, but that has to be health for everybody. With COVID-19, we have an example where that has not turned out to be the case. We need to do everything we can going forward to identify ways to change that.

## Document Analysis

On May 18, 2020 Dr. Francis Collins, Director of NIH, interviewed Dr. Eliseo Pérez-Stable, Director of NIMHD about the impact of COVID-19 on racial and ethnic minority communities. Before the interview began, it was noted that recent studies have revealed that "blacks, Hispanics, tribal communities and some other racial, ethnic, and disadvantaged socioeconomic groups are bearing the brunt of COVID-19." Most notably, a recent study found that 22 percent of US counties are disproportionately black. These same counties have accounted for 52 percent of COVID cases and 58 percent of COVID deaths.

The interview with Pérez-Stable begins with his acknowledgement that there is still a lot to be learned about the impact of COVID on minority communities. As the pandemic spread throughout the United States, the focus was understandably on helping patients and not collecting data "on race and other sociodemographic variables." He notes that a similar scenario occurred in the 1980s during the HIV epidemic, when it took some time before the medical community properly investigated its impact on different communities. However, after more than 60,000 people died of COVID, it was becoming clearer that African Americans and other minorities were dying at disproportionate rates.

Pérez-Stable notes that one of the likely reasons for this disparity is that African Americans in particular are disproportionately impacted by "co-morbidities" such as cardiovascular disease, obesity, and diabetes. However, there are also socio-economic circumstances that explain the disproportionate impact of COVID on African Americans and other minority communities. He notes that in cities, like Chicago, Milwaukee, Atlanta, and especially New York with large minority communities, social distancing is much more difficult as populations are more congested, and housing is often shared between more people.

Pérez-Stable also argues that minority communities are more likely to have problems accessing health care. This problem has only increased during COVID as a high percentage of "elective ambulatory visits and elective admissions to the hospital have been postponed, delayed, or cancelled." Not helping matters, sick people who might otherwise seek medical care avoid going to the doctor for fear of contracting COVID. These barriers become all the more pronounced for people with inadequate health insurance policies or no insurance at all. CO-VID testing has also been a major challenge. Pérez-Stable points out that COVID testing so far has been fairly narrow as only medical workers, those showing obvious symptoms, and people who have interacted with people who have tested positive for COVID have had full access to testing.

Pérez-Stable identifies a number of other economic factors that may explain high rates of infection among minority communities. He notes that minorities and poor people are more likely to work in employment that places them at disproportionate risk for contracting CO-VID. He argues that "the minorities, the poor people—work in service jobs where they're on the front line. They were the restaurant servers and people in the kitchen, they're still the bus drivers and the Uber drivers, and those working in pharmacies and supermarkets." Working in these jobs places them at high risk of exposure because they constantly deal with the public. As well, given that these jobs are mostly low paying and lack adequate benefits, workers holding them often can not afford to take leave of work, let alone quarantine in response to possible exposure. If they miss work, they risk losing their jobs. They are in a difficult, if not impossible position.

Pérez-Stable acknowledges that there is still a lot to learn about why COVID has had such a disproportionate impact on minority communities, African Americans and Latinos in particular. Although there could be medical reasons why these communities could be more susceptible to COVID, he thinks that this is not the case. He notes that "Infectious diseases usually seem to affect all people; sort of equal opportunity invaders."

However, Pérez-Stable is also adamant that it is the responsibility of medical professionals to respond properly and effectively to the spread of COVID in minority communities. This will require short-term solutions like encouraging so-cial distancing, as well as "enhancing access to healthcare for our populations, both to manage chronic conditions and for diagnosis and treatment of acute COVID-19." As well, the long-term economic impact of the pandemic must be dealt with, including unemployment and loss of medical insurance.

Lastly, it is important that the medical profession recognizes that many communities mistrust the medical system because of past historical injustices. It is imperative that medical professionals provide an inclusive and welcoming environment for all communities, but especially those disproportionately impacted by COVID. Pérez-Stable concludes with a plea that we understand the "importance of race, ethnicity, socioeconomic status, the built environment, the social environment, and systems" when discussing the impact of COVID-19.

## Essential Themes

In the months following Collins's interview with Pérez-Stable, the number of COVID cases continued to rise both globally and within the United States. By the end of June, the number of cases globally had reached 10,475,817 with 511,251 deaths. The United States represented 25 percent of both the total number of cases, 2,627,584, and deaths, 127,251. (The United States' population as a percentage of the world population is 4.25 percent.)

As the number of cases of COVID rose, available evidence continued to suggest that the pandemic disproportionately impacted minority communities. On July 14, 2020, an article published by the American Heart Association confirmed many of Pérez-Stable's claims. It noted another study that found that African Americans account for 33 percent of COVID hospitalizations despite comprising 18 percent of the sample population. It also cited another study that found that while African Americans comprised 32 percent of the population in Louisiana, they accounted for 70 percent of COVID related deaths. It also identified some of the same socio-economic factors that Pérez-Stable mentioned as responsible for high rates of infection among African Americans.

Equally significant on July 24, the Centers for Disease Control and Prevention (CDC) released a statement titled "Health Equity Considerations and Racial and Ethnic Minority Groups" which acknowledged that there is considerable evidence that COVID-19 has had a disproportionate impact on racial and ethnic minority groups. Echoing Pérez-Stable's earlier analysis, the CDC cited "long-standing systematic health and social inequalities" as contributing factors for the high rates of COVID-19 among minority groups. Although there remains much to be learned about the full impact of COVID on minority communities, this statement confirms Pérez-Stable's arguments that COVID has thus far had a disproportionate impact on racial and ethnic minority communities. As well, long-standing socio-economic inequalities have also contributed to its disproportionate impact on minority communities.

—*Gerald F. Goodwin, PhD*

## Bibliography and Additional Reading

Haynes, Norrisa,et al. "At the Heart of the Matter: Unmasking and Addressing the Toll of COVID-19 on Diverse Populations," *Journal of American Heart Association*, vol. 42, no. 2, 14 July 2020, pp. 105–07, org/10.1161/CIRCULATIONAHA.120.048126. Accessed 18 Aug. 2020.

"Health Equity Considerations and Racial and Ethnic Minority Groups," *Centers for Disease Control and Prevention*, 24 July 2020, www.cdc.gov/coronavirus/2019-ncov/community/health-equity/race-ethnicity.html. Accessed 18 Aug. 2020.

Price-Haygood, E.G. et al. "Hospitalization and Mortality among Black Patients and White Patients with Covid-19," *New England Journal of Medicine*, 2020, vol. 382, pp. 2534–43, doi:10.1056/NEJMsa2011686. Accessed 18 Aug. 2020.

"A Timeline of COVID-19 Developments in 2020," *The American Journal of Managed Care*, 3 July 2020, www.ajmc.com/view/a-timeline-of-covid19-developments-in-2020. Accessed 18 Aug. 2020.

# SCOURGES OF WAR

War has often proved an incubator of disease outbreaks. During the Peloponnesian War (431–404 BCE), an epidemic of plague in 430 BCE killed some 30,000 Athenians and caused their enemies, the Spartans, to abandon plans for an invasion of Attica because their troops feared contracting the illness. During the Spanish colonization of the Americas, the conquistadores brought numerous diseases with them to the New World, killing in some cases up to 90 percent of indigenous populations, the members of which had no natural immunity against these scourges.

The American Civil War was accompanied by massive numbers of deaths—possibly as much as 60 percent or more of all war deaths—due to outbreaks of dysentery, malaria, measles, typhoid fever, typhus, scarlet fever, pneumonia, tuberculosis, syphilis, and other diseases. Letters sent home to families of victims generally named action in a specific engagement as the cause of death, but the reality was that death came just as often as a result of disease outbreaks in soldier camps and field hospitals.

In World War I, many of these same diseases were present (though not in the same proportions) even as Allied troops, in addition, faced chemical attacks (e.g., mustard gas) and soldiers in the trenches everywhere experienced the effects of shell shock, or what we would call today post-traumatic stress disorder (PTSD). Near the end of the war, a worldwide pandemic of influenza ("Spanish Flu") impacted troops and civilian populations alike, ultimately infecting some 500 million people and killing between 15 and 45 million—the worst disease outbreak in human history in terms of sheer numbers dead.

World War II saw the use of nuclear weapons, which killed around 200,000 civilians in Hiroshima and Nagasaki (Japan), and likely an equal number in post-bombing cases of radiation poisoning, cancer, fatal birth defects, and other complications due to radiation exposure. As a result, international controls were put in place on the use of such weapons—together with a comprehensive biological weapons ban in 1972. The latter came also in the aftermath of the use of the toxic defoliant Agent Orange during the Vietnam War, which left lingering damaging effects in both US and Vietnamese soldier populations as well as in exposed civilian populations.

# ■ The First Gas Attack

**Date:** April 22, 1915 (account published 1921)
**Authors:** Amos A. Fries and Clarence J. West
**Genre:** article; essay

## Summary Overview

This document, taken from the second chapter of the book *Chemical Warfare*, was an attempt to keep poison gas warfare in the minds of the public and to convince them that this was not only a weapon to be used in warfare, but something that might serve other purposes. Thus, in this section of the book, in addition to a description of the horrendous results of the first gas attack, there is also an editorial section lauding the use of these chemical weapons as "most humane." General Fries was a strong advocate of chemical warfare throughout his time in the army. This short essay presented 1) the military reason why gas attacks might be used in the future, 2) an opposite view as to why they would not owing to the terrible consequences of such attacks, and 3) strong advocacy for keeping chemical weapons in use by the person in charge of the Chemical Warfare Service of the United States Army.

## Defining Moment

Although European agreements against using poisoned weapons go back to the seventeenth century, the scale on which poisonous gases were used in World War I exceeded anything that most people could have imagined. Although these weapons did not swing the tide of the war in either direction, they did inflict more than a million casualties—i.e., injuries or deaths. The images of the human destruction that had occurred affected many millions more. Even though in 1899 most nations had agreed not to use "asphyxiating or deleterious gases," that agreement had not held. General Fries, as head of the Chemical Warfare Service, was charged with keeping the United States safe from gas attacks, as well as with using these weapons against potential enemies if it came to that. With the United States finally ready to sign a peace treaty with Germany in 1921, diplomats started to look at other areas where there might be cooperation. A new treaty outlawing the *use* of chemical weapons was one such area.

Fries believed that it was necessary not only to give an accurate account of events during the First World War, but to advocate for continued research and preparation for the future use of chemical weapons. As a result, he and Clarence West wrote this book to convey their knowledge and views on the subject.

Because of the technical nature of the book, it is highly unlikely that leaders in the American government ever read the full text; but its publication did raise the issue of preparedness. The treaty proposed by the United States in 1922 was not accepted by all the European powers because it included provisions on the use of submarines in addition to chemical weapons. However, in 1925, the Geneva Protocol was accepted by all of the major nations of the world, thus outlawing the use of chemical weapons. While this might seem to have been a loss for Fries, and for those with similar mindsets, it was actually a victory. It allowed him to continue the work that had been his focus since World War I. The Geneva Protocol outlawed the use of such weapons, not any research, development, production, or deployment of them (e.g., as a deterrent). While Fries did advocate using gas, both militarily and in selected civilian applications, his point of view on preparedness did carry the day in Geneva. The United States, and other countries, were able to continue their chemical weapons research as they might desire. Articles and books such as this one by Fries and West resulted in a much more limited international agreement than many had sought.

## Author Biography

Amos A. Fries (1873–1963) was a graduate of the US Military Academy and served more than thirty years on active duty. He was in the Army Corps of Engineers, and worked on diverse projects, such as roads in Yellowstone Park, a canal in Oregon, and the Los Angeles Harbor. In World War I, he was assigned to develop the emerging Gas Service Section, later the Chemical Warfare Service. From that time on, he ad-

vocated for the use of, and preparedness for, gas attacks. He also pushed civilian uses, such as in security systems, and he helped develop the gas chamber for criminal executions. He was an active anti-communist, viewing most who opposed him as communists. He was politically outspoken, including by his strong advocacy of chemical weapons.

Clarence Jay West (1886–1953) was a chemist pulled into what became the Chemical Warfare Service during World War I. West was a career employee of the National Research Council, ending up as director of the Research Information Service. For most of his career, he worked on technical issues and compiled lists/bibliographies of chemistry publications. His contribution would seem to have been more in the seventeen chapters (out of twenty-six) that dealt with the chemistry of chemical weapons and defenses, rather than in the sections like the one represented by this document

## HISTORICAL DOCUMENT: The First Gas Attack

The first suggestion of a gas attack came to the British Army through the story of a German deserter. He stated that the German Army was planning to poison their enemy with a cloud of gas, and that the cylinders had already been installed in the trenches. No one listened to the story, because, first of all, the whole procedure seemed so impossible and also because, in spite of the numerous examples of German barbarity, the English did not believe the Germans capable of such a violation of the Hague rules of warfare. The story appeared in the summary of information from headquarters and, as [British Colonel S.J.M.] Auld says, "was passed for information for what it is worth." But the story was true, and on the afternoon of the 22nd of April [1915], all the conditions being ideal, the beginning of "gas warfare" was launched. Details of that first gas attack will always be meager, for the simple reason that the men who could have told about it all lie in Flanders field where the poppies grow.

The place selected was in the northeast part of the Ypres salient, at that part of the line where the French and British lines met, running southward from where the trenches left the canal near Boesinghe. The French right was held by the Regiment of Turcos, while on the British left were the Canadians. Auld describes the attack as follows:

Try to imagine the feelings and the condition of the colored troops as they saw the vast cloud of greenish-yellow gas spring out of the ground and slowly move down wind towards them, the vapor clinging to the earth, seeking out every hole and hollow and filling the trenches and shell holes as it came. First wonder, then fear; then, as the first, fringes of the cloud enveloped them and left them choking and agonized in the fight for breath—panic. Those who could move broke and ran, trying, generally in vain, to outstrip the cloud that followed inexorably after them.

> **I**t was the most fiendish, wicked thing I have ever seen.

It is only to be expected that the first feeling connected with gas warfare was one of horror. That side of it is very thrillingly described by Rev. O. S. Watkins in the *Methodist Recorder* (London). After describing the bombardment of the City of Ypres from April 20th to 22nd, he relates that in the midst of the uproar came the poison gas:

> Going into the open air for a few moments' relief from the stifling atmosphere of the wards, our attention was attracted by very heavy firing to the north, where the line was held by the French. Evidently a hot fight—and eagerly we scanned the country with our field glasses hoping to glean some knowledge of the progress of the battle. Then we saw that which almost caused our hearts to stop beating—figures running wildly and in confusion over the fields.

> "The French have broken," we exclaimed. We hardly believed our words…. The story they told we could not believe; we put it down to their terror-stricken imaginings—a greenish-gray cloud had swept down upon them, turning yellow as it traveled over the country, blasting everything it touched, shriveling up the vegetation. No human courage could face such a peril.

> Then there staggered into our midst French soldiers, blinded, coughing, chests heaving, faces an ugly purple color—lips speechless with agony, and behind them, in the gas-choked trenches, we learned that they had left hundreds of dead and dying comrades. The impossible was only too true.

> It was the most fiendish, wicked thing I have ever seen.

It must be said here, however, that this was true only because the French had no protection against the gas. Indeed, it is far from being the most horrible form of warfare, provided both sides are prepared defensively and offensively. Medical records show that out of every 100 Americans gassed less than two died, and as far as records of four years show, very few are permanently injured. Out of every 100 American casualties from all forms of warfare other than gas more than 25 per cent died, while from 2 to 5 per cent more are maimed, blinded or disfigured for life. Various forms of gas, as will... make life miserable or vision impossible to those without a mask. Yet they do not kill.

Thus instead of gas warfare being the most horrible, it is the most humane where both sides are prepared for it, while against savage or unprepared peoples it can be made so humane that but very few casualties will result...

Methods of defense against gas [were developed] later... Suffice to say here that, in response to an appeal from Lord Kitchener, a temporary protection was quickly furnished the men. This was known as the "Black Veiling" respirator, and consisted of a cotton pad soaked in ordinary washing soda solution, and later, in a mixture of washing soda and "hypo," to which was added a little glycerine. These furnished a fair degree of protection to the men against chlorine, the only gas used in the early attacks.

## GLOSSARY

**Boesinghe:** (now Boezinge) a town north of Ypres

**"Flanders field..."** : a rephrasing of a line from the famous poem "In Flanders Field" by Canadian Lt. Col. John McCrae

**hypo:** sodium thiosulphate, normally used to remove chlorine from substances

**Turcos:** French troops from Algeria

**Ypres:** Ypres, Belgium

## Document Analysis

This document had two major purposes. One was historical, in retelling some of the observations that were made on the day of the first gas attack by the Germans. The second was to advocate for the continued preparations to defend against, and to use, chemical weapons. However, Fries and West were better able to achieve the first than the second. Although part of a book that contained additional material related to both goals, the horrors of the first attacks were always easier to convey than was the ultimate utility of the weapons.

While Germany had used tear gas in 1914, that nation had been working on a way to use lethal chlorine gas as a weapon, contrary to the 1899 agreement in The Hague that poison gas weapons would not be used in warfare. Although told of the impending attack by a German deserter, the British dismissed the warning. When unleashed, French troops from Algeria

(Turcos) at the center of the German gas attack suffered heavy casualties, including death for all at the front of the trench. Although not mentioned in this document, this first attack was an experiment by the Germans, which meant that they were not prepared to take advantage of the situation by advancing their troops into the void left by the death of so many French troops and others "running wildly in confusion over the fields." The words used to describe the situation in the first-hand accounts quoted by Fries and West are vivid and accurate. "Choking and agonized," "panic," and soldiers "blinded, coughing, chests heaving, faces an ugly purple color" all indicate events that had never been imaged. If German leaders had thought that the results would be so dramatic, their troops could have moved uncontested through the Allied lines. At the end of this document, there is a brief reference to the initial defense used against the next chlorine attacks.

As gruesome as the images detailed by those who witnessed the first attack at a distance were, however, Fries and West paint a different vision in the closing paragraphs of the document. Fries, as head of the CWS service until the end of the 1920s, gave this vision repeatedly in the first decade after the war. For him, gas attacks were a perfectly acceptable form of combat, even more "humane" than conventional forms. He gives two conflicting arguments in this section, however, and the statistics differ from those appearing later in the book. Fries argues that chemical weapons should continue to be used because they are "humane," with a low casualty rate. To gain support for such weapons, he argues this while ignoring the question of why the Army would want to continue to support what is, by Fries' own account, a relatively ineffective weapon. In fact, however, as recorded in a quote from the Surgeon General later in the book, more than twenty-seven percent of American deaths were gas related. Considering that statistic, claims for neither the ineffective-

ness of gas attacks nor their humaneness would be accurate. By the time the United States entered the First World War, Germany was mainly using mustard gas to incapacitate soldiers so that they could be killed more easily by other means, rather than deploying more lethal gases. The lack of permanent injury to those attacked with mustard gas is a point understated by Fries and West. The figures from the records demonstrated that the use of gas attacks was not entirely lethal, but neither was it particularly humane.

## Essential Themes

Although it was not the authors' stated intention, the stigma attached to chemical weapons is brought to light by them in the vivid recounting they give of the effects of the first gas attack on French forces. This was then and remains the image that many have had regarding the use of gas in World War I, even though, as made clear at the end of the article, most of the later attacks had less of an effect on the troops. That, for many, the non-lethal effects of gas attacks made life "miserable" is something of an understatement. In 1675, there had been a treaty outlawing poisoned bullets, and, in 1899, a declaration was accepted to extend this restriction to gas attacks. In response to what many soldiers had witnessed on the battlefield, and including documents such as this one that kept the image in people's minds, the leading nations of the world met in Geneva in 1925 and developed the Geneva Protocol, banning chemical and bacteriological weapons. That ban was ultimately accepted by 137 nations. Images of World War I, as well as more recent uses of gas attacks in violation of the Geneva Protocol, have kept support for the ban of these weapons strong.

Fries' and West's assertion that these types of weapons are no worse than, and perhaps even better than, other types of weapons has never really been widely accepted. Their indirect argument in this document, however, an argument made more directly later in the book, is that the United States should continue to research chemical weapons and defenses against them; and this has largely been accepted. In the 1910s and 1920s, the cautious move by American leaders to retain the ability to attack with, and defend against, chemical weapons, was in line with standing military philosophy regarding the need to be prepared for any and all weapons during war.

*—Donald A. Watt, PhD*

### Bibliography and Additional Reading

Addison, James Thayer. *The Story of the First Gas Regiment*. Boston: Houghton Mifflin, 1919. Print.

Fries, Amos A., and Jay West. *Chemical Warfare*. New York: McGraw-Hill, 1921. Print. Google eBook. Web. 3 June 2014.

Tucker, Jonathan B. *War of Nerves: Chemical Warfare from World War I to Al-Qaeda*. New York: Pantheon Books, 2006. Print.

Vilensky, Joel A., and Pandy R. Sinish. "Weaponry: Lewisite—America's World War I Chemical Weapon," *MHQ: The Quarterly Journal of Military History*. Weider History Network, 12 Jun. 2006. Web. 3 June 2014.

# ■ The Effects of Shell Shock

**Date:** March 25, 1917
**Author:** W. R. Houston, M.D.
**Genre:** article; journal

## Summary Overview

This document is a physician's account of the effects of shell shock on the soldiers who were injured in the trenches in World War I. At a time when the traumatic effects of war on the brain were not well understood, hysteria was assumed to be at the root of many injuries, if no external cause could be found. Dr. Houston goes into significant detail concerning the physical symptoms that occur with shell shock along with some of the ways they could be treated. The various and terrible injuries that soldiers fighting in the trenches faced are explained, and the relative lack of knowledge about how to treat such injuries is indicated. Dr. Houston, a distinguished neurologist, does his best to explain how to deal with these injuries, but he leaves the readers of his article without a clear idea of what treatment would be helpful or effective—such was the state of medical knowledge at the time.

## Defining Moment

World War I was a war unlike any that had occurred before. The day-to-day rain of mortar shells on men stuck in trenches and surrounded by mud, death, and offal created conditions that broke the spirits of many a soldier. Men who suffered from injuries, such as shell shock—also known as war neurosis—were often deemed weak or prone to failures of the nervous system and could be considered cowards because they seemed unable to cope with the pressures of battle. The explosions from shells created obvious physical injuries, but they also produced injuries that were not necessarily apparent through a physical examination. The Great War was one of the first times in history that mental trauma struck so many soldiers and to such a marked degree. This document is one that resulted from this new area of study—namely, how soldiers' mental states played a role in their ability, or inability, to fight. Almost nothing was known about how the mind reacted to the stress of battle. Doctors tried to understand the problem, but not always with great results. Depression, anxiety, memory loss, and many other symptoms are now known to result from exhaustion and combat stress. In 1917, however, these issues were just emerging.

This article was published in the *New York Times* just weeks before the United States entered World War I. But even though American soldiers had not yet entered the trenches, American doctors, along with much of the country, were hungry for news and information from the front lines. Dr. W. R. Houston was interested in the new medical issues that arose from the fighting and presented his own observations on the subject. The main issue with such a document, especially since the true reasons for shell shock were not yet known, was that it spread the idea that suffering from shell shock—or what is now known as combat stress and post-traumatic stress disorder (PTSD)—was something shameful and only happened to weak men. Documents like this show how much neuroscience has advanced, due in large part to the study of soldiers in the twentieth and twenty-first centuries.

## Author Biography

Very little information survives about the author of this document, Dr. W. R. Houston, other than the previously stated point about his being a doctor of neurology and a professor of clinical medicine at the University of Georgia. During World War I, Dr. Houston visited France in order to see first-hand the injured soldiers and the effects of the war traumas on their brains. It was from these experiences that he wrote the article examined below, which attempts to understand the physical reasons for the mental breakdowns experienced by so many soldiers. Dr. Houston wrote an article in *The Annals of Internal Medicine* in 1938 entitled "The Doctor Himself as a Therapeutic Agent." That article examines the idea that a doctor needs to be more involved with his patient in order to create the best outcome. It is possible that this interest in healing the patient, beyond simply treating the symptoms, stemmed from his experiences with World War I injuries.

## HISTORICAL DOCUMENT

When the entire manhood of a nation is mustered into battle, it follows that the nervously frail, the men of unstable equilibrium, must go, too. The shocks and sudden emotional strains of civil life have made a certain number hysterical. It might be expected that under the stress of warfare many would break. The number of such cases arising in the course of war is far greater than in time of peace, but, after all, they form but a small fraction of the total number of nervous crises in the neurological centres.

We have considered them, however, less because of their intrinsic interest than for comparison with another class of cases — the commotionnes, that very large and novel group of cases, comprising several thousand admissions to the neurological hospitals of France, which the French physicians named cerebral commotion, the English shell shock.

In the accounts of the great bombardments we have all read of men who were found dead in the trenches, unwounded. Death had resulted from air concussion in the zone contiguous to the exploding shell. The concussion is more intense and the danger greater if the shell explodes in a closed space, as in the deep chambered trenches of the western front.

### Countless Internal Wounds

Most of our commotion cases were injured in the trenches. Often they were hurled some distance, dashed against a wall, and buried alive. If an examination is made of the bodies of these dead, or of those who have survived a few days before death, it is found that there has taken place an intimate tearing of the finer structures throughout the body. The lungs are torn; there are abundant hemorrhages in the pleura and stomach. The blood vessels in the brain are ruptured, and minute hemorrhages are found throughout.

Many are killed outright, but most survive. Even these survivors bleed in many cases from the ears, the lungs, the stomach, the bladder, and bowels. There are sometimes hemorrhages into the retina and under the conjunctivae. The normally clear cerebro-spinal fluid is found blood tinged. Even after blood is no longer found the fluid is often discovered to be under high pressure, the white cells and globulins that indicate damage to the meninges continue to be found in it for months.

The patients seldom regain memory of the beginning of their accidents. At most they recall the whistling sound that preceded the arrival of the shell. In certain cases there will be found only a more or less transient clouding of consciousness, or a very painful sensation of having been beaten on the head. Usually the patient is unable to walk, and as he is carried on the stretcher every movement is painful. The limbs are inert, the head drops on the shoulder. Even when sitting he collapses if not supported. Any movements made are maladroit and imprecise. The sphincters are relaxed; almost all arrive at the aid stations soiled with excrements. Later they may have retention, but in the beginning the contrary is the rule.

The facial expression is typical—comparable to that seen in the cerebral type of infantile paralysis—the corners of the mouth droop, the tongue is paretic, the lids droop, and the eyeballs are without motion. The pupils are dilated, almost always unequal.

In all cases is found the sign of Babinski—irritation of the foot sole, provoking an obvious and prompt elevation of the great toe and a fanlike spreading of the other toes — an unequivocal indication of damage to the motor pathways leading from the brain; and, as further indication of this damage, the tendinous reflexes are generally strongly exaggerated…. Cortical irritation is present….

In severe cases, and sometimes from milder ones, there develop a series of most bizarre clinical pictures. It is the general nervous system that is most often and most strikingly affected. As the patient emerges from his clouding of consciousness, he seems to be in a state of confusion. His memory is weakened. He has lost in power of voluntary attention. He has hallucinations. These psychopathic states may persist for days or months, and are accompanied almost always by persistent nightmares of fire and battle that startle and disturb the rest.

> "When the entire manhood of a nation is mustered into battle…the men of unstable equilibrium must go too.

It is at this stage extraordinarily difficult to disentangle symptoms that are due to gross organic injury from those that would be reckoned hysterical. Very frequently there are convulsive attacks that seem frankly similar to that described above; occasionally a case that resembles … epilepsy.

### Sight and Hearing Affected

There is often deafness associated with injury to the ears; again, deafness is present with ears apparently normal. Sometimes the deafness is associated with vertigo such as suggests damage to the inner ear.

As to the sight, we encounter every degree of disability, from slight cloudiness of vision and narrowing of the visual field to complete blindness. In a considerable number of cases these troubles are due to damage done the retina. In a larger number, however, so far as examination can determine, they are purely subjective. These troubles of sight and hearing are almost never isolated. They are found associated with an assemblage of other symptoms referable to the nervous system.

Much more frequent than the troubles of the special senses are the paralyses—paralysis of a single member, of both legs, or of a lateral half of the body. Some of these paralyses are obviously due to hemorrhage within the brain, others are a flaccid paralysis with loss of sensation. In all the characteristics that are accessible to investigation most resemble hysterical paralysis, and the greater number are associated with contracture of the muscles.

The foot will be drawn into the position of a clubfoot and firmly fixed there. The hand is tightly clenched, and the wrist and elbow bent. The contracted muscles of half the body may draw the trunk and head to one side. The neck may be fixed as a wry neck. A very frequent deformity is the bent back. A peculiar circumstance is the violent fit of coughing that is induced by any attempt to straighten the bent back, either in bed or against the wall.

The vocal cords may be paralyzed and the tongue incapable of being protruded, so that the patient is entirely mute, unable to make the slightest sound, to whistle or to blow, or even to imitate the movements of the lips in speech. His breathing muscles are contracted so that he cannot draw a long breath. In milder cases there is a stammering to the degree of almost complete unintelligibility.

A muscular trouble, often of the most striking and startling sort, is the shaking and trembling. This may be a fine tremor… or a very coarse, irregular shaking and jerking of the head, arms, legs, in contortions that make walking or any coordinated movement nearly or quite impossible.

---

**GLOSSARY**

**cerebral:** pertaining to the brain

**conjunctivae:** the mucous membrane that covers the eyeball and the inner surface of the eyelid

**contiguous:** close together; very near continuous

**cortical:** pertaining to the cerebral cortex or the outer layer of the brain

**hemorrhages:** profuse discharge of blood; heavy bleeding

**maladroit:** unskillful; awkward; clumsy

---

## Document Analysis

The aim of this document is to address and explain some of the reports and rumors that were coming across the Atlantic Ocean concerning the war and its effects on soldiers. Dr. Houston, although he went to France in order to gain experience with these new forms of injury, also wants to enlighten the public about the conditions from which the soldiers were suffering. The article was written about two years after the term "shell shock" was first coined, and the condition's nature was still largely unknown. About all that was known was that it was a stigmatized sort of injury and one that was said mainly to affect the cowardly and the weak.

Dr. Houston, in fact, opens his account with a theory of the type of men that are affected by shell shock. This theory has now been shown to be invalid, as most anyone can become deeply troubled by the horrors of war and develop physiological reactions or symptoms. At the time, however, shell shock was mostly associated with "the nervously frail, the men of unstable equilibrium." Houston, in his opening paragraphs, does mention that there were many types of neurological conditions that have resulted from the war and its associated injuries. He seems to associate these types of injuries with the "air concussion" produced by exploding shells, as with internal injuries that sometimes left soldiers dead, yet seemingly uninjured to the eye. The link between the ideas that the internal organs can be injured to the point of death and that the brain can be injured to the point of breakdown, seems to be operative in Houston's account, although perhaps not explicitly so.

As the author continues in the article, he describes the terrible wounds and ailments that left soldiers bed-bound and unable to fight or even care for themselves. His understanding of the physical nature of these injuries—even those that cause hemorrhages in the brain—is confident. What he seems unable to get at are other physical traces of damage to the brain and what such damage can lead to, such as partial paralysis or the inability to speak. Because shell shock was not fully understood, Houston does not fully differentiate between the mental inability to cope with war and the physical damage done to the brain that produced bodily symptoms. The instances in which Houston mentions such problems as loss of memory, "convulsive attacks…similar to…epilepsy," and uncontrollable tremors show that, as is now known, the brain was likely damaged in such a way as to be mostly invisible to the naked eye. Traumatic brain injury and post-traumatic stress can be extremely harmful conditions, with lasting effects on one's physical and mental health.

It may hinder a soldier's ability to move on in postwar life.

## Essential Themes

The identification of shell shock and the evolution of understanding and treating it began with early physicians, such as Dr. Houston, venturing to the army hospitals and reporting what they saw. These doctors were experts in various fields, but this new type of trauma lay outside their empirical knowledge. Shell shock was seen as evidence of cowardice or internal weakness. In the military, cowardice is and was punishable, even by death—though, often, soldiers were simply hospitalized and sent back to the trenches. In the case of Houston and his article, the aim is to provide a medical description for lay persons in an attempt to address rumors and perhaps lighten American fears. He provides some answers as to why soldiers have died in the trenches without a wound on them and lays out the basics regarding shell shock.

Reports like Houston's ultimately created a basis for the expansion of neurological and psychiatric understanding of concussive impact and emotional trauma and their effects on the body and the brain. Even today, although traumatic brain injury is generally accepted as a medical condition, there remains some stigma attached to post-traumatic stress disorder. Fortunately, this is beginning to change and more people now recognize mental conditions as legitimate—and treatable—medical conditions. This change is thanks, in part, to neurological specialists like Dr. Houston.

—*Anna Accettola, MA*

## Bibliography and Additional Reading

Babington, Anthony. *Shell Shock: A History of the Changing Attitude to War Neurosis*. Wiltshire: Redwood Books, 1990. Print.

Hipp, Daniel. *The Poetry of Shell Shock: Wartime Trauma and Healing in Wilfred Owen, Ivor Gurney, and Siegfried Sassoon*. Jefferson, NC: McFarland, 2005. Print.

Houston, Dr. W. R. "The Doctor Himself as a Therapeutic Agent." *The Annals of Internal Medicine* 11 (1938): 1416–1425.

Jones, Edgar, and Simon Wessely. *Shell Shock to PTSD: Military Psychiatry from 1900 to the Gulf War*. East Sussex: Psychology Press, 2005. Print.

"Shell Shock and War Neuroses." *British Medical Journal* 2 (1918): 260.

# ■ An Army Physician on the 1918 Flu Pandemic

**Date:** September 29, 1918
**Author:** anonymous
**Genre:** letter

## Summary Overview

During the late stages of World War I, a new threat to the global community emerged: an influenza pandemic. Arriving in the United States in the spring of 1918, the disease quickly spread throughout the country. At the overcrowded Camp Devens in Massachusetts, thousands of US soldiers suddenly became ill in a matter of days. Nearly one thousand men died at this site alone. In a letter to a friend and fellow physician, a camp doctor known only by his first name, Roy, describes the scene and conditions at Camp Devens, where an average of one hundred men were dying each day during the pandemic. He cites rapidly appearing symptoms, followed by severe pneumonia and a "horrible," suffocating death.

## Defining Moment

World War I (1914–18) was one of the most destructive conflicts in history. More than sixty-five million military personnel were mobilized by sixteen nations, including the United States, which mobilized nearly 4.4 million troops. More than twenty-one million soldiers, who were sent to the battlefield, were wounded, and more than eight million soldiers were killed. The battlefield was a harsh environment; in addition to gunfire and chemical attacks, troops were exposed to extremely unsanitary conditions in the cramped and damp foxholes and trenches.

When the Great War began to wind down, a new threat emerged from that environment: influenza. The disease was first reported in the United States in January 1918, cropping up mainly in military camps. Very little attention was paid to this first wave, as the US government was more focused on the ongoing war effort. In the fall of 1918, however, a second, more virulent wave of influenza could not be ignored. The widespread mobilization of troops across the world facilitated the spread of the disease. Merchant and military ships carrying troops and military hardware also brought influenza to ports all across the United States.

This letter by an anonymous physician provides a fascinating snapshot of the effects of the influenza pandemic at one Massachusetts military installation. Camp Devens, located about thirty miles northwest of Boston, was one of the main military hospitals and training installations in the Northeast. The camp (later renamed Fort Devens) was built to house up to thirty-five thousand people. However, by the summer of 1918, it had exceeded this capacity by some ten thousand men. Soldiers slept in cramped, crowded quarters that further facilitated the transmission of the disease.

Influenza began its rapid spread through Camp Devens by mid-September 1918. On September 22 alone, more than fifteen hundred soldiers went to the camp infirmary complaining of flu-like symptoms. That infirmary was only supposed to house about twelve hundred patients. Due to the overcrowding, the camp's barracks became makeshift hospitals as well. One barracks even became a morgue, as the staggering death toll from the pandemic filled the existing morgue beyond its capacity. The military quarantined the camp, but locking it off from traveling soldiers took a great deal of time; by the time the camp was contained, far too many soldiers had been exposed for the quarantine to be effective. Meanwhile, there was a lack of medical personnel to treat the ill—far too many physicians were overseas assisting the war effort, leaving medical students and volunteers to treat the sick. More than one thousand people at Camp Devens died from what one doctor described as a powerful form of pneumonia that ultimately asphyxiated them. Writing to a fellow physician, "Roy," as he signed his letter, illustrated how influenza had affected those at Camp Devens.

## HISTORICAL DOCUMENT: An Army Physician on the 1918 Flu Pandemic

Camp Devens is near Boston, and has about 50,000 men, or did have before this epidemic broke loose… This epidemic started about four weeks ago, and has developed so rapidly that the camp is demoralized and all ordinary work is held up till it has passed. All assemblages of soldiers taboo. These men start with what appears to be an attack of *la grippe* or influenza, and when brought to the hospital they very rapidly develop the most viscous type of pneumonia that has ever been seen. Two hours after admission they have the mahogany spots over the cheek bones, and a few hours later you can begin to see the cyanosis extending from their ears and spreading all over the face, until it is hard to distinguish the coloured men from the white. It is only a matter of a few hours then until death comes, and it is simply a struggle for air until they suffocate. It is horrible. One can stand it to see one, two or twenty men die, but to see these poor devils dropping like flies sort of gets on your nerves. We have been averaging about 100 deaths per day, and still keeping it up…

The normal number of doctors here is about 25 and that has been increased to over 250… We have lost an outrageous number of nurses and doctors, and the little town of Ayer is a sight. It takes special trains to carry away the dead. For several days there were no coffins and the bodies piled up something fierce… It beats any sight they ever had in France after a battle. An extra long barracks has been vacated for the use of the morgue, and it would make any man sit up and take notice to walk down the long lines of dead soldiers all dressed up and laid out in double rows. We have no relief here; you get up in the morning at 5:30 and work steady till about 9:30 p.m., sleep, then go at it again.

## GLOSSARY

**cyanosis:** a bluish discoloration of the skin and mucous membranes

**grippe:** flu, or, more specifically, Spanish flu

## Document Analysis

Camp Devens, one of the US military's main training and hospital installations in the Northeast during the Great War, became a microcosm of the second wave of the 1918 influenza outbreak in the United States. Because of wartime censorship in the United States and Europe, little attention was paid to the first wave of influenza. In September 1918, however, the second wave was so powerful and devastating that it killed thousands within days. Troops died, as did civilians and even the health care workers assigned to treat them. In a letter to a friend named Burt, a doctor at Camp Devens described the scene—the deplorable conditions, the rapidity and intensity with which the contagion spread, and the horrific images of the dead being stored in and transported out of the camp.

According to Roy, the onset of the influenza pandemic at Camp Devens was extremely quick and more devastating than any weapon deployed on the battlefield. The doctor writes how he and his fellow physicians at the camp "used to go down to the morgue (which is just back of my ward) and look at the boys laid out in long rows. It beats any sight they ever had in France after a battle." He tells his friend that there were nearly fifty thousand people at Camp Devens prior to the outbreak; within a matter of weeks, that figure was significantly reduced. Soldiers arrived at the infirmary complaining of respiratory ailments. The symptoms resembled those of "la grippe" (otherwise known as "Spanish flu"). However, he says, the strain that afflicted countless men at Camp Devens overtook the afflicted with far greater speed than was expected.

As soon as the men came to the infirmary, Roy says, they fell victim to "the most viscous type of pneumonia" he had ever seen. Within hours, the patients' inability to breathe would lead to cyanosis, a condition in which the skin becomes discolored (purple or blue) due to a lack of oxygen. The cases the doctor recalls witnessing were so severe that patients' entire faces became discolored, making it "hard to distinguish the coloured men from the white." After the appearance of cyanosis, "it is only a matter of a few hours then until death comes, and it is simply a struggle for air until they suffocate. It is horrible." As a physician in the early twentieth century, Roy could be expected to see a handful of such cases from time to time, but at Camp Devens, he witnessed hundreds of agonizing deaths over four weeks.

The doctor says that the hospital was normally staffed by only about twenty-five doctors, but saw its physician rolls increase to 250 during the epidemic. Nevertheless, these extra doctors and nurses were still overworked. He recalls how he worked sixteen-hour days, without rest, writing, "we have no relief here." Such stressful demands continued for weeks.

He also offers a surreal picture of the nearby town of Ayer. The normally picturesque town, he says, became a central venue for the removal of the dead from Camp Devens. Bodies were not loaded onto trains in coffins, as there were none available. Instead, the bodies were simply piled one on top of the other, awaiting a special train to take them away from the area. Back in the camp, the morgue was completely full, as was an extra-long barracks that had been converted into a temporary morgue. The letter explains that such images were reminiscent of those on the battlefield, although he believed (rightly or wrongly) that what he witnessed at Devens was far more horrific than any scene at the front during the Great War.

## Essential Themes

Unlike many Americans, the doctor who wrote this letter knew of the first wave of influenza that had occurred a few months earlier, beginning in January 1918. When the second wave of influenza arrived at Camp Devens and other military installations, the doctor had a relatively informed understanding of the fact that it was the flu. However, the virus's virulence far exceeded his expectations as a physician, and he remained at a loss as to how to treat his patients. In his letter, he notes, "There is no doubt in my mind that there is a new mixed infection here, but what I don't know." The letter simultaneously reveals the tremendous efforts of the physicians who assisted infected patients, as well as the significant limitations to their medical knowledge in containing and treating the influenza.

In his letter to a colleague, the doctor suggests that the strength and speed with which this form of influenza attacked the Devens population could not have been anticipated. Indeed, droves of men entered the hospital daily complaining of flu-like symptoms, only to be quickly overcome by cyanosis and die within hours of their admission. The doctor describes his efforts to identify the characteristic sign of the disease in his patients by listening to their breathing for rales, or abnormal breathing sounds, noting "they all mean but one thing here . . . and that means in about all cases death." The high mortality rate he witnessed at Camp Devens was characteristic of the disease worldwide: Approximately ten to twenty percent of all persons who became infected with this strain of influenza died. In total, nearly one-third of the global population became infected and more than fifty million people died, making the influenza pandemic responsible for nearly as many deaths as the war itself.

—*Michael P. Auerbach, MA*

## Bibliography and Additional Reading

Barry, John M. *The Great Influenza: The Story of the Deadliest Pandemic in History*. New York: Penguin, 2004. Print.

Billings, Molly. "The Influenza Pandemic of 1918." *Human Virology at Stanford*. Stanford University, Feb. 2005. Web. 31 Jan. 2014.

Kent, Susan K. *The Influenza Pandemic of 1918–1919*. Boston: Bedford, 2012. Print.

Marciniak, Kristin. *The Flu Pandemic of 1918*. Minneapolis: ABDO, 2014. Print.

# ■ The Atomic Bombings of Hiroshima and Nagasaki: The Nature of An Atomic Explosion

**Date:** June 19, 1946
**Author:** US Army
**Genre:** report

## Summary Overview

Shortly after the US Army detonated the first atomic weapons over the Japanese cities of Hiroshima and Nagasaki in August 1945, the Army assembled a special Manhattan Project Bomb Investigating Group to assess the sites of the atomic bomb detonations. This military report summarizes the strategy, execution, and aftermath of the bombings. In this section, the report explains the scientific nature of an atomic explosion and its impact by describing the force, heat, and radiation generated in comparison to the more traditional explosive TNT. It emphasizes the great deal of energy generated and released as heat at the moment of detonation, capable of raising temperatures to high levels so rapidly as to cause instant incineration. The report also discusses the radioactive forces unleashed by nuclear weapons, including gamma and beta rays. Along with the physical forces of heat and pressure, radiation is acknowledged as one of the most damaging effects of the atomic bomb and the most unique compared to traditional explosives.

## Defining Moment

During the early twentieth century, new theories by innovative physicists such as Albert Einstein greatly advanced human understanding of energy. As early as 1939, research was already underway in Europe to harness the energy released by the division of atoms. Mastering this force would enable the development of weaponry with immense physical power.

In the spring of 1945, Harry S. Truman became president upon the death of Franklin D. Roosevelt. Truman had been vice president only a short time before Roosevelt's death and had little knowledge of the secret military strategies of World War II. It was with great surprise, therefore, that he learned after taking office of an ongoing military program to develop a powerful new kind of weapon based on the principles of nuclear physics. Even more surprising was that such a weapon was nearly ready to be used. That July, scientists in New Mexico successfully detonated the first atomic bomb. Soon thereafter, Truman and other Allied countries fighting Japan issued the Potsdam Declaration, which demanded that the Japanese agree to an unconditional surrender or face "prompt and utter destruction."

No immediate surrender was forthcoming. Truman faced a choice between either mounting a traditional military invasion of the Japanese islands or authorizing the use of an atomic weapon on a combined civilian and military Japanese target. An invasion involving ground, sea, and air attacks was likely to require many more months of fighting and tens of thousands of American lives as well as hundreds of thousands of Japanese civilian casualties. An atomic attack, by contrast, was expected to kill many thousands of Japanese without any US human costs. It also had the benefit of making a very public demonstration of the incredible new destructive power controlled, at that time, solely by the United States. Some advisers, including a group of scientists who had worked on the bomb and fully grasped its potential for devastation, opposed a nuclear attack, however.

Truman decided to proceed with the nuclear bombing in the hopes that it would force a Japanese surrender and avoid the need for a large-scale invasion. On August 6, 1945, a US bomber dropped the first atomic bomb on the city of Hiroshima. The devastation was immense, but the Japanese government did not immediately agree to a surrender. Three days later, the Soviet Union declared war on Japan and the United States used a second nuclear weapon against the city of Nagasaki. Facing certain defeat, the Japanese surrendered. The atomic age, however, was just beginning, as US scientists and military experts embarked on a period of continued nuclear research and consideration of further applications of their newly proven destructive force.

## Author Biography

The US Army Corps of Engineers officially oversaw the development and implementation of the atomic bomb through its management of a top-secret research program known as the Manhattan Project, taken from the name of the administering Manhattan Engineer District. Under the leadership of Major General Leslie Groves, Manhattan Project teams across the country worked to solve the numerous technological challenges required to create the uncontrollable nuclear reaction needed for a successful weapon. In conjunction with high-ranking political officials, they also considered how, where, and whether the weapons they constructed should be used.

After the attacks on Hiroshima and Nagasaki, some of these same military and scientific experts contributed to the US Army's summative report on the matter. These experts included Hans Bethe—a nuclear physicist whose ideas are specifically referenced in this section of the report—along with other physicists active in the Manhattan Project.

## HISTORICAL DOCUMENT: The Nature of An Atomic Explosion

The most striking difference between the explosion of an atomic bomb and that of an ordinary T.N.T. bomb is of course in magnitude; as the President announced after the Hiroshima attack, the explosive energy of each of the atomic bombs was equivalent to about 20,000 tons of T.N.T.

But in addition to its vastly greater power, an atomic explosion has several other very special characteristics. Ordinary explosion is a chemical reaction in which energy is released by the rearrangement of the atoms of the explosive material. In an atomic explosion the identity of the atoms, not simply their arrangement, is changed. A considerable fraction of the mass of the explosive charge, which may be uranium 235 or plutonium, is transformed into energy. Einstein's equation, $E = mc^2$, shows that matter that is transformed into energy may yield a total energy equivalent to the mass multiplied by the square of the velocity of light. The significance of the equation is easily seen when one recalls that the velocity of light is 186,000 miles per second. The energy released when a pound of T.N.T. explodes would, if converted entirely into heat, raise the temperature of 36 lbs. of water from freezing temperature (32 deg F) to boiling temperature (212 deg F). The nuclear fission of a pound of uranium would produce an equal temperature rise in over 200 million pounds of water.

The explosive effect of an ordinary material such as T.N.T. is derived from the rapid conversion of solid T.N.T. to gas, which occupies initially the same volume as the solid; it exerts intense pressures on the surrounding air and expands rapidly to a volume many times larger than the initial volume. A wave of high pressure thus rapidly moves outward from the center of the explosion and is the major cause of damage from ordinary high explosives. An atomic bomb also generates a wave of high pressure which is in fact of, much higher pressure than that from ordinary explosions; and this wave is again the major cause of damage to buildings and other structures. It differs from the pressure wave of a block buster in the size of the area over which high pressures are generated. It also differs in the duration of the pressure pulse at any given point: the pressure from a blockbuster lasts for a few milliseconds (a millisecond is one thousandth of a second) only, that from the atomic bomb for nearly a second, and was felt by observers both in Japan and in New Mexico as a very strong wind going by.

The next greatest difference between the atomic bomb and the T.N.T. explosion is the fact that the atomic bomb gives off greater amounts of radiation. Most of this radiation is "light" of some wave-length ranging from the so-called heat radiations of very long wave length to the so-called gamma rays which have wave-lengths even shorter than the X-rays used in medicine. All of these radiations travel at the same speed; this, the speed of light, is 186,000 miles per second. The radiations are intense enough to kill people within an appreciable distance from the explosion, and are in fact the major cause of deaths and injuries apart from mechanical injuries. The greatest number of radiation injuries was probably due to the ultra-violet rays which have a

*The most striking difference between the explosion of an atomic bomb and that of an ordinary T.N.T. bomb is of course in magnitude.*

wave length slightly shorter than visible light and which caused flash burn comparable to severe sunburn. After these, the gamma rays of ultra short wave length are most important; these cause injuries similar to those from over-doses of X-rays.

The origin of the gamma rays is different from that of the bulk of the radiation: the latter is caused by the extremely high temperatures in the bomb, in the same way as light is emitted from the hot surface of the sun or from the wires in an incandescent lamp. The gamma rays on the other hand are emitted by the atomic nuclei themselves when they are transformed in the fission process. The gamma rays are therefore specific to the atomic bomb and are completely absent in T.N.T. explosions. The light of longer wave length (visible and ultra-violet) is also emitted by a T.N.T. explosion, but with much smaller intensity than by an atomic bomb, which makes it insignificant as far as damage is concerned.

A large fraction of the gamma rays is emitted in the first few microseconds (millionths of a second) of the atomic explosion, together with neutrons which are also produced in the nuclear fission. The neutrons have much less damage effect than the gamma rays because they have a smaller intensity and also because they are strongly absorbed in air and therefore can penetrate only to relatively small distances from the explosion: at a thousand yards the neutron intensity is negligible. After the nuclear emission, strong gamma radiation continues to come from the exploded bomb. This generates from the fission products and continues for about one minute until all of the explosion products have risen to such a height that the intensity received on the ground is negligible. A large number of beta rays are also emitted during this time, but they are unimportant because their range is not very great, only a few feet. The range of alpha particles from the unused active material and fissionable material of the bomb is even smaller.

Apart from the gamma radiation ordinary light is emitted, some of which is visible and some of which is the ultra violet rays mainly responsible for flash burns. The emission of light starts a few milliseconds after the nuclear explosion when the energy from the explosion reaches the air surrounding the bomb. The observer sees then a ball of fire which rapidly grows in size. During most of the early time, the ball of fire extends as far as the wave of high pressure. As the ball of fire grows its temperature and brightness decrease. Several milliseconds after the initiation of the explosion, the brightness of the ball of fire goes through a minimum, then it gets somewhat brighter and remains at the order of a few times the brightness of the sun for a period of 10 to 15 seconds for an observer at six miles distance. Most of the radiation is given off after this point of maximum brightness. Also after this maximum, the pressure waves run ahead of the ball of fire.

The ball of fire rapidly expands from the size of the bomb to a radius of several hundred feet at one second after the explosion. After this the most striking feature is the rise of the ball of fire at the rate of about 30 yards per second. Meanwhile it also continues to expand by mixing with the cooler air surrounding it. At the end of the first minute the ball has expanded to a radius of several hundred yards and risen to a height of about one mile. The shock wave has by now reached a radius of 15 miles and its pressure dropped to less than 1/10 of a pound per square inch. The ball now loses its brilliance and appears as a great cloud of smoke: the pulverized material of the bomb. This cloud continues to rise vertically and finally mushrooms out at an altitude of about 25,000 feet depending upon meteorological conditions. The cloud reaches a maximum height of between 50,000 and 70,000 feet in a time of over 30 minutes.

It is of interest to note that Dr. Hans Bethe, then a member of the Manhattan Engineer District on loan from Cornell University, predicted the existence and characteristics of this ball of fire months before the first test was carried out.

To summarize, radiation comes in two bursts - an extremely intense one lasting only about 3 milliseconds and a less intense one of much longer duration lasting several seconds. The second burst contains by far the larger fraction of the total light energy, more than 90%. But the first flash is especially large in ultra-violet radiation which is biologically more effective. Moreover, because the heat in this flash comes in such a short time, there is no time for any cooling to take place, and the temperature of a person's skin can be raised 50 degrees centigrade by the flash of visible and ultra-violet rays in the first millisecond at a distance of 4,000 yards. People may be injured by flash burns at even larger distances. Gamma radiation danger does not extend nearly so far and neutron radiation danger is still more limited.

The high skin temperatures result from the first flash of high intensity radiation and are probably as significant for injuries as the total dosages which come mainly from the second more sustained burst of radiation. The combination of skin temperature increase plus large ultra-violet flux inside 4,000 yards is injurious in all cases to exposed personnel. Beyond this point there may be cases of injury, depending upon the individual sensitivity. The infra-red dosage is probably less important because of its smaller intensity.

## GLOSSARY

**incandescent:** glowing or white with heat

**nuclear fission:** in physics, the splitting of the nucleus of an atom into nuclei of lighter atoms, accompanied by the release of energy

## Document Analysis

This portion of the US Army's report on the bombings of Hiroshima and Nagasaki focuses on the scientific and technical details of the bomb's detonations and effects. To do this, the report explores three key areas: the overall force and unique features of the atomic bomb as compared to that of existing explosive substances, the immediate effects of the bomb's blast, and the short-term impacts of the radioactive energy released as a by-product of the detonations.

Prior to the development of the atomic bomb, bombs typically employed TNT, or trinitrotoluene, as the main explosive force. TNT's relative stability and predictability had long made it the favored explosive for military use and for civilian applications, such as clearing large rocky areas for mining or construction, and its force has become a standard for comparison. The report therefore compares the nuclear explosions to those of TNT in order to give readers a sense of the immense scale of the atomic bomb's power. For example, the report notes that the detonation of one pound of TNT would generate enough energy to heat thirty-six pounds of water "from freezing temperature . . . to boiling temperature," whereas the detonation of one pound of uranium, a radioactive element used in atomic weapons, would generate enough energy to cause an equal rise in temperature of two hundred million pounds of water. The scale of energy released by an atomic explosion was therefore almost unimaginably greater than those of the past.

The contrast between the effects of a traditional explosion and a nuclear one was even starker. In a certain understatement, the report notes that "the atomic bomb gives off greater amounts of radiation" than an explosion of TNT. The radiation released by atomic weapons has immediate effects on living creatures, physical structures, and the environment. The report then describes the creation of flash burns from the intense heat and radiation of the detonation and notes that the various forms of radiation emitted from the explosion were "the major cause of deaths and injuries apart from mechanical injuries" caused by the explosions' pressure waves. The report then delves into the impact of the different types of energy waves formed by a nuclear explosion. Gamma rays, the shortest and most powerful of all energy waves in the electromagnetic spectrum, are unique to atomic explosions and can disrupt the structure of atoms, making these waves especially devastating. The report explains that an atomic explosion also emits a large amount of beta and alpha rays, although their effect is less significant due to their limited range. Along with gamma, beta, and alpha rays, the report also notes that an atomic explosion emits high levels of visible and ultraviolet rays, which produce an intense fireball that "remains at the order of a few times the brightness of the sun for a period of 10 to 15 seconds for an observer at six miles distance." The report concludes by summarizing the various bursts of radiation released by an atomic explosion and their effects.

**Essential Themes**

The immense power of nuclear blasts described by this text had significant short- and long-term

consequences for the people of Hiroshima and Nagasaki. The heat and pressure created by the atomic explosions were so great that thousands of individuals in the blast zone were incinerated instantly. Flash burns charred human skin, and a high wave of pressure from the explosion and fires from the intense heat damaged structures over a few square miles surrounding each explosion center. Radiation sickness, a condition resulting from exposure to high levels of ionizing radiation that causes cell death throughout the body, caused people to experience symptoms ranging from nausea and vomiting to organ failure and death.

The Radiation Effects Research Foundation has estimated that the effects of the nuclear bomb caused 90,000 to 166,000 acute deaths in Hiroshima and 60,000 to 80,000 acute deaths in Nagasaki within four months of the bombings. In Japan, survivors of the bombings at Hiroshima and Nagasaki became known as the *hibakusha*, meaning "those who were bombed." Exposure to intense radiation also made the *hibakusha* prone to long-term struggles with radiation sickness, higher rates of cancer (particularly leukemia), and biological and psychological problems for decades after the attacks.

—*Vanessa E. Vaughn, MA*

**Bibliography and Additional Reading**

Hersey, John. *Hiroshima*. New York: Knopf, 1946. Print.
"'Hibakusha': Those Who Survived and How They Survived." *Children of the Atomic Bomb.* University of California at Los Angeles, 10 Oct. 2007. Web. 5 Dec. 2014.
Hogan, Michael J., ed. *Hiroshima in History and Memory.* New York: Cambridge UP, 1996. Print.
Kort, Michael. *Columbia Guide to Hiroshima and the Bomb.* New York: Columbia UP, 2007. Print.

# ■ Biological Weapons Convention

**Date:** April 10, 1972
**Geographic Region:** London, England; Moscow, Soviet Union; and Washington, DC
**Genre:** treaty

## Summary Overview

The Convention on the Prohibition of the Development, Production, and Stockpiling of Bacteriological (Biological) and Toxin Weapons and on Their Destruction, commonly known as the Biological Weapons Convention (BWC), represented the first multilateral disarmament treaty to ban certain types of weapons of mass destruction (WMDs). The UN convention prohibited each signatory from developing, producing, and stockpiling chemical and biological weapons. It also called upon each nation to destroy whatever WMDs it already possessed and to prevent distribution of such weapons in other countries. With the United States, the Soviet Union, and the United Kingdom acting as depositaries (charged with the administrative management of the convention), the BWC was established as a living document, enabling new signatories, amendments, party withdrawals, and periodic reviews over the course of its unlimited duration of activity. The BWC entered into force on March 26, 1975. As of 2015, there have been seven review conferences of the convention, with the eighth set for December 2016.

## Defining Moment

By the early twentieth century, the torturous effects of poisonous clouds created by chemical and biological weapons had changed the complexion of war, giving rise to debate over the morality of nonconventional weaponry. Chemical weapons started to be deployed on a large scale during World War I, which was nicknamed by many "the chemist's war," in light of the many technological and scientific innovations that came into use. During the war, the first major chemical weapons attack took place, when the German army released chlorine, mustard, and other toxic chemicals onto unsuspecting French forces. These weapons generated approximately 1.3 million casualties, including some ninety thousand deaths. The French, British, and US militaries attempted to develop their own WMDs, but these programs lagged far behind the Germans.

When World War I ended in 1918, there were multiple attempts to abolish such weapons. Multiple conferences were held in pursuit of this goal, but it was not until 1925 that such an initiative bore fruit in international law. The Geneva Protocol prohibited the use of offensive chemical weapons. However, the Protocol did not prohibit the production and/or stockpiling of these WMDs, nor did it ban the use of these weapons when attacked with chemical weapons by noncompliant states. During World War II, many of the participating nations (including the United States) used chemical weapons. During the Cold War, countries continued to develop and stockpile WMDs, including napalm and Agent Orange (both of which the United States used in Vietnam). Meanwhile, in the Middle East, Egypt reportedly used a variety of chemical weapons—such as nerve and mustard gases—against insurgents in Yemen during the Six-Day War in 1967.

By the end of the 1960s, the United States began focusing less on chemical weapons development, despite decades of experiments with such weapons systems. The danger of exposure to civilian populations, experts warned, far outbalanced the perceived need for stockpiling those WMDs. In 1969, the United Nations published the report "Chemical and Bacteriological (Biological) Weapons and the Effects of Their Possible Use," which raised the issue of the grave long-term effects of deployed chemical weapons. A report issued by the World Health Organization published the following year discussed the threat to civilians of such weapons. In 1970, President Richard M. Nixon called for the ban and dismantlement of American chemical weapons stockpiles. In 1972, the United States, acting as one of three depositaries in the United Nations, joined what would be known as the Biological Warfare Convention

## HISTORICAL DOCUMENT: Biological Weapons Convention

The States Parties to this Convention,

Determined to act with a view to achieving effective progress towards general and complete disarmament, including the prohibition and elimination of all types of weapons of mass destruction, and convinced that the prohibition of the development, production and stockpiling of chemical and bacteriological (biological) weapons and their elimination, through effective measures, will facilitate the achievement of general and complete disarmament under strict and effective international control,

Recognising the important significance of the Protocol for the Prohibition of the Use in War of Asphyxiating, Poisonous or Other Gases, and of Bacteriological Methods of Warfare, signed at Geneva on 17 June 1925, and conscious also of the contribution which the said Protocol has already made and continues to make, to mitigating the horrors of war,

Reaffirming their adherence to the principles and objectives of that Protocol and calling upon all States to comply strictly with them,

Recalling that the General Assembly of the United Nations has repeatedly condemned all actions contrary to the principles and objectives of the Geneva Protocol of 17 June 1925,

Desiring to contribute to the strengthening of confidence between peoples and the general improvement of the international atmosphere,

Desiring also to contribute to the realisation of the purposes and principles of the Charter of the United Nations,

Convinced of the importance and urgency of eliminating from the arsenals of States, through effective measures, such dangerous weapons of mass destruction as those using chemical or bacteriological (biological) agents,

Recognising that an agreement on the prohibition of bacteriological (biological) and toxin weapons represents a first possible step towards the achievement of agreement on effective measures also for the prohibition of the development, production and stockpiling of chemical weapons, and determined to continue negotiations to that end,

Determined, for the sake of all mankind, to exclude completely the possibility of bacteriological (biological) agents and toxins being used as weapons,

Convinced that such use would be repugnant to the conscience of mankind and that no effort should be spared to minimise this risk,

Have agreed as follows:

Article I
Each State Party to this Convention undertakes never in any circumstances to develop, produce, stockpile or otherwise acquire or retain:

(1) microbial or other biological agents, or toxins whatever their origin or method of production, of types and in quantities that have no justification for prophylactic, protective or other peaceful purposes;

(2) weapons, equipment or means of delivery designed to use such agents or toxins for hostile purposes or in armed conflict.

Article II
Each State Party to this Convention undertakes to destroy, or to divert to peaceful purposes, as soon as possible but not later than nine months after the entry into force of the Convention, all agents, toxins, weapons, equipment and means of delivery specified in Article I of the Convention, which are in its possession or under its jurisdiction or control. In implementing the provisions of this Article all necessary safety precautions shall be observed to protect populations and the environment.

Article III
Each State Party to this Convention undertakes not to transfer to any recipient whatsoever, directly or indirectly, and not in any way to assist, encourage, or induce any State, group of States or international organisations to manufacture or otherwise acquire any of the agents, toxins, weapons, equipment or means of delivery specified in Article I of the Convention.

Article IV
Each State Party to this Convention shall, in accordance with its constitutional processes, take any necessary measures to prohibit and prevent the development, production, stockpiling, acquisition or retention of the agents, toxins, weapons, equipment and means of delivery specified in Article I of the Convention, within the territory of such State, under its jurisdiction or under its control anywhere.

Article V
The States Parties to this Convention undertake
to consult one another and to co-operate in solv-
ing any problems which may arise in relation to
the objective of, or in the application of the provisions of, the Convention. Consultation and
co-operation pursuant to this Article may also
be undertaken through appropriate international
procedures within the framework of the United
Nations and in accordance with its Charter.

> *With a view to achieving... disarmament, including the prohibition and elimination of all types of weapons of mass destruction.*

Article VI
(1) Any State Party to this Convention which
finds that any other State Party is acting in breach
of obligations deriving from the provisions of the Convention may lodge a complaint
with the Security Council of the United Nations. Such a complaint should include all
possible evidence confirming its validity, as well as a request for its consideration by
the Security Council.
(2) Each State Party to this Convention undertakes to co-operate in carrying out
any investigation which the Security Council may initiate, in accordance with the provisions of the Charter of the United Nations, on the basis of the complaint received by
the Council. The Security Council shall inform the States Parties to the Convention
of the results of the investigation.

Article VII
Each State Party to this Convention undertakes to provide or support assistance, in
accordance with the United Nations Charter, to any Party to the Convention which so
requests, if the Security Council decides that such Party has been exposed to danger
as a result of violation of the Convention.

Article VIII
Nothing in this Convention shall be interpreted as in any way limiting or detracting
from the obligations assumed by any State under the Protocol for the Prohibition
of the Use in War of Asphyxiating, Poisonous or Other Gases, and of Bacteriological
Methods of Warfare, signed at Geneva on 17 June 1925.

Article IX
Each State Party to this Convention affirms the recognised objective of effective prohibition of chemical weapons and, to this end, undertakes to continue negotiations
in good faith with a view to reaching early agreement on effective measures for the
prohibition of their development, production and stockpiling and for their destruction,

and on appropriate measures concerning equipment and means of delivery specifically designed for the production or use of chemical agents for weapons purposes.

Article X

(1) The States Parties to this Convention undertake to facilitate, and have the right to participate in, the fullest possible exchange of equipment, materials and scientific and technological information for the use of bacteriological (biological) agents and toxins for peaceful purposes. Parties to the Convention in a position to do so shall also co-operate in contributing individually or together with other States or international organisations to the further development and application of scientific discoveries in the field of bacteriology (biology) for the prevention of disease, or for other peaceful purposes.

(2) This Convention shall be implemented in a manner designed to avoid hampering the economic or technological development of States Parties to the Convention or international co-operation in the field of peaceful bacteriological (biological) activities, including the international exchange of bacteriological (biological) agents and toxins and equipment for the processing, use or production of bacteriological (biological) agents and toxins for peaceful purposes in accordance with the provisions of the Convention.

Article XI

Any State Party may propose amendments to this Convention. Amendments shall enter into force for each State Party accepting the amendments upon their acceptance by a majority of the States Parties to the Convention and thereafter for each remaining State Party on the date of acceptance by it.

Article XII

Five years after the entry into force of this Convention, or earlier if it is requested by a majority of Parties to the Convention by submitting a proposal to this effect to the Depositary Governments, a conference of States Parties to the Convention shall be held at Geneva, Switzerland, to review the operation of the Convention, with a view to assuring that the purposes of the preamble and the provisions of the Convention, including the provisions concerning negotiations on chemical weapons, are being realised. Such review shall take into account any new scientific and technological developments relevant to the Convention.

Article XIII

(1) This Convention shall be of unlimited duration.

(2) Each State Party to this Convention shall in exercising its national sovereignty have the right to withdraw from the Convention if it decides that extraordinary events, related to the subject matter of the Convention, have jeopardised the supreme interests of its country. It shall give notice of such withdrawal to all other States Parties

to the Convention and to the United Nations Security Council three months in advance. Such notice shall include a statement of the extraordinary events it regards as having jeopardised its supreme interests.

Article XIV

(1) This Convention shall be open to all States for signature. Any State which does not sign the Convention before its entry into force in accordance with paragraph 3 of this Article may accede to it at any time.

(2) This Convention shall be subject to ratification by signatory States. Instruments of ratification and instruments of accession shall be deposited with the Governments of the United Kingdom of Great Britain and Northern Ireland, the Union of Soviet Socialist Republics and the United States of America, which are hereby designated the Depositary Governments.

(3) This Convention shall enter into force after the deposit of instruments of ratification by twenty-two Governments, including the Governments designated as Depositaries of the Convention.

(4) For States whose instruments of ratification or accession are deposited subsequent to the entry into force of this Convention, it shall enter into force on the date of the deposit of their instruments of ratification or accession.

(5) The Depositary Governments shall promptly inform all signatory and acceding States of the date of each signature, the date of deposit of each instrument of ratification or of accession and the date of the entry into force of this Convention, and of the receipt of other notices.

(6) This Convention shall be registered by the Depositary Governments pursuant to Article 102 of the Charter of the United Nations.

Article XV

This Convention, the English, Russian, French, Spanish and Chinese texts of which are equally authentic, shall be deposited in the archives of the Depositary Governments. Duly certified copies of the Convention shall be transmitted by the Depositary Governments to the Governments of the signatory and acceding States.

## Document Analysis

The goals of the Biological Weapons Convention are that all biological, chemical, and similar weapons should be dismantled and that no such WMDs should be developed in the future. Citing as abhorrent the weapons identified in the Geneva Protocol of 1925, the BWC requires that every signatory and depositary country not only stop production of these weapons but also destroy existing stockpiles. Participating states also agree to prevent the proliferation of biological, chemical, or similar weapons to nonparticipating states. Furthermore, the participants agree to remain in communication with one another, as well as with the United Nations, to ensure that these WMDs will never be used and eventually be eradicated.

The BWC begins by stating that each participant recognizes the need for total global chemical, biological, and bacteriological WMD disarmament. The introductory statement notes that the United Nations "has repeatedly condemned" the use of these weapons in light of the Geneva Protocol and hints at the torturous effects of these weapons, noting that future use of WMDs "would be repugnant to the conscience of mankind." Citing "the sake of all mankind," this section recognizes an imperative to halt both the "production and stockpiling" of these weapons.

The fifteen articles of the convention state clearly the commitment to total disarmament. Each party agrees not to develop, manufacture, stockpile, or otherwise receive biological, chemical, and similar WMDs. Additionally, existing stockpiles are to be destroyed or "divert[ed] to peaceful purposes." The BWC implicitly raises the point that not every state in the world (indeed, not every member of the United Nations) will agree to the terms of the BWC. In fact, the document implies, many states might be pursuing such weapons. Therefore, to further prevent the use of these WMDs, the BWC calls upon each signatory not to share with other states information about such weapons and to actively discourage the development or proliferation programs of other countries.

Article 5 of the BWC encourages participating nations to work with one another should issues arise that undermine their ability to carry out the provisions of the BWC. Through such communication, the parties involved cooperate with one another in the pursuit of the lofty goals of the BWC.

Although the BWC encourages bi- and multilateral communication and cooperation, the convention recognizes the United Nations as the central authority for carrying out this agreement. Nations with concerns about biological, chemical, and/or bacteriological weapons issues are, under the terms of article 6, encouraged to file official complaints with the UN Security Council, which would in turn launch an investigation. Each party to the BWC is required to support the Security Council's investigation into such matters, upon request.

The BWC is intended to have a fluid lifespan, capable of being amended as pertinent issues arise over the course of the convention's unlimited duration. Over time, new countries will be accepted, each of which would submit to one of the three depositaries managing the BWC's administration—the United States, the Soviet Union, and Great Britain. The signatory nations also have the right to withdraw from the convention if they deem it necessary to do so, but they must include "a statement of the extraordinary events it regards as having jeopardized its supreme interests."

## Essential Themes

Born of both the actual and potential horrors of biological, chemical, and bacteriological weapons, the Biological Weapons Convention called for the curtailment of weapons development, the dismantling of weapons stockpiles, and, the nondeployment of additional such weapons. Working with one another through proper communications channels, sponsored by the United Nations, the participating states took a positive step toward peacefully reducing the prevalence of these weapons within their borders. The BWC also noted that proliferation of these WMDs was as dangerous to the world order as their development, manufacturing, and stockpiling. The Convention called upon every signatory to take the proper steps to prevent the proliferation of these deadly weapons. With the safety of all humanity in mind, the BWC stated, every avenue by which these weapons might appear should be closed. At the time of the conventions, twenty-two countries signed the agreement. Since then, more than 170 states have either acceded to or ratified the treaty.

—*Michael P. Auerbach, MA*

## Bibliography and Additional Reading

"The Biological Weapons Convention." *United Nations Office for Disarmament Affairs*, 2015. Web. 11 Mar. 2016.

Gerstein, Daniel M. *National Security and Arms Control in the Age of Biotechnology: The Biological and Toxin Weapons Convention*. Lanham: Rowman, 2013. Print.

Goldblat, Jozef. "The Biological Weapons Convention: An Overview." *International Review of the Red Cross. Intl. Committee of the Red Cross*, 30 June 1997. Web. 11 Mar. 2016.

Rissanen, Jenni. "The Biological Weapons Convention." *NTI. Nuclear Threat Initiative*, 1 Mar. 2003. Web. 11 Mar. 2016.

**SUPPLEMENTAL HISTORICAL DOCUMENT: The American Civil War as a biological phenomenon: did Salmonella or Sherman win the war for the North?**

Michael D. Brown, Chicago, Illinois, United States

### Reexamining Civil War deaths

A demographic historian, J. David Hacker, recently discovered an unfortunate truth; using newly digitized data from the 1860, 1870, and 1880 censuses, he construct-ed new estimates of Northern and Southern Civil War deaths. In his pivotal analysis published in 2012, the death toll in the American Civil War was far higher than previously re-ported.[1] The long-held belief derived from muster-out rolls and battle reports and compiled by amateur historians had previously esti-mated 618,222 mili-tary deaths (360,222 from the North and

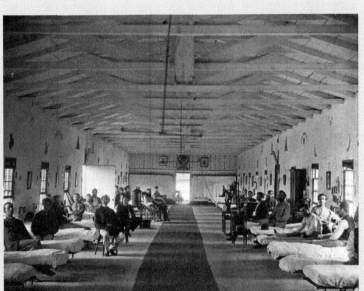

*Patients in Ward K of Armory Square Hospital – Washington, DC, 1865*

258,000 from the South) during the Civil War. Data from the South was particularly untrustworthy, however, due to the post-war destruction of the Southern army and many of its documents. Nonetheless, the previously quoted numbers have stood as accurate totals for the last 150 years. Hacker's pivotal population study suggests a new number for total war dead at approximately 750,000-800,000 deaths, a 20% increase. Hacker clearly extends our understanding of the carnage and suffering wrought upon the United States by the American Civil War.

### Was it bugs or ballistics?

What the new numbers do not reveal is the cause of those deaths. Hacker's study serves as a reminder that many more of these deaths were related to infectious dis-eases than to ballistic injuries. It postulates that most of the additional deaths were due to greater medical and disease losses in the South.[1] Army records for the North suggest that 62% of Union Army deaths were caused by disease, whereas less accurate Southern records suggest that deaths by disease exceeded 65% of all deaths. By contrast, infectious diseases accounted for 70% of hospital admissions in the Vietnam War, but deaths from infections were less than 0.5% of battle-related causalities.2

A wide variety of biological diseases were noted during the Civil War.3 In order of frequency these were dysentery and diarrheal disorders (Salmonella, Shigella, Amoeba), malaria, measles, typhoid fever and typhus, smallpox, scarlet fever, pneumonia, tuberculosis, "camp itch" (lice infestations), scurvy, rheumatism, mumps, yellow fever, and venereal diseases. Typhoid fever was likely the most common infectious disease of the war, and diarrheal illnesses due to Salmonella and Shigella accounted for significant death and disability.4 Ninety percent of all new recruits to the Confederate Army developed diarrhea upon entering camp, and soldiers on both sides rarely had formed bowel movements. A Southern minister noted, "The disease that seems to breakdown the willpower more than any other was chronic diarrhea, and the patients seemed to lose not only their desire to live but all manliness and self-respect."5 Medical theory of the early 1860s suffered from a rudimentary concept of hygiene and no knowledge of the infectious causes of illnesses such as dysentery or malaria.6 Without an accurate understanding of the infectious nature of these illnesses, prevention was impossible and spread rapid and complete. It would be ten years before Louis Pasteur's germ theory would finally begin to alter medical thinking.

The prevailing therapy of medical illness favored the concept of "ill humors" or "noxious effluvia" as causative agents. Indeed, Dr. John Brown's theory that inflammation represented "excessive stimulation and overexcitement" was widely accepted. Misguided attempts to eliminate these "vapors" and stimulations led to the use of toxic and unnecessary diaphoretics, cathartics, irritants, counter irritants, astringents, emetics, bleedings, and purgatives that further injured or killed the patient.6 These precepts of medical theory, however, did not differ between the North and the South.

The medical corps in the military differed significantly in the North and South, however, which led to significant disparities in medical management.3,7 William Hammond was the U.S. surgeon general for the Union Army until his court-martial in 1864. Hammond, an eleven-year US Army veteran who had spent five years on the faculty of the University of Maryland, was able to run an efficient military medical corps. He ordered hazardous medications out of the formulary, weeded out incompetent physicians, pushed for hygienic conditions, and was able to hire nurses and doctors on the spot as needed. He also invoked the Letterman System, which modernized the use of battlefield ambulances, standardized medical field kits, and restructured the medical command system to favor experience over social status. Hammond's counterpart in the South, Samuel Preston Moore, was also an army veteran but his attempts to modernize Southern medical care were hampered by social hierarchy, small hospitals, and inadequate physician and nurse staffing. He received a mere $350,000 to initiate medical services for the entire Southern army.5

Demographic factors also played a role in the increased Southern casualties from infectious diseases. Inadequate physical exams, in which unqualified and very young and very old conscripts were brought into the army, increased the morbidity and mortality wrought by infection. A preponderance of troops from rural areas in the South brought individuals into large populations of men where their lack of immunity placed them at a uniquely high risk for infectious disorders. Exposure, lack of clothing and shoes, poor and insufficient foods, and impure water were more pervasive in the Southern ranks, thus increasing their infectious risk.3,4

These differences raise the question: did the Confederate Army's increased susceptibility to infection, and specifically to diarrheal disorders, lead to a reduction in force that subsequently lost the war? It is important to remember that invasion and conquest were required for the North to win the war, whereas the South needed simply to defend and survive in order to win. It is possible that the South might have succeeded if it had been able to achieve infectious disease rates similar to those in the North.

### Contingency points: Vicksburg and Atlanta

Stanford Civil War historian James M. McPherson has noted five critical contingency points during the Civil War where the outcome and duration, far from inevitable at the time, may have significantly changed: 1) McClellan's failure to capture Richmond, 2) the Union victory at Antietam, 3) The Union victory at Vicksburg, 4) Lee's loss at Gettysburg, and 5) Sherman's successful capture of Atlanta.8 The outcomes of two of these five contingency points, the Vicksburg campaign and the capture of Atlanta may have been largely determined by differences in medical care and the toll of infectious diseases. The inability of the South to deal with these diseases and their preferential suffering at the hands of these illnesses placed them in a tenuous situation in both scenarios and may have ensured a victory for the North.

The siege of Vicksburg, Mississippi took place between May 18 and July 4, 1863. The conclusion of the siege, with the surrender of Lieut. Gen. John C. Pemberton's Confederate defenders, secured the Mississippi River for the North and successfully ended the Vicksburg campaign, strengthening Gen. Ulysses S. Grant's stature in the Union Army.

Two attempts to control the city by frontal assaults were unsuccessful, forcing Grant to enter a prolonged siege beginning on May 25 and ending with the surrender on July 4. Although Pemberton had only 18,500 troops at his disposal compared to Grant's 35,000, he had a city with nearly impenetrable defenses. Approximately one-quarter of Grant's Union Army of the Tennessee was ill with malaria, but overall its medical condition was improving throughout the siege. Conversely, 50% of the Confederate defenders were ill and not with Pemberton's command at the time of the battle of Champion Hill on May 16, 1863 or later during the siege. It was the loss of this battle that forced Pemberton back into a defensive position around Vicksburg.

Excess Confederate losses from illness were likely due to dysentery syndromes such as *Salmonella* and *Shigella* infections, a direct result of water contamination, poor and insufficient food, lack of appropriate clothing with subsequent exposure, and poor hygiene which resulted in infestations of insects and other vermin.[4,5] These were well-documented issues for those defending Vicksburg and certainly played a role in Grant's successful siege. One could postulate that if Pemberton's army had been at full field strength, or even increased by 25% of its size at the Battle of Champion's Hill, that a repulsed Union Army of the Tennessee would by necessity have fallen back into disarray to the Mississippi River and retreated to Northern-held territory. In this alternate history, Grant, of somewhat tenuous stature in the Union Army, might have lost his command or resigned, leaving Vicksburg and the Mississippi River under Confederate control. This might have prolonged the war beyond 1865, ultimately leaving the South intact as an independent nation through negotiations with the North.

The Battle of Atlanta took place on July 22, 1864 southeast of Atlanta, Georgia. The Union Army under Gen. William Tecumseh Sherman was successful that day in repulsing Gen. Joe Johnston's Confederate defenders into Atlanta and setting up siege lines around the city. Sherman then proceeded to attempt to cut the city's supply lines from Macon, Georgia. On August 31, 1864 his army was successful, and on September 2 the city was surrendered to him. Sherman then set up headquarters in the city and remained there until November 15, 1864 when, after burning the majority of the city, he proceeded on his March to the Sea and the capture of Savannah, Georgia.

Sherman's successful march through the South and capture of Atlanta is typically attributed to his brilliance and ruthlessness as a commander, but perhaps also to Johnson's hesitation and Confederate Gen. John Bell Hood's impetuosity.[3] It is equally likely, however, that the inability of the Confederate Army to mount an effective defense of Atlanta was due to extraordinary medical losses in its troop strength. Interestingly, any Confederate soldier lost to illness during the Battle of Atlanta never returned to combat. In the last two months of the battle for Atlanta, 30,000 Confederate soldiers were lost to medical transfer and furlough. At the same time, Sherman's army was considered the healthiest in the Union as it proceeded to live off the land during its march to Atlanta. If the Confederate defenders of Atlanta had a troop health even close to that of the Union Army, an expected increase in true strength of 15,000 to 20,000 soldiers might have stymied Sherman into a stalemate in northern Georgia in 1864. In this alternate history, it is quite possible that Abraham Lincoln might have lost the 1864 election to Gen. George B. McClellan, whose political peace platform called for the cessation of hostilities and negotiations with the Confederacy to allow for its continued existence.

## One nation

In our brief review of two of McPherson's five Civil War contingency points, it seems clear that infectious diseases and specifically dysenteric disorders had a significant impact on the outcome on the war, favoring the North. In the two specific campaigns discussed, those of Vicksburg and Atlanta, diarrheal diseases were decisive in decimating the ranks of Confederate defenders. The South's significant medical disadvantages and increased risk of infectious diseases ensured a Northern victory. If not for Salmonella typhi, the United States, if it even would even be called that, would be a very different place today.

## References

1. Hacker JD. A Census-Based Count of Civil War Dead. *Civil War History.* 2011;57(4):307-348.

2. Affairs USDoV. Military Health History for Clinicians:Vietnam. *Military Health History* 2012, 2013.

3. Freemon FR. *Gangrene and Glory: Medical Care during the American Civil War.* 1st ed. Urbana, IL: University of Illinois Press; 1998.

4. Gilchrist MR. Disease and Infection in the American Civil War. *The American Biology Teacher.* 1998;60(4):258-261.

5. Cunnignham HH. *Doctors in Gray.* 2nd ed. Baton Rouge, LA: Louisiana State University Press; 1960.

6. M.D. CKW. *Civil War Medicine.* 1st ed. Guilford, CN: The Globe Pequot Press; 1998.

7. Adams GW. *Doctors in Blue.* 1st ed. Baton Rouge, LA: Louisiana State University Press; 1952.

8. McPherson JM. *Drawn with the Sword.* 1st ed. New York, NY: Oxford University Press; 1996.

MICHAEL D. BROWN, MD, MACM, FACP, FACG, AGAF, is a professor of medicine at Rush University Medical Center in Chicago in the Section of Digestive Diseases. He is particularly interested in the area of functional bowel diseases. As an undergraduate biology major with a history minor at the University of Colorado, he developed a strong academic interest in the American Civil War that continues to this day.

*SOURCE:* https://hekint.org/2017/01/22/the-american-civil-war-as-a-biological-phenomenon-did-salmonella-or-sherman-win-the-war-for-the-north/

## SUPPLEMENTAL HISTORICAL DOCUMENT: Gulf War Syndrome

### Findings in Brief

This report was produced by the federal Research Advisory Committee on Gulf War Veterans' Illnesses (RACGWVI), which was established by Congress under Public Law 105-368. Membership includes veterans of the 1990-91 Gulf War, scientists who have studied illnesses affecting these veterans, clinicians who care for ill Gulf War veterans and a member of the general public.

The Committee periodically releases reports that summarize research to date on the health of veterans of the 1990-1991 Gulf War. The most recent report was published in 2008, and the current report updates knowledge from that time by reviewing published scientific papers that appeared after the last report and through December 2013.

The present research review is divided into four sections. The first summarizes the new information available on rates of Gulf War illness and other illnesses and disabilities that affect groups of veterans from the Gulf War (Section 1, Epidemiologic Research). The second reviews the human and animal research that has been carried out to identify the causes of Gulf War illness and other health problems in Gulf War veterans (Section 2: Etiologic Investigations). The third section focuses on studies of the disruptions in normal body functions that underlie the symptoms of Gulf War illness and other health problems (Section 3: Pathobiology of Gulf War illness). And the fourth reviews clinical trials that are underway to treat Gulf War illness (Section 4: Gulf War Illness Treatment Research).

In this section, the findings of the report are described in brief.

### General conclusions

Scientific research published since the 2008 Committee report supports and further substantiates the conclusions of the 2008 report that Gulf War illness is a serious physical disease, affecting at least 175,000 veterans of the 1990-1991 Gulf War, that resulted from hazardous exposures in the Gulf War theater. Important progress has been made in improving scientific understanding of Gulf War illness. Research has begun to identify probable underlying mechanisms, promising treatments and biomarkers. However, much work remains to be done.

We support the scientists and clinicians working to improve the health of Gulf War veterans and to protect the health of current and future American servicemen and women at risk of similar exposures. Effective treatments for Gulf War illness could also lead to treatments for other exposure-related occupational health problems. The Committee recommends a robust federal research effort to monitor and improve the health of Gulf War veterans, with the identification of treatments for Gulf War illness the highest priority.

A wide-ranging scientific literature review of this problem published after 2008, the Institute of Medicine's 2010 *Gulf War and Health* report, also recommended a renewed federal research effort and concluded that treatments and hopefully preventions can likely be found with the right research.

### What is Gulf War illness and how common is it?

Gulf War illness refers to the chronic symptoms that affect veterans of the 1990-1991 Gulf War at markedly elevated rates compared to other veteran groups and to the U.S. population as a whole. The individual symptoms experienced by ill Gulf War veterans can vary from person to person, but overall the types of symptoms reported are similar in the many groups of ill veterans that have been studied since the war. Symptoms typically include some combination of widespread pain, headache, persistent problems with memory and thinking, fatigue, breathing problems, stomach and intestinal symptoms, and skin abnormalities.

In the early years after the war, this disorder was commonly called "Gulf War Syndrome" by the media and has since been referred to by a variety of names such as undiagnosed illness, Gulf War illness, chronic multisymptom illness and other terms. "Gulf War illness" is the term most commonly used by scientists, clinicians, veterans' groups and the Department of Defense and is used in this report to refer to the illness associated with military service in the 1990-1991 Gulf War.

Based on its review of the research that has been published since 2008, the Committee concludes that Gulf War illness has been consistently reported in all studies of Gulf War veterans and that it is seen in about 25-30% of Gulf War veterans, or about 175,000 to 250,000 of the 700,000 troops deployed to the war in 1990-91. The same conclusion was reached in 2008.

Little new information has become available on whether the health of ill Gulf War veterans has improved over time. The research published in the 2008 RACGWVI report suggests that there is little to no improvement among veterans with Gulf War illness. The effect that aging will have on this vulnerable population remains a matter of concern.

### *What other kinds of health problems are experienced by Gulf War veterans?*
Studies published since 2008 continue to find that veterans from the 1990-91 Gulf War have poorer general health and greater disability than other veterans of the same era who did not deploy to the Gulf.

Studies reviewed in this report show that Gulf War veterans who were most exposed to the release of nerve gas by the destruction of the Khamisiyah Iraqi arms depot have significantly elevated rates of death due to brain cancer. Veterans who were exposed to the highest level of contaminants from oil well fires also have increased rates of brain cancer deaths. Studies conducted prior to 2008 show that Gulf War veterans experienced higher than expected rates of amyotrophic lateral sclerosis (ALS).

Very little other research has yet been conducted to determine rates at which Gulf War veterans have been affected by other medical conditions of possible concern, including neurological diseases such as multiple sclerosis or Parkinson's disease, cancers, sleep disorders, adverse pregnancy outcomes or rates of birth defects in veterans' children.

Persons with disorders like chronic fatigue syndrome, fibromyalgia and multiple chemical sensitivity have similar symptoms to veterans with Gulf War illness, but most Gulf War illness patients cannot be diagnosed with these disorders using standard diagnostic rules. Gulf War illness is a distinct disorder and Gulf War veterans who can be diagnosed with these disorders often differ significantly from non-veteran populations who are diagnosed with them.

Studies of psychological and psychiatric disorders in Gulf War veterans since 2008 continue to show that combat and other stressors are associated with post-traumatic stress disorder, anxiety, depression and alcohol abuse in Gulf War veterans but that these disorders are clinically distinct from Gulf War illness. They are typically reported to occur in less than 10% of Gulf War veterans, far below the rate of these disorders in veterans of other recent wars and far below the rate of Gulf War illness in Gulf War veterans.

Very little is known about whether service in the Gulf War or having Gulf War illness affects veterans' life expectancy. Much more needs to be learned about this. Despite specific recommendations over many years from both RACGWVI and Institute of Medicine panels, research in this area remains seriously inadequate.

### Which exposures and experiences in the Gulf War theater caused ill health and functional disability in Gulf War veterans?

Once it became clear that veterans of the Gulf War had returned home with persistent health problems, the question immediately arose as to the cause or causes of ill health in this veteran group. Although a highly publicized initial argument was that their ill health was due to deployment related stressors and psychological trauma, scientific studies consistently demonstrated that Gulf War illness was associated with chemical, pharmaceutical and other environmental exposures in theater, rather than stress. Research in this area has expanded since 2008 and has included investigations of effects of veterans' exposures to specific chemicals and drugs during the war as well as extensive exploration of the persistent effects of single and combined Gulf War-related exposures in animal models. Further, many studies have shown that environmental and occupational exposure to pesticides in other populations are associated with health problems similar to Gulf War illness.

The research reviewed in this report supports and reinforces the conclusion in the 2008 RACGWVI report that exposures to pesticides and pyridostigmine bromide are causally associated with Gulf War illness. Evidence also continues to demonstrate that Gulf War illness is not the result of psychological stressors during the war.

Hazardous exposures in theater are also related to certain other health problems seen in Gulf War veterans. Exposure to the nerve gas agents sarin and cyclosarin has been linked in two more studies to changes in structural magnetic resonance brain imaging that are associated with cognitive decrements, further supporting findings on the nervous system effects of these agents reported in the 2008 report. New evidence has emerged suggesting that oil well fire exposures may be important in the development of Gulf War illness and brain cancer. It is unclear if vaccine exposures may also be contributing to Gulf War veteran health symptoms, because current results have been conflicting and include weak associations. Although exposure to depleted uranium has been demonstrated, with continuing levels in body tissue, its contribution to ill health is unclear: studies on this substance have focused on small groups of individuals.

### How are basic body functions affected in veterans with Gulf War illness?

Studies reviewed in the 2008 RACGWVI report and research published since then have shown that Gulf War illness is associated with changes in the brain, autonomic nervous system, endocrine system and immune system. Other health problems have also been demonstrated in subgroups of veterans who experienced exposures to specific chemicals in the Gulf War theater.

### What effective treatments are available for patients with Gulf War illness and how should new treatments be developed?

Treatment research has increased significantly since 2008, particularly reflecting the efforts of the Gulf War Illness Research Program (GWIRP) of the Department of Defense (DoD)'s Office of Congressionally Directed Medical Research Programs (CDMRP) to fund such research. However, most of these studies are still underway, with few results yet available. Promising preliminary reports from the limited trials to date indicate possible benefits provided by coenzyme Q10 (a dietary supplement), acupuncture and use of continuous positive airway pressure (CPAP) during sleep in veterans with sleep apnea.

The Committee believes that the first priority of federal Gulf War illness research must be the identification of effective treatments to improve the health of Gulf War veterans and to protect the health of current and future American servicemen and women at risk of similar exposures.

Treatment approaches based on what is known about the underlying physiological changes that occur in veterans with Gulf War illness may be the most effective. Promising laboratory research is underway to develop cutting-edge treatment approaches by studying the effects of Gulf War exposures in animals and then targeting and testing treatments for these effects. Effective treatments of Gulf War illness could lead to treatments for exposure-related occupational and environmental health problems in other groups of people. It may be possible to leverage support from other federal health agencies interested in exposure-related diseases and disorders for this effort.

# Executive Summary

This report was produced by the federal Research Advisory Committee on Gulf War Veterans' Illnesses (RACGWVI), established by Congress under Public Law 105-368. The Committee periodically releases reports that summarize research to date on the health of veterans of the 1990-1991 Gulf War. The most recent report was published in 2008, and the current report updates knowledge since that time by reviewing published papers that appeared after the last report and through December 2013.

The research review is divided into four sections that summarize the epidemiological issues and research on Gulf War illness, the human and animal research that has addressed causes of the illness and other health problems in Gulf War veterans, studies that focus on the underlying pathobiology of illness manifestations and the clinical trials that are underway to treat Gulf War illness.

In this Executive Summary, the Committee summarizes its conclusions about the findings from research to date on Gulf War illness and other health problems in Gulf War veterans and provides recommendations about how to further understand and, most importantly, how to identify and evaluate effective treatments.

## *General conclusions*

Scientific research published since the 2008 Committee report supports and further substantiates the conclusions of the 2008 report that Gulf War illness is a serious physical disease, affecting at least 175,000 veterans of the 1990-1991 Gulf War, that resulted from hazardous exposures in the Gulf War theater. Important progress has been made in improving scientific understanding of Gulf War illness. Research is beginning to identify probable underlying mechanisms, promising treatments and biomarkers. However, much work remains to be done.

We support the scientists and clinicians working to improve the health of Gulf War veterans and to protect the health of current and future American servicemen and women at risk of similar exposures. Effective treatments for Gulf War illness could also lead to treatments for other exposure-related occupational health problems. The Committee recommends a robust federal research effort to monitor and improve the health of Gulf War veterans, with the identification of treatments for Gulf War illness the highest priority.

A wide-ranging scientific literature review of this problem published after 2008, the Institute of Medicine's 2010 *Gulf War and Health* report, also recommended a renewed federal research effort and concluded that treatments and hopefully preventions can likely be found with the right research.

## *What is Gulf War illness and how prevalent is it?*

As described in previous Committee reports, Gulf War illness refers to the chronic symptoms that affect veterans of the 1990-1991 Gulf War at markedly elevated rates compared to other veteran groups and to the U.S. population as a whole. The individual symptoms experienced by ill Gulf War veterans can vary from person to person, but overall the types of symptoms reported are similar in the many groups of ill veterans that have been studied since the war. Symptoms typically include some combination of widespread pain, headache, persistent problems with memory and thinking, fatigue, breathing problems, stomach and intestinal symptoms and skin abnormalities.

In the early years after the war, this disorder was commonly called "Gulf War Syndrome" by the media and has since been referred to by a variety of names such as undiagnosed illness, Gulf War illness, chronic multisymptom illness and various other terms. Gulf War illness, the term most commonly used by scientists, clinicians, veterans' groups and the Department of Defense, is used throughout this report to refer to the chronic symptomatic illness associated with military service in the 1990-1991 Gulf War.

Based on its review of the data published since 2008, the Committee concludes that all population-based studies conducted since the Gulf War have continued to identify a significant excess rate of chronic symptomatic illness, variously defined, in 1990-1991 Gulf War veterans. The large majority of studies indicate that the prevalence of Gulf War illness is in the range of 25-30% in Gulf War veterans, as reported in 2008.

Little additional information on the long-term prognosis of Gulf War illness has become available since 2008. Prior data reported in 2008 suggest that there is little to no improvement in the health of ill Gulf War veterans over time. The effect that aging will have on this vulnerable population remains a matter of concern.

### *What other kinds of health problems are experienced by Gulf War veterans?*
Studies published since 2008 continue to document poorer general health status and greater disability among Gulf War veterans than in contemporary veterans who did not deploy to the Gulf. Despite the extensive number of studies conducted with Gulf War veterans in the 23 years since Desert Storm, medical surveillance in this population remains seriously inadequate.

Very little research has yet been conducted to determine rates at which Gulf War veterans have been affected by many medical conditions of possible concern. As a result, it is not currently known if Gulf War veterans have experienced excess prevalence or incidence rates of most medical conditions. Disorders of concern reviewed in this report include the following:

1. Neurological disorders. Although neurological conditions are a prominent concern for Gulf War veterans and research has found an elevated incidence of amyotrophic lateral sclerosis (ALS), rates of multiple sclerosis, Parkinson's disease and other neurological diseases (e.g., seizures, stroke, migraines) in Gulf War veterans are currently unknown. Research studies on the prevalence of neurological diseases have not been conducted despite repeated recommendations by this Committee and the Institute of Medicine and explicit legislation by Congress. The prevalence of these disorders is particularly important because they can be expected to increase as the Gulf War veteran population ages.

2. Cancer. Since 2008, research using state cancer registries has suggested that there may be an increased rate of lung cancer in Gulf War veterans. Brain cancer mortality has been shown in two studies conducted by VA to be significantly increased in the subgroup of Gulf War veterans with greatest exposure to oil well fire smoke and to low-level nerve agents released by the destruction of Iraqi facilities at Khamisiyah. In general, cancer risk remains unknown and understudied.

3. Other diagnosed medical conditions reported at excess rates. Research since 2008 continues to indicate that Gulf War veterans report being diagnosed with a variety of medical conditions at significantly higher rates than nondeployed era veterans. These include chronic digestive disorders, respiratory conditions, heart disease and skin disorders. Although consistently reported by Gulf War veterans, these conditions have not been further evaluated or characterized by epidemiologic or clinical studies.

4. Sleep dysfunction. A single study published since 2008 has identified sleep abnormalities in a

group of Gulf War veterans compared to obesity-matched controls. Sleep disturbance is an extremely common symptom in veterans with Gulf War illness and continuous positive airway pressure (CPAP) has shown some promise for treating a range of symptoms in veterans with sleep apnea in a small treatment trial.

5. Adverse reproductive outcomes and birth defects. No definitive new information is available on birth defects in offspring of Gulf War veterans, and no research has ever been published concerning neurological or other medical conditions affecting veterans' children. It is important that medical and reproductive outcomes be assessed in children of veteran subgroups of interest (e.g. exposure, location, illness subgroups).

Multisymptom conditions, including chronic fatigue syndrome, fibromyalgia and multiple chemical sensitivity, share similar symptoms with Gulf War illness, but most Gulf War illness patients do not meet diagnostic criteria for them. Gulf War veterans who meet criteria for these disorders often differ significantly on tested parameters from non-veteran populations who are diagnosed with them. It may be necessary to consider people with these disorders who are and are not Gulf War veterans separately in research studies, including treatment research.

Studies of psychological and psychiatric morbidity in Gulf War veterans since 2008 continue to show that combat and other stressors are associated with post-traumatic stress disorder (PTSD), anxiety, depression and alcohol abuse but are not independently associated with Gulf War illness.

Lack of current information on overall and disease-specific mortality among U.S. Gulf War veterans is an important issue. No comprehensive information has been published on the mortality experience of U.S. Gulf War era veterans after the year 2000. The 13 years for which no mortality figures are available represent more than half of the 23 years since Desert Storm. Mortality information from the last decade is particularly crucial for understanding the health consequences of the Gulf War, given the latency periods associated with many chronic diseases of interest. Despite specific recommendations over many years from both the current Committee and Institute of Medicine panels, federal research efforts to monitor the mortality experience of 1990-1991 Gulf War veterans remain seriously inadequate.

## How can research on the health of Gulf War veterans be improved?
**Case definition of Gulf War illness**
In the absence of a consensus case definition of Gulf War illness 23 years after the appearance of this condition, it can be difficult to assess and compare research findings in epidemiological, pathobiological or treatment research on the disorder. The Committee recommends the following approaches to the development of such a definition.

1. An evidence-based, expert consensus-driven case definition for Gulf War illness should be developed. This process should include a) a review of the existing literature relevant to case definitions for Gulf War illness, b) in-depth statistical and epidemiologic assessment of the strengths and weaknesses of different case definition approaches using datasets that provide representative data on symptoms and medical conditions affecting 1990-1991 Gulf War era veterans and c) final case definition parameters and guidelines developed by an expert consensus panel that includes scientists experienced in Gulf War illness research and symptom-based case definitions in veterans affected by Gulf War illness (see http://www.va.gov/RAC-GWVI/VA_draft_strategic_plan.pdf Section 5.3). The recent IOM panel on case definitions of Gulf War illness also commented that a data-based case definition of the disorder could be derived (Institute of Medicine, 2014). This effort should involve representatives from VA, a broad spectrum of scientists conducting research in Gulf War

veterans, clinicians knowledgeable about the problem and Gulf War veterans. It could be organized through the Gulf War Illness Research Program of the Department of Defense Congressionally Directed Medical Research Program (CDMRP) through its competitive grant proposal process with scientific review.

2. VA should adopt the name Gulf War illness for the symptomatic condition associated with military service in the 1990-1991 Gulf War. This recommendation is also supported by the 2014 Institute of Medicine report on case definitions of the illness (Institute of Medicine, 2014).

**Monitoring the effect of Gulf War service on long-term health**
Ongoing monitoring and surveillance of the Gulf War veteran population is critical as this veteran group ages. A strategy for such monitoring was included in a plan proposed by a VA Strategic Planning group composed of representatives from RACGWVI, the VA National Research Advisory Council and VA staff. Such surveillance should include outcomes described in this document, including Gulf War illness; neurological disorders, including Parkinson's disease; autoimmune conditions such as multiple sclerosis; brain, lung and other cancers; cardiovascular disorders and dysfunction; sleep dysfunction; adverse reproductive outcomes and birth defects; general ill health and disability; mortality, and other disorders and outcomes that emerge as important during the surveillance process. This effort must include the following elements.

1. Ongoing assessment of Gulf War illness and its impact on the health and lives of Gulf War veterans is critical. VA's longitudinal survey currently in process should be extended to add a symptom inventory adequate to define the illness according to existing commonly-used case definitions, as previously recommended by the Committee: "[The current survey instrument] cannot determine the prevalence, progression, or correlates of this illness… [I]t is unthinkable that the largest national study of Gulf War veterans would not provide the data required to evaluate the signature problem of the 1991 Gulf War" (Research Advisory Committee on Gulf War Veterans' Illnesses, 2012).

2. VA's longitudinal survey can be effectively used to assess rates of physician-diagnosed medical conditions in Gulf War and era veterans. Survey data should be used to flag conditions of possible importance and followed up with detailed investigation, including any clinical evaluations that are required to determine specific medical diagnoses affecting Gulf War veterans at excess rates.

3. A study on the prevalence of "multiple sclerosis, Parkinson's disease, and brain cancers, as well as central nervous system abnormalities that are difficult to precisely diagnose" in Gulf War and recent Iraq/Afghanistan war veterans was required by Congress in 2008 (Public Law 110-389, 2008, Section 804) and should be carried out. These assessments should be repeated and published at a minimum of 5-year intervals.

4. Systematic assessment of overall and disease-specific mortality in all Gulf War veterans and in specific subgroups of interest is essential. The results of these assessments should also be published at 5-year intervals.

5. VA's longitudinal survey should be used to assess rates of medical conditions, including neurological and behavioral disorders and birth defects, in children of Gulf War era veterans. Survey data can be used to flag conditions of possible concern and followed up. It is also

important that VA publish results from studies of veterans' children that were conducted over 10 years ago.

6. Evaluation of health outcomes in Gulf War veterans in subgroups of potential importance is critical as some health outcomes are related to specific exposures and experiences in theater. These subgroups can be defined by suspected or documented exposures in theater, geographical locations in the Gulf War theater or other predictors.

**Improved methodology in Gulf War epidemiologic research**
It is important that VA work with CDMRP to establish guidelines for improved methodology in Gulf War research that can be included in requests for proposals and subject to research application reviews. Such guidelines should include the following:

1. Systematic methods for assessing symptoms and other health outcomes in Gulf War veterans.

2. Evaluation of health outcomes in Gulf War veteran subgroups of importance—for example, subgroups defined by relevant exposure history or location in theater.

3. Consideration of subpopulations with multiple health outcomes.

4. In evaluating risk factors for Gulf War illness and other health outcomes, use of analytic methods that control as fully as possible for confounding effects of multiple exposures and etiologic factors that may be associated both with the exposures and outcomes of interest. Consideration of the effects of mixed exposures is also key.

## Which exposures and experiences in the Gulf War theater caused ill health and functional disability in Gulf War veterans?

Once it became clear that veterans of the Gulf War had returned home with persistent health problems, the question immediately arose as to the cause or causes of ill health in this veteran group. Although a highly publicized initial argument was that their ill health was due to deployment related stressors and psychological trauma, the evidence ultimately demonstrated that chemical, pharmaceutical and other environmental exposures in theater underlie the development of Gulf War illness. Research in this area has expanded since 2008 and has included research on exposure-outcome relationships in veterans as well as extensive use of animal models to explore the chronic, persistent effects of single and combined exposures to substances and conditions that occurred in theater.

Taken together, the scientific literature published since 2008 supports and reinforces the conclusion in the 2008 RACGWVI report that exposures to pesticides and pyridostigmine bromide are causally associated with Gulf War illness and that exposures to low-level nerve agents, oil well fires, receipt of multiple vaccines, and combinations of Gulf War exposures cannot be ruled out as contributing factors to this condition. Studies also continue to show that Gulf War illness is not caused by psychological stressors during the war.

**Epidemiologic research**
Overall, studies published since the 2008 report continue to show that exposures to pesticides and pyridostigmine bromide are etiologically important in the development of Gulf War illness and in the behavioral and cognitive dysfunction experienced by Gulf War veterans. The findings in Gulf War veteran populations are consistent with those seen in other occupational and environmental groups (see Appendix C). Exposure to the nerve gas agents sarin/cyclosarin has been linked in two more studies to changes in structural magnetic resonance brain imaging findings that are associated with cognitive

decrements, further supporting the conclusion from evidence reviewed in the 2008 report that exposure to these agents is etiologically important to the central nervous system dysfunction that occurs in some subsets of Gulf War veterans.

New evidence has emerged suggesting that oil well fire exposures may be important in the development of Gulf War illness and brain cancer. It is unclear if vaccine exposures may also be contributing to Gulf War veteran health symptoms, because current results are conflicting and include weak associations. Although exposure to depleted uranium has been demonstrated, with continuing levels in body tissue, its contribution to ill health is unclear; studies on this substance have focused on small groups of individuals.

Most veterans experienced exposures to chemical mixtures in theater and effects of these complex exposures remain unknown. Improved modeling of contributions of individual and mixed exposures would inform the assessment of mixed exposures, as would the development of biomarkers of exposures to specific chemicals that occurred in the past.

Exposure studies in Gulf War veterans to identify the etiologic agents that may have been causative in Gulf War illness remain important because they can help to determine treatment targets in subgroups of veterans with specific exposures for which there are known mechanistic pathways that cause illness and symptoms. Results from this work can be useful in protecting the health of future military personnel who will experience these exposures as well as non-military populations with occupational or environmental exposure to them. The Committee recommends that additional research in this area be carried out utilizing objective markers of exposure whenever feasible. These include environmental sampling and modeling of conditions in theater. Identification of biomarkers of exposure and downstream effects of exposures since the war that are present years after the exposure occurred have strong potential for improving scientific understanding of the physiological effects of Gulf War theater exposures and the relationship of these exposures to Gulf War illness. Applicable methods might include genomic, genetic, epigenetic, proteomic, lipidomic or metabolomic assays to explore suspected physiological effects and to identify novel, unsuspected pathways of illness. Research and statistical methods that consider the mixed exposure scenario experienced by Gulf War veterans in theater are essential. These should focus on assessing effects of individual exposures as well as various exposure combinations and mixtures. Mixed exposures include not only mixtures of chemicals but also chemicals combined with heat, dehydration, infection and other environmental stressors.

**Animal studies**
As noted in the RACGWVI 2008 report, animal studies have identified biological effects of Gulf War exposures and combinations of exposures that were previously unknown. The evidence concerning these effects has burgeoned since 2008, with new animal models of Gulf War illness and exposures in theater. It is axiomatic that animals are not humans and conclusions from animal studies must be used as clues that can be further investigated in appropriate human research. However, the outcomes from animal studies are important because data on exposure-outcome relationships can be collected rapidly and efficiently, with confidence in the exposures (since they are controlled). Animal models of Gulf War-relevant exposures to individual chemicals, chemical mixtures, and chemicals plus other stressors have demonstrated alterations in nervous system outcomes (behavior, cognition, neurotransmission, intracellular signaling, molecular and cellular disruptions of axonal transport); liver and cardiovascular function; genomic, proteomic, lipidomic and metabolomic profiles, and mitochondrial changes. These studies have confirmed hypotheses that exposures are important in the development and expression of Gulf War illness symptomatology, that health effects due to exposures and exposure mixtures can be delayed and occur after exposure has ended and that persistent effects can be seen following exposure cessation. Animal models are also critical for treatment research. The systemic alterations and physiological changes identified in exposure research can provide the targets for treatment approaches, and animal models can be used to pre-test promising treatments.

The Committee recommends that research using animal models of Gulf War illness continue to examine the immediate, delayed, and persistent effects of acute exposures to chemicals and chemical mixtures. Research in this area should include the following elements:

1. Future animal model research should focus on studies that characterize persistent effects of Gulf War-related exposures, alone and in combination, on proinflammatory processes in the central nervous system, autonomic nervous system and peripheral target organs, including those that encompass mitochondrial dysfunction and accumulation of reactive oxygen species.

2. Studies that evaluate systemic immune and endocrine parameters in animal models, with an emphasis on those parameters that sensitize ill veterans to Gulf War illness, should also be informative.

3. Animal research to identify biomarkers indicative of past exposures to Gulf War-related toxic compounds that can be applied to Gulf War veterans is important. This includes studies that identify persistent or "downstream" changes in biochemical processes in relation to past neurotoxicant exposure(s) and that identify persistent changes in the central nervous system and in autonomic function associated with Gulf War-related exposures and conditions. Exploratory biomarker research in animal models that assesses genomic, genetic, epigenetic, proteomic, metabolomic and lipidomic pathways of exposure effect may also be informative.

4. Animal models of Gulf War illness are recommended for rapid screening of potential therapeutics.

### What are the physiological mechanisms that underlie Gulf War illness, ill health and functional disability in Gulf War veterans?

In order to understand the health problems seen in the Gulf War veteran population and to generate clues about how to treat their health conditions, is important to learn the underlying pathobiological changes associated with Gulf War illness and with exposures experienced in theater. This report reviews research on structure and function in the central nervous system (using brain imaging, electroencephalography (EEG) and cognitive assays) and work that assesses neuroendocrine, autonomic nervous system, and immunological functions.

Overall, the Committee concludes that the evidence to date continues to point to alterations in central and autonomic nervous system, neuroendocrine, and immune system functions in Gulf War illness and in subsets of Gulf War veterans with specific exposures in theater.

Consistent with evidence presented in the 2008 Committee report, new neuroimaging and EEG research has assessed veterans with Gulf War illness and veterans with sarin/cyclosarin exposure. Fourteen of fifteen new studies show structural and electrical abnormalities in the central nervous system associated with Gulf War illness or with exposure to the nerve gas agents sarin and cyclosarin.

Recent studies on cognitive function in Gulf War veterans provide further support for the conclusion of the 2008 report that cognitive dysfunction is a central issue for Gulf War veterans with Gulf War illness and for Gulf War veterans who experienced specific exposures in theater. These findings support the evidence from imaging and EEG probes that nervous system dysfunction is a key element in veterans' ill health.

Studies continue to support the conclusion from the 2008 report that neuroendocrine function, as assessed by altered hypothalamic pituitary axis (HPA) functioning in Gulf War veterans, is present and is not consistent with the typical pattern seen in post-traumatic stress disorder.

The 2008 RACGWVI report discussed a number of scientific publications documenting autonomic nervous system dysregulation in Gulf War veterans. Since 2008, the only published study that looked specifically at autonomic function in Gulf War veterans confirmed diminished night-time heart rate variability in all three Haley Syndrome Gulf War illness groups.

Six of eight studies conducted on immune system alterations in Gulf War veterans since 2008 showed immune dysregulation. Research in this area appears to be narrowing in on changes occurring to the expression of certain cell lines. Additionally, changes occurring during or following exercise reiterate that immunological (and other) manifestations of Gulf War illness may only become apparent in specific experimental or clinical settings under "challenge" conditions.

The Committee recommends that research on the pathobiological underpinnings of Gulf War illness and ill health in Gulf War veterans continue to focus on the central and autonomic nervous systems and on immunological and neuroendocrine outcomes in this population in order to identify targets for treatment interventions and outcomes that should be improved during such treatments.

1. Clear, operationalized case definitions are important for this work. Findings may differ in differing patient populations, either defined with different Gulf War illness criteria or experiencing different health problems. For example, non-veteran patients with multisymptom illnesses like chronic fatigue syndrome or fibromyalgia may show different patterns of immunological or neurological function than veterans who have Gulf War illness and meet criteria for these disorders.

2. Similarly, Gulf War theater exposures, age and other variables likely moderate pathobiological effects and should be carefully addressed in research.

3. In some studies that have included female Gulf War veterans, it appears that gender differences may play a role in the pathobiological expression of Gulf War illness and its effects. Gender should be considered whenever possible in mechanistic and treatment research on Gulf War illness.

4. Since the pathobiological mechanisms underlying Gulf War illness are poorly understood, exploratory probes such as genomics, metabolomics and proteomics may yield useful information that can lead to more focused research.

5. Epigenetic and genetic approaches to research on Gulf War illness pathobiology are likely also to be informative.

6. In order to effectively pursue "omics" and genetic correlates of Gulf War illness, standardized sample collections in research that uses biological specimens can expedite exploratory and hypothesis-driven research. Standardized protocols for sample collections should be established and followed.

7. Increased emphasis should be placed on the study of alterations in regulatory dynamics both within and across the principal regulatory axes, including the endocrine, immune and nervous systems. These should include response to standardized challenges at different time scales, i.e. acute response to exercise, circadian rhythm, and monthly cycles as well as long-term illness

progression. Statistical analysis should be integrative and deployed across these interacting systems whenever possible using methodologies that formally acknowledge regulatory control.

8. Animal models may be appropriate to investigate some mechanistic hypotheses and illness or exposure effects.

### *What effective treatments are available for patients with Gulf War illness and how should new treatments be developed?*

Treatment research has increased significantly since 2008, particularly reflecting the work of the Gulf War Illness Research Program (GWIRP) of the DoD Congressionally Directed Medical Research Program (CDMRP). However, most of these studies are underway, with results pending. Promising preliminary reports from the limited trials to date indicate possible benefits provided by coenzyme Q10 (a dietary supplement), acupuncture, and use of continuous positive airway pressure (CPAP) during sleep in veterans with sleep disorders.

Early results provide encouraging signs that the treatment goals identified in the 2010 Institute of Medicine report are achievable: "Veterans who continue to suffer from these discouraging symptoms deserve the very best that modern science and medicine can offer . . . to speed the development of effective treatments, cures, and, it is hoped, preventions. The committee suggests a path forward to accomplish these goals and we believe that, through a concerted national effort and rigorous scientific input, answers can likely be found" (Institute of Medicine, 2010, p. x).

It will continue to be important to explore both conventional medical approaches (such as medications or devices) as well as alternative therapies. Treatments based on proposed mechanisms of illness presentation and on specific symptoms are currently under development through two CDMRP-funded collaborative consortia and through other trials by individual investigators. These projects have the potential to identify treatments that address the fundamental physiological alterations underlying the illness, rather than simply the symptoms.

The Committee believes that the first priority of federal Gulf War illness research must be the identification of effective treatments to improve the health of Gulf War veterans and to protect the health of current and future American servicemen and women at risk of similar exposures.

This research should include a number of critical elements.

1. Clear, operationalized case definitions for Gulf War illness and other diagnostic subgroups for whom treatments are designed are essential.

2. Clear, operationalized definitions of the clinical targets for treatment must be included in the research plan.

3. Treatment outcomes must be clearly defined so that it is possible to quantify improvements associated with interventions.

4. Where possible, treatment outcomes should include improvement in measures associated with expressions of underlying pathology (abnormal laboratory and functional assays).

Treatment approaches based on known mechanistic pathways of Gulf War illness should be pursued. Effective treatments of Gulf War illness could also lead to significant breakthroughs in the treatment of other exposure-related occupational and environmental health problems. Funding agencies should support intervention development at the proof-of-concept level as well as large-scale clinical trials as they become appropriate. It may be possible to leverage support from other federal health agencies interested in exposure-related diseases and disorders for this effort.

Although the perfect animal model of Gulf War illness has not yet been developed, preclinical animal models can and should be used to develop and test new treatments focused on pathobiological mechanisms of Gulf War illness and the effects of Gulf War theater exposures.

Center- and consortium based treatment research efforts can capitalize on multi-disciplinary expertise and multi-pronged approaches to treatment targets and pre-clinical trials. The CDMRP treatment consortia are an important step in developing integrated treatments for ill Gulf War veterans as an initial assessment of treatment safety and efficacy in Phase I/II trials. Since CDMRP has limited capacity to fund larger clinical trials, validation studies through the VA Cooperative Studies Program (CSP) or similar large, multi-site, government sponsored programs are necessary to provide validation of the safety and efficacy outcomes identified in initial Phase I/II trials. When a pilot treatment study funded by VA or CDMRP shows promising results and is judged to have scientific merit, VA should follow up with a larger trial or other systematic assessment of the treatment's potential benefits.

Data on effective treatments from VA's 2005 longitudinal survey should be published. Information from veterans with Gulf War illness and their treating physicians on treatments that they believe have been effective should be collected and published. This should include reconducting the IOM review of treatments by Gulf War veterans' medical practitioners ordered by Congress in 2010 (Public Law 111-275, 2010, Section 805). This study was transformed into a literature review of treatments for mainly mental health problems by a group with no experience in treating Gulf War illness.

VA Annual Reports to Congress on Gulf War illness research funded by VA should include only studies and treatment trials in which the health of Gulf War veterans is the central focus and in which the study participants are primarily Gulf War veterans.

Congress should maintain its funding to support the effective treatment-oriented Gulf War Illness Research Program at the DoD Office of Congressionally Directed Medical Research Programs for openly competed, peer-reviewed studies to identify:

1. Effective treatments for Gulf War illness,

2. Objective measures that distinguish veterans with Gulf War illness from healthy veterans, and

3. Underlying biological mechanisms potentially amenable to treatment.

# SUBSTANCE ABUSE AND PUBLIC HEALTH

Drug abuse in the United States has a history that stretches back to the late nineteenth century, when opium use reached near epidemic proportions in some cities. Yet even before that, concerns over alcohol abuse (alcoholism) led to calls for the banning of alcoholic beverages. In both cases a strongly moralistic perspective was employed, where not the addictive substance but the individual person (and his or her moral depravity) was held responsible. Drug, alcohol, and tobacco regulation tells the story of a nation grappling with substance abuse as a public health crisis. It also tells the story of ideological differences, conservative versus progressive attitudes, racial and ethnic biases, criminal stereotypes, medical advances, and the power of corporations.

# ■ The Nature and Occasions of Intemperance

**Date:** 1828
**Author:** Beecher, Lyman
**Genre:** political sermon; sermon

## Summary Overview

In the opening decades of the nineteenth century in the United States, the Second Great Awakening was a Protestant revival movement that saw an increase in agitation for conservative Christian moral and social reforms, one of which was the ban of alcoholic beverages. Believing alcohol to be the root of many social and moral problems, these early reformers would give rise to the prohibition movement later in the century and, ultimately, to the passing of the Eighteenth Amendment to the United States Constitution in 1919, which made the production, sale, and consumption of alcohol illegal. A prominent leader in the Second Great Awakening, Congregationalist minister Lyman Beecher was active in efforts to ban alcohol in the early nineteenth century. Drawing from his experience as a clergyman and a moral reformer, Beecher used his sermons to extol the virtues of temperance to those who came to hear him speak. For Beecher, the key to a happy, healthy, fulfilling life was religion, not alcohol.

## Defining Moment

The tumultuous opening decades of the nineteenth century in America gave rise to the Second Great Awakening, a Protestant religious movement that emphasized salvation for all. Led in large part by Methodist and Baptist churches, the movement was known for its elaborate and well-attended religious revivals at which well-known preachers would give stirring sermons aimed at the conversion of souls. One of the target areas for the movement was the so-called burned-over district of present-day upstate New York. In the early years of the nineteenth century, this area was considered to be frontier land in need of religious renewal, and it was so popular a destination for revivals and camp meetings that opportunities for new religious converts were ultimately considered to have "burned" out.

The Second Great Awakening was also a period in which ardent Christians in America took up social causes such as abolition, women's rights, and temperance. In a period of moral reform, it became abundantly clear to reformers that society's ills were in large part due to the prevalence of alcohol consumption. Men in particular were the focus of this movement. Once part of a domestic economy in which men and women worked together in the home, men increasingly had to leave their families during the day for work as American industries grew. Reformers targeted these men, who they believed had turned away from the morality of the home and toward the corruption of secular, industrialized society. Those who advocated for temperance viewed alcohol, usually indulged in outside of the home, as a further division between men and their families.

The Reverend Lyman Beecher, a strong advocate for moral improvement, was among the temperance reformers. For Beecher, alcohol not only took men away from their families but also distracted them from God. Beecher believed that men mistook the sensations that they experienced under the influence of alcohol for those granted naturally by God; one of his primary concerns was that alcohol would push individuals farther away from salvation in the life to come.

## Author Biography

Lyman Beecher was born on October 12, 1775, in New Haven, Connecticut. After his mother's death when Beecher was just days old, his father, blacksmith David Beecher, sent him to be raised by his mother's sister and her family in nearby Guilford, Connecticut. Beecher graduated from Yale University in 1797 and subsequently worked as a pastor in Long Island, New York; Litchfield, Connecticut; and Boston, Massachusetts, before taking a position as the president of Lane Theological Seminary in Cincinnati, Ohio, in 1832. Beecher married Roxana Foote in 1799. After her death, he married Harriet Porter in 1817. Between them, Foote and Porter bore Beecher thirteen children, including Harriet Beecher Stowe, Catharine Beecher, and well-known Congregationalist minister Henry Ward Beecher. Lyman Beecher's career-long desire for social reform undoubtedly had an impact on his equally famous and influential children. After his second wife's death in 1835, Beecher married Lydia Beals Johnson, but he had no more children.

In the early nineteenth century, Beecher, newly graduated from college, applied his religious education to secular issues such as intemperance and slavery, which he considered to be immoral and corrupting forces in American society. As a revivalist during the Second Great Awakening, Beecher used his sermons and public role to support his causes while also speaking out against the Catholic and Unitarian churches, which he opposed. For Beecher and his religiously minded contemporaries, religious reform was the best way to remedy the moral turmoil in society. Although Beecher advocated an end to slavery, he believed that the best means to that end was not sudden, radical nationwide abolition but a gradual change, so that the nation would not experience too dramatic of a cultural shift. Beecher returned to the East Coast in the 1850s. He died in Brooklyn on January 10, 1863.

## HISTORICAL DOCUMENT: The Nature and Occasions of Intemperance

This is a glowing description of the sin of intemperance. None but the pencil of inspiration could have thrown upon the canvass so many and such vivid traits of this complicated evil, in so short a compass. It exhibits its woes and sorrows, contentions and babblings, and wounds and redness of eyes; its smiling deceptions in the beginning, and serpent-bite in the end; the helplessness of its victims, like one cast out upon the deep; the danger of destruction, like that of one who sleeps upon the top of a mast; the unavailing lamentations of the captive, and the giving up of hope and effort. "They have stricken me, and I was not sick; they have beaten me, and I felt it not: when shall I awake? I will seek it yet again"; again be stricken and beaten; again float upon the deep, and sleep upon the mast.

No sin has fewer apologies than intemperance. The suffrage of the world is against it; and yet there is no sin so naked in its character, and whose commencement and progress is indicated by so many signs, concerning which there is among mankind such profound ignorance. All reprobate drunkenness; and yet, not one of the thousands who fall into it, dreams of danger when he enters the way that leads to it.

The soldier, approaching the deadly breach, and seeing rank after rank of those who preceded him swept away, hesitates sometimes, and recoils from death. But men behold the effects upon others, of going in given courses, they see them begin, advance, and end, in confirmed intemperance, and unappalled rush heedlessly upon the same ruin.

A part of this heedlessness arises from the undefined nature of the crime in its early stages, and the ignorance of men, concerning what may be termed the experimental indications of its approach. Theft and falsehood are definite actions. But intemperance is a state of internal sensation, and the indications may exist long, and multiply, and the subject of them not be aware that they are the signs of intemperance. It is not unfrequent, that men become irreclaimable in their habits, without suspicion of danger. Nothing, therefore, seems to be more important, than a description of this broad way, thronged by so many travelers, that the temperate, when they come in sight of it, may know their danger and pass by it and turn away. What I shall deliver on this subject, has been projected for several years, has been delayed by indisposition, and the pressure of other labors, and is advanced now without personal or local reference Intemperance is the sin of our land, and, with our boundless prosperity, is coming in upon us like a flood; and if anything shall defeat the hopes of the world, which hang upon our experiment of civil liberty, it is that river of fire, which is rolling through the land, destroying the vital air, and extending around an atmosphere of death. It is proposed in this and the subsequent discourses, to consider the nature, the occasions, the signs, the evils, and the remedy of intemperance. In this discourse we shall consider

## THE NATURE AND OCCASIONS OF INTEMPERANCE

The more common apprehension is that nothing is intemperance, which does not supercede the regular operations of the mental faculties and the bodily organs. However much a man may consume of ardent spirits, if he can command his mind, his utterance, and his bodily members, he is not reputed intemperate. And yet, drinking within these limits, he may be intemperate in respect to inordinate desire, the quantity consumed, the expense incurred, the present effect on his health and temper, and moral sensibilities, and what is more, in respect to the ultimate and inevitable results of bodily and mental imbecility, or sottish drunkenness.

God has made the human body to be sustained by food and sleep, and the mind to be invigorated by effort and the regular healthfulness of the moral system, and the cheering influence of his moral government. And whoever, to sustain the body, or invigorate the mind, or cheer the heart, applies habitually the stimulus of ardent spirits, does violence to the laws of his nature, puts the whole system into disorder, and is intemperate long before the intellect falters, or a muscle is unstrung.

The effect of ardent spirits on the brain, and the members of the body, is among the last effects of intemperance, and the least destructive part of the sin. It is the moral ruin which it works in the soul that gives it the denomination of giant-wickedness. If all who are intemperate, drank to insensibility, and on awaking, could arise from the debauch with intellect and heart uninjured, it would strip the crime of its most appalling evils. But among the woes which the scriptures denounce against crime, one is, "wo unto them that are mighty to drink wine, and men of strength to consume strong drink." These are captains in the bands of intemperance, and will drink two generations of youths into the grave, before they go to lie down by their side. The Lord deliver us from strong-headed men, who can move the tongue when all are mute around them, and keep the eye open when all around them sleep, and can walk from the scene of riot, while their companions must be aided or wait until the morning.

*No sin has fewer apologies than intemperance.*

It is a matter of undoubted certainty, that habitual tippling is worse than periodical drunkenness. The poor Indian, who, once a month, drinks himself dead all but simple breathing, will out-live for years the man who drinks little and often, and is not, perhaps, suspected of intemperance. The use of ardent spirits daily, as ministering to cheerfulness, or bodily vigor, ought to be regarded as intemperance. No person, probably, ever did, or ever will, receive ardent spirits into his system once a day, and fortify his constitution against its deleterious effects, or exercise such discretion and self government, as that the quantity will not be increased, and bodily infirmities and mental imbecility be the result, and, in more than half the instances, inebriation. Nature may hold out long against this sapping and mining of the constitution, which daily tippling is carrying on; but, first or last, this foe of life will bring to the assault enemies of its own formation, before whose power the feeble and the mighty will be alike unable to stand.

All such occasional exhilaration of the spirits by intoxicating liquors, as produces levity and foolish jesting, and the loud laugh, is intemperance, whether we regard those precepts which require us to be sober-minded, or the effect which such exhilaration and lightness has upon the cause of Christ, when witnessed in professors of religion. The cheerfulness of health, and excitement of industry, and social intercourse, is all which nature demands, or health or purity permits.

A resort to ardent spirits as a means of invigorating the intellect, or of pleasurable sensation, is also intemperance. It is a distraint upon nature, to extort, in a short time, those results of mind and feeling, which in her own unimpelled course would flow with less impetuosity, but in a more equable and healthful current. The mind has its limits of intellectual application, and the heart its limits of feeling, and the nervous system of healthful exhilaration; and whatever you gain through stimulus, by way of anticipation, is only so much intellectual and vital power cut off at the latter end of life. It is this occult intemperance, of daily drinking, which generates a host of bodily infirmities and diseases: loss of appetite—nausea at the stomach—disordered bile—obstructions of the liver—jaundice—hoarseness of voice—coughs—consumptions—rheumatic pains— epilepsy—gout—colic—palsy—apoplexy—insanity— are the body-guards which attend intemperance, in the form of tippling, and where the odious name of drunkenness may perhaps be never applied.

A multitude of persons, who are not accounted drunkards, create disease, and shorten their days, by what they denominate a "prudent use of ardent spirits." Let it therefore be engraven upon the heart of every man, THAT THE DAILY USE OF AR-DENT SPIRITS, IN ANY FORM, OR IN ANY DEGREE, IS INTEMPERANCE. Its effects are certain, and deeply injurious, though its results may be slow, and never be ascribed to the real cause. It is a war upon the human constitution, carried on ostensibly by an auxiliary, but which never fails to subtract more vital power than it imparts. Like the letting out of waters by little and little, the breach widens, till life itself is poured out. If all diseases which terminate in death, could speak out at the grave, or tell their origin upon the coffin-lid, we should witness the most appalling unexpected disclosures. Happy the man, who so avoids the appearance of evil, as not to shorten his days by what he may call the prudent use of ardent spirits. . . .

THERE IS NO NUTRITION IN ARDENT SPIRIT. ALL THAT IT DOES IS, TO CONCENTRATE THE STRENGTH OF THE SYSTEM FOR THE TIME, BE-YOND ITS CAPACITY FOR REGULAR EXERTION. It is borrowing strength for an occasion, which will be needed for futurity, without any provision for payment, and with the certainty of ultimate bankruptcy.

The early settlers of New-England endured more hardship, and performed more labor, and carried through life more health and vigor, than appertains to the existing generation of laboring men. And they did it without the use of ardent spirits.

Let two men, of equal age and firmness of constitution, labor together through the summer, the one with and the other without the excitement of ardent spirits, and the latter will come out at the end with unimpaired vigor, while the other will be comparatively exhausted. Ships navigated as some now are without the habitual use of ardent spirits—and manufacturing establishments carried on without—and extended agricultural operations— all move on with better industry, more peace, more health, and a better income to the employers and the employed. The workmen are cheerful and vigorous, friendly and industrious, and their families are thrifty, well fed, well clothed and instructed; and instead of distress and poverty, and disappointment and contention— they are cheered with the full flow of social affection, and often by the sustaining power of religion.

But where ardent spirit is received as a daily auxiliary to labor, it is commonly taken at stated times—the habit soon creates a vacancy in the stomach, which indicates at length the hour of the day with as much accuracy as a clock. It will be taken besides, frequently, at other times, which will accelerate the destruction of nature's healthful tone, create artificial debility, and the necessity of artificial excitement to remove it; and when so much has been consumed as the economy of the employer can allow, the growing demand will be supplied by the evening and morning dram, from the wages of labor—until the appetite has become insatiable, and the habit of intemperance nearly universal—until the nervous excitability has obliterated the social sensibilities, and turned the family into a scene of babbling and wo—until voracious appetite has eaten up the children's bread, and abandoned them to ignorance and crime—until conscience has become callous, and fidelity and industry have disappeared, except as the result of eye service; and wanton wastefulness and contention, and reckless wretchedness characterize the establishment.

## GLOSSARY

**ardent spirits:** strong distilled alcohol such as brandy, rum, or whiskey

**distraint:** compulsion or seizure by means of distress

**intemperance:** lack of moderation, especially when drinking alcohol

**sottish:** stupid or foolish

**tippling:** frequent or continuous drinking of alcohol in relatively small amounts

## Document Analysis

Lyman Beecher's "The Nature and Occasions of Intemperance" is the introductory sermon in a series of six sermons in which Beecher outlines the sins and individual and social repercussions of intemperance. Although Beecher was concerned about alcohol consumption in America from the perspective of a social activist, his claims about intemperance are largely rooted in morality and religion. His approach, therefore, is one that condemns alcohol for its negative impact on society while considering the long-term effects of intemperance on one's soul. In the early nineteenth century in America, the divisions between church and state had been drawn with the disestablishment of state churches, but in reality, the nation was still very much fixed in Protestant Christian beliefs and practices. For Beecher to consider temperance from the perspective of an activist and clergyman would therefore have been not just socially permissible but widely accepted.

As the introductory statement for Beecher's longer series of grievances about intemperance and its increasingly concerning effects on American society and life, this initial sermon in many ways merely sets the stage for the author's much broader arguments about the signs and evils of intemperance and his proposed remedies for them. Beecher's forceful language and vivid imagery would have been particularly interesting to audiences listening to his sermons before they were published. The image that Beecher presents of soldiers marching blindly to a certain death in battle is a good example of this. Although not all those in his audience would have been on the brink of alcoholism, many Americans were familiar with war imagery, as it had been just decades since the Revolutionary War and the War of 1812. According to Beecher's analogy, those individuals who chose to drink were likewise heedlessly entering into what would ultimately be a losing battle leading to death, despite the sad examples of those who had met a similar demise before them.

When Beecher composed this sermon and presented it in the 1820s, the idea of temperance was not a new one. From the time of the Revolution through the Civil War, social and religious reformers responded to crises in the nation by attempting to eliminate what they saw as the sins for which the country was being punished, particularly slavery and intemperance. These two "evils" were especially emphasized, as they were both considered to be the source of many other social and domestic problems. In the case of slavery, tensions existed between Christians who were in support of slavery and those who were against it. This raised questions about whether or not God intended for slavery to be part of American life and if Christian morality could possibly be used to support proslavery arguments. In the case of intemperance, reformers like Beecher connected excessive alcohol consumption to poor health, the breakdown of family units, violence, reduced productivity, and, ultimately, the risk of not being able to attain salvation upon one's death. For these reformers, religion and social tensions were inextricably linked, and all of one's actions in life translated to one's state after death.

In his sermons on intemperance, Beecher is expressly dumbfounded by the public, and therefore obvious, trouble that intemperance causes. For Beecher, the problem is not just the impact of alcohol on the individual but the social influence that intemperance has on those who are in contact with the intemperate. It is most concerning to him that the destructive actions of "sottish" drinkers do not stop others from going down the same path to self- and social degradation. Beecher is concerned that despite the many social ills caused by intemperance, including selfishness, wastefulness, poverty, and illness, the consumption of alcohol continued to grow in America as the nineteenth century progressed.

For Beecher to note health issues surrounding the temperance cause is to put his observations into dialogue with the many wellness movements of the era. It was during these same decades that Sylvester Graham introduced the graham cracker, a food made with whole grains instead of bolted flour (a type of wholewheat flour from which the majority of bran has been removed), along with a strict diet that eliminated meat and alcohol in order to purify one's body and mind. Graham's efforts would lead to continued dietary movements later in the century by Seventh-Day Adventists Ellen G. White and John Harvey Kellogg, both of whom advocated temperate, vegetarian diets for physical and spiritual well-being at their Battle Creek Sanitarium in Michigan. Beecher's observations about intemperance in relation to the overall condition of the body are therefore very much in tune with the contemporary wellness movements of his day.

Although Beecher was concerned for the condition of the body due to intemperance, his fears were not merely about the impact of alcohol on one's health. For Beecher, and other religious reformers like him, the body was a creation of God, to be "sustained by food and sleep," not by alcohol or other artificial means. Beecher also

warns against intemperance as a means for al-
leviating of pain or generating happiness. As a
clergyman heavily steeped in Christian doctrine
and practice, Beecher argues that the only true
paths to peace and joy are those that lead to
and are created by God, not the artificial ones
shaped by drunkenness. According to Beecher,
drink is not only an unnatural way to evoke emo-
tions but also a sinful one. For a religious revivalist like Beecher, salvation was the ultimate goal
of conversion experience, and a happy position
in the life to come. Therefore, Beecher suggests
that it is not just one's temporal comfort that is
at stake when one is intemperate but the condition of one's very soul.

As Beecher reiterates throughout his sermons on the subject, the term intemperance
in the nineteenth century came to encompass
much more than simply excess in drink. Intemperance, for Beecher, extended beyond drinking too much alcohol to include excessive poor
judgment, increased poverty due to men spending their earnings on alcohol rather than their
responsibilities at home, and more and more
instances of poor physical and mental health. In
talking about intemperance in this way Beecher
reiterates the negative effects of alcohol consumption on many aspects of American life.

The author, and later activists like those from
the American Society for the Promotion of Temperance (1826) and the Women's Christian
Temperance Union (1873), used this emphasis
on the totality of social reform achieved through
temperance as their platform into the early years
of the twentieth century. It is important to note
here that the initial reforms for alcohol consumption were at first aimed at abstinence, not
the total exclusion of alcohol. However, as time
went on, reformers increasingly argued for the
complete elimination of alcohol consumption as
a model for social reform.

According to these advocates for temperance,
one's awareness of alcohol consumption could
be heightened simply by agreeing to abstain

from using alcohol for anything other than medicinal purposes. "Ardent spirits" were dangerous because one did not start out drinking with
the intention of becoming a regular drunkard.
As an example, Beecher points to an "Indian"
whom he notes as being occasionally intoxicated
to the point of oblivion. While he certainly did
not consider this to be acceptable, Beecher suggests that it would be far worse for one to consume alcohol in smaller amounts but constantly
and daily, with equally destructive, though perhaps not as immediately noticeable, effects.
This alludes not only to historical criticisms of
colonists for introducing alcohol to American
Indians but also to the implication that alcohol
is in some ways a rather sneaky vice. Beecher
suggests that it is only over time that one truly
begins to notice the effects of regular alcohol
consumption on one's physical body and life,
and by the time that awareness of the problem
of intemperance sets in, it is too late for one to
do much about it.

In summary, Lyman Beecher as clergyman,
revivalist, and social activist argues in "The Nature and Occasions of Intemperance" that alcohol is dangerous because it mimics the natural
state of man granted to him by God, and it is
therefore not healthy either for one's physical
body or for one's prospects of salvation. During
the profoundly religious period of the Second
Great Awakening, Beecher offered religion as
the alternative to alcohol consumption for en-
dowing one's life with cheerfulness and providing comfort during difficult times. Beecher argues that those who are intemperate are neither
useful nor productive—truly a problem in an increasingly industrialized and urbanized society.
In order for a more productive and moral society to emerge, in which the family would come
first, he believed, alcohol would ultimately need
to be eliminated, as it was the source of many
social ills. In order to appeal to his audience of
what would presumably have been fellow be-
lievers Beecher anchors his argument in strong

support of the use of one's faith, not alcohol, to get through life in order that one's soul might be saved upon death. These are all themes that continued to be played out by temperance reformers through the later decades of the nineteenth century and into the twentieth, until the successful passage of the Eighteenth Amendment to the Constitution in 1919, which forbade the legal production, sale, and consumption of alcohol in the United States until its repeal in 1933.

## Essential Themes

The temperance movement extended from the United States into Europe as the decades of the nineteenth century progressed. Lyman Beecher's religious view of temperance was not unique. Many others, from Elizabeth Cady Stanton to Herbert Hoover, found intemperance to be one of the central social and moral problems in nineteenth- and early twentieth-century America. This was a period in American history marked by great social and religious change; from the revivals of the Second Great Awakening to the rise of sects and new religions midcentury to the Gilded Age and subsequent Progressive Era and Social Gospel movement, Americans were looking for outlets for their awe and frustration in a country increasingly influenced by immigration, industrialization, urbanization, capitalism, advances in transportation, slavery, and the devastating effects of the Civil War and World War I.

Temperance, despite its widespread influence, was by no means embraced by all Americans. In particular, those who made and sold alcohol were not pleased by the limitations suggested by temperance reformers. While the passing of the Eighteenth Amendment in the early twentieth century curbed the open production and consumption of alcohol, it was illegally served to patrons in speakeasies, secret rooms in buildings all over the country. Such establishments were often associated with those involved in organized crime, which further supported Beecher's theories that the consumption of alcohol was connected to many negative activities in American life.

—*Emily Bailey, MA*

## Bibliography and Additional Reading

Beecher, Lyman. Six Sermons on the Nature, Occasions, Signs, Evils, and Remedy of Intemperance. New York: Amer. Tract Soc., 1827. Print.

Beecher, Lyman, and Harriet Beecher Stowe. The American Woman's Home; or, Principles of Domestic Science: Being a Guide to the Formation and Maintenance of Economical, Healthful, Beautiful, and Christian Homes. Boston: Brown, 1869. Print.

Bordin, Ruth. Frances Willard: A Biography. Chapel Hill: U of North Carolina P, 1986. Print.

Clark, Norman H. Deliver Us from Evil: An Interpretation of American Prohibition. New York: Norton, 1976. Print.

Dorsey, Bruce. Reforming Men and Women: Gender in the Antebellum City. Ithaca: Cornell UP, 2002. Print.

Hamm, Richard F. Shaping the Eighteenth Amendment: Temperance Reform, Legal Culture, and the Polity, 1880–1920. Chapel Hill: U of North Carolina P, 1995. Print.

Henry, Stuart. Unvanquished Puritan: A Portrait of Lyman Beecher. Grand Rapids: Eerdmans, 1973. Print.

Mattingly, Carol. Well-Tempered Women: Nineteenth- Century Temperance Rhetoric. Carbondale: Southern Illinois UP, 2000. Print.

Wacker, Grant. Religion in Nineteenth Century America. New York: Oxford UP, 2000. Print.

Willard, Frances E. Women and Temperance; or, The Work and Workers of the Women's Christian Temperance Union. Hartford: Park, 1883. Print.

Williams, Susan. Food in the United States, 1820s– 1890. Westport: Greenwood, 2006. Print.

# ■ Address before the Second Biennial Convention of the World Women's Christian Temperance Union

**Date:** October 1893
**Author:** Frances Willard
**Genre:** Speech

## Summary Overview

On the heels of the Civil War, a range of Americans called for the prohibition of alcohol. Without the right to vote and largely absent from American politics before this point, women nevertheless comprised a large share of the movement. Frances Willard, the author of this document, had been a prominent part of the Women's Christian Temperance Union (WCTU), the group she addresses in this speech, since its founding in 1874. She became the Union's president in 1879 and strongly advocated for the women's temperance group to take up a host of issues related to temperance such as women's suffrage and labor rights. The speech featured in this document showcases Willard's broad approach. She explains and argues for what she calls her "Do Everything" policy, trying to allay the fears of her fellow prohibitionists who preferred a narrower focus on temperance alone. Willard died five years after giving this speech, but the interconnected movements she helped to galvanize continued to thrive in the twentieth century, resulting in constitutional amendments that both granted women suffrage and (temporarily) put a prohibition on alcohol.

## Defining Moment

Alcohol played a ubiquitous role in colonial America, and advocates for its prohibition are as old as the United States itself. Benjamin Rush, a founding father and signer of the Declaration of Independence who was also a physician, penned the medical treatise *An Inquiry into the Effects of Ardent Spirits upon the Human Body and Mind* in 1785. The document details the detrimental effects that alcohol has on physical and mental health and catalyzed a sentiment among some that the drug should be outlawed. Temperance advocacy groups and publications popped up in a swath of states of the infant nation in the first decades of the nineteenth century. The movement gained a particularly Christian makeup with many of the leaders being ministers and many of the groups being led and housed by churches.

The movement waned during the Civil War as the nation had other focuses but came back strong in the closing decades of the nineteenth century. The Catholic Total Abstinence Union of America was founded in 1872 as a voluntarist organization, meaning the members supported abstinence from alcohol but believed it to be a moral decision that individuals should make free of legal compulsion. Frances Willard and other women founded the Woman's Christian Temperance Union (WCTU) in 1874. The Union was a prohibitionist group, meaning they did not rely on moral persuasion like the voluntarists but instead argued alcohol should be prohibited by law. The newly formed group elected Annie Wittenmyer as their first president and then Frances Willard as their second in 1879.

As this document exhibits, the WCTU, especially under Willard's guidance, expanded its focus beyond temperance. Willard only alludes to women's suffrage under the broader category of "Woman's Liberation" in the excerpt featured in this chapter, but she was an ardent suffragist, and women's suffrage made up a significant pillar of her "Do Everything" policy. The wider temperance and women's suffrage movements similarly dovetailed. Prominent American suffragist Susan B. Anthony fought for the cause of temperance; north of the border, Nellie Mc-Clung took up both causes in Canada. Some advocates of temperance used racist tropes and arguments to argue their case. Willard herself denounced lynching upon pressure from civil rights activist Ida B. Wells but nevertheless used provocative and racist language especially when speaking in the South.

The American temperance movement culminated in the early twentieth century. Building on the work of the WCTU and others, the Anti-Saloon League brought the movement to its crescendo. Rev. Howard Hyde Russell had formed the league in 1894, and it led the charge that resulted in Congress passing the Eighteenth Amendment prohibiting "intoxicating liquors" on December 18, 1917. After enough states ratified the amendment, it took effect on January 16, 1920. The lasting influence of Willard and the WCTU lies not with this amendment, which was repealed in 1933 by the Twenty-First Amendment, but with the other issues they tied to the temperance movement, including women's suffrage. Congress passed the Nineteenth Amendment granting women the right to vote on June 4, 1919; the amendment was ratified the following year, almost two decades after Willard's death.

## Author Biography

Frances Willard was a prominent advocate of the temperance movement and women's suffrage. She was born on September 28, 1839 in upstate New York before moving with her family to Ohio and then Illinois. Willard graduated from North Western Female College and held several teaching positions before becoming president and then dean of Evanston College for Ladies, later renamed Woman's College of Northwestern University. She resigned after a disagreement with Charles Henry Fowler, the university president, and devoted her life to activism. She began, focused on temperance. She attended the inaugural convention of the WCTU in 1874 and became the corresponding secretary of the newly founded organization. Five years later, she became the Union's president, a position she would hold for the rest of her life. As witnessed in this document, Willard often pushed the Union and the temperance movement in general to include other issues within their fight. In various states, she helped raise age of consent laws and establish eight-hour workdays. She died at the age of fifty-eight in February 1898 after a bout with influenza.

## HISTORICAL DOCUMENT

*Beloved Comrades of the White Ribbon Army:*

WHEN we began the delicate, difficult, and dangerous operation of dissecting out the alcohol nerve from the body politic, we did not realize the intricacy of the undertaking nor the distances that must be traversed by the scalpel of investigation and research. In about seventy days from now, twenty years will have elapsed since the call of battle sounded its bugle note among the homes and hearts of Hillsboro, Ohio. We have all been refreshing our knowledge of those days by reading the "Crusade Sketches" of its heroic leader, Mrs. Eliza J. Thompson, "the mother of us all," and we know that but one thought, sentiment and purpose animated those saintly "Praying Bands" whose name will never die out from human history. "Brothers, we beg you not to drink and not to sell!" This was the one wailing note of these moral Paganinis, playing on one string. It caught the universal ear and set the key of that mighty orchestra, organised with so much toil and hardship, in which the tender and exalted strain of the Crusade violin still soars aloft, but upborne now by the clanging cornets of science, the deep trombones of legislation, and the thunderous drums of politics and parties. The "Do Everything Policy" was not of our choosing, but is an evolution as inevitable as any traced by the naturalist or described by the historian. Woman's genius for details, and her patient steadfastness in following the enemies of those she loves "through every lane of life," have led her to antagonise the alcohol habit and the liquor traffic just where they are, wherever that may be. If she does this, since they are everywhere, her policy will be "Do Everything."

A one-sided movement makes one-sided advocates. Virtues, like hounds, hunt in packs. Total abstinence is not the crucial virtue in life that excuses financial crookedness, defamation of character, or habits of impurity. The fact that one's father was, and one's self is, a bright and shining light in the total abstinence galaxy, does not give one a vantage ground for high-handed behaviour toward those who have not been trained to the special virtue that forms the central idea of the Temperance Movement. We have known persons who, because they had "never touched a drop of liquor," set themselves up as if they belonged to a royal line, but whose tongues were as biting as alcohol itself, and whose narrowness had no competitor save a straight line. An all-round movement can only be carried forward by all-round advocates; a scientific age requires the study of every subject in its correlations. It was once supposed that light, heat, and electricity were wholly separate entities; it is now believed and practically proved that they are but different modes of motion. Standing in the valley we look up and think we see an isolated mountain; climbing to its top we see that it is but one member of a range of mountains many of them of well-nigh equal altitude.

Some bright women who have opposed the "Do-Everything Policy" used as their favourite illustration a flowing river, and expatiated on the ruin that would follow if that river (which represents their do-one-thing policy) were diverted into many channels, but it should be remembered that the most useful of all rivers is the Nile, and that the agricultural economy of Egypt consists in the effort to spread its waters upon as many fields as possible. It is not for the river's sake that it flows through the country but for the sake of the fertility it can bring upon adjoining fields, and this is pre-eminently true of the Temperance Reform.

Joseph Cook, that devoted friend of every good cause has wisely said:- "If England were at war with Russia, and the latter were to have several allies, it would obviously be necessary for England to attack the allies as well as the principal enemy. Not to do this would be foolishness, and might be suicide. In the conflict with the liquor traffic, the policy of the W.C.T.U. is to attack not only the chief foe, but also its notorious and open allies." This is the course dictated not only by common sense, but by absolute necessity. If the home is to be protected, not only must the dram-shop be made an outlaw, but its allies, the gambling hells, the houses of unreportable infamy, the ignorance of the general population as to alcoholics and other narcotics, the timidity of trade, the venality of portions of the press, and especially the subserviency of political parties to the liquor traffic, must be assailed as confederates of the chief enemy of the home. . . . It is certain that the broad and progressive policy of the W.C.T.U. in the United States makes the whiskey rings and time-serving politicians greatly dread its influence. They honour the Union by frequent and bitter attacks. It is a recognised power in international affairs. If its policy were made narrow and non-partisan, its influence would immensely wane in practical matters of great importance.

> **M**ake a chain, for the land is full of bloody crimes and the city of violence.

"The department of Scientific Temperance Instruction, conducted by the W.C.T.U., and led by Mrs. Mary H. Hunt, of Boston, has now made such instruction mandatory in thirty-six States of the Republic. This is a very large and substantial triumph of the broad and progressive policy. "Instead of the National W.C.T.U. having lost the confidence of the churches by its broad policy, I believe, after much travel and years of observation, that it never had more of that confidence than at the present hour. At a recent Congressional Hearing, in Washington, I heard a distinguished Presbyterian Professor of Theology, Rev. Dr. Herrick Johnson, of Chicago, call the W.C.T.U. the most powerful, the most beneficent, and the most successful organization ever formed by women. Similar testimony abounds in all the most enlightened circles of the land."

Let us not be disconcerted, but stand bravely by that blessed trinity of movements, Prohibition, Woman's Liberation and Labour's uplift.

Everything is not in the Temperance Reform, but the Temperance Reform should be in everything.

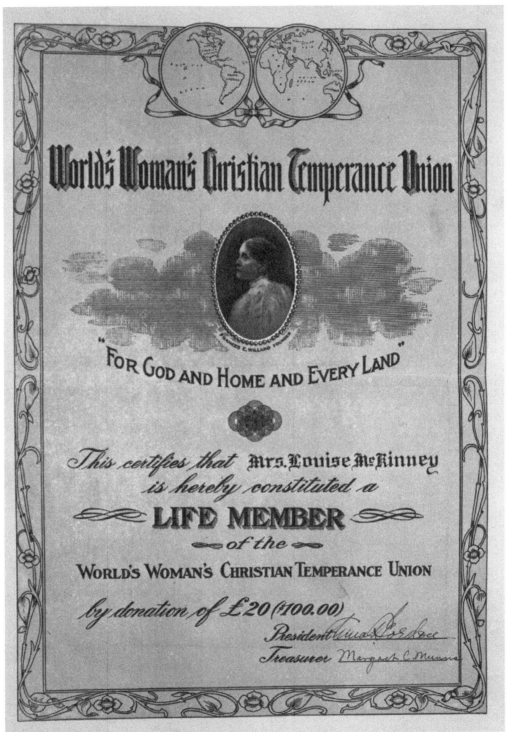

*World's Women's Christian Temperance Union Certificate awarded to Louise McKinney, the first woman elected to the Legislative Assembly of Alberta and the first woman elected to a legislative assembly in Canada or anywhere in the British Commonwealth. Provincial Archives of Alberta, A10047.*

There is no better motto for the "Do-Everything-Policy," than this which we are saying by our deeds: "Make a chain, for the land is full of bloody crimes and the city of violence."

If we can remember this simple rule, it will do much to unravel the mystery of the much controverted "Do-Everything-Policy," viz: that every question of practical philanthropy or reform has its temperance aspect, and with that we are to deal.

Methods that were once the only ones available may become, with the passage of years, less useful because less available. In earlier times the manly art of hunting was most helpful to civilization, because before fields could be cleared and tilled, they had to be free from the danger of wild beasts, and no method of obtaining food was more important than the chase; but when the forests have been cleared away and the pastoral condition of life has supervened, nay, more, when the highest civilization peoples the hills and valleys, it certainly evinces a lack of imagination to present such a spectacle as do the hunters who in England to-day place a poor stag in a van, convey him on four wheels to a wood, let him out through a door, and set trained dogs upon him, while they follow with guns and halloos, and call it "sport"! The same absurdity has been illustrated by Baron Hirsch, who recently imported 6,000 caged partridges to his country place, let them loose in the groves, and set himself and friends peppering away at them. Surely such conduct is the reverse of manly, and must bring what was once a noble occupation into contempt. But, in a different way, we illustrate the same principle, when we forget that:

"New occasions teach new duties,
Time makes ancient good uncouth."

We are too apt to think that what makes for us makes for the truth, and what makes for the truth must be true. Such a circle of reasoning leaves us, so far as logic goes, in the attitude said to have been assumed by the coffin of Mohammed-suspended between earth and heaven. A reformer is very apt to fall into this line of argumentation, a tendency which is perhaps most likely to be corrected by studying the correlated movements of other groups of men and women equally excellent, and by allying to the reform of which he is an advocate as many others germane to it as may be practicable, always asking this question as the touchstone of the natural selection he would make "What is the Temperance aspect of this cognate reform and what its aspect toward the liquor traffic?"

The Temperance cause started out well night alone, but mighty forces have joined us in the long march. We are now in the midst of the Waterloo battle, and in the providence of God the Temperance army will not have to fight that out all by itself. For Science has come up with its glittering contingent, political economy deploys its legions, the woman question brings an Amazonian army upon the field, and the stout ranks of labor stretch away far as the eye can reach. As in the old Waterloo against Napoleon, so now against the Napoleon of the liquor traffic, no force is adequate except the allied forces…

## GLOSSARY

**Paganinis:** Niccolò Paganini (b. October 27, 1782, d. May 27, 1840), a famous Italian violinist

## Document Analysis

This document constitutes the opening of Frances Willard's lengthy address to the Second Biennial Convention of the World Women's Christian Union in 1893. Willard used this opening excerpt and the speech as a whole to explain and support her "Do Everything" policy.

The "Do Everything" policy, Willard's approach to temperance, argues for a broad focus and engagement with a host of issues connected, related, and similar to temperance. At one point, she names "Prohibition, Woman's Liberation and Labour's uplift" as a "blessed trinity of movements." She introduces this inclusivity as inevitable, claiming it "was not of our choosing." Women's inherent attention to details and steadfastness, she argues, "led her to antagonise the alcohol habit and the liquor traffic just where they are, wherever that may be. If she does this, since they are everywhere, her policy will be 'Do Everything.'" The policy, in her telling, is both a positive and a product of the organization's female membership with their particular virtues.

Willard employs political and natural metaphors to describe the need for her broad approach. For her first political metaphor, she quotes the Union's friend Joseph Cook: "If England were at war with Russia, and the latter were to have several allies, it would obviously be necessary for England to attack the allies as well as the principal enemy… the policy of the W.C.T.U. is to attack not only the chief foe, but also its notorious and open allies." Willard places their conflict into the well studied arena of geopolitics in attempt to make the need for the "Do Everything" policy more clear. She returns to the realm of national conflict to face a different metaphorical foe: "We are now in the midst of the Waterloo battle… As in the old Waterloo against Napoleon, so now against the Napoleon of the liquor traffic, no force is adequate except the allied forces." Whereas the first metaphor stressed the allies of the alcohol industry, this one emphasizes the allies of the temperance movement. Together these metaphors posit the fight over temperance as far reaching and widely applicable.

Willard takes up a natural metaphor used by the opponents of her broad policy and appropriates it for her own purposes. These prohibitionists support a narrow focus on alcohol and, Willard says, compare the temperance movement to "a flowing river." They detail "the ruin that would follow if that river (which represents their do-one-thing policy) were diverted into many channels." She answers them by citing one of the world's largest and most famous rivers: "It should be remembered that the most useful of all rivers is the Nile, and that the agricultural economy of Egypt consists in the effort to spread its waters upon as many fields as pos-

*Officers and delegates of the first convention of the Women's Christian Temperance Union (W.C.T.U.), Skagway, AK. Courtesy of George and Edna Rapuzzi Collection, Rasmuson Foundation, Klondike Gold Rush National Historical Park (inventory #000147).*

sible." The conflation of the reach, fertility, and utility of the Nile with the temperance movement elevates the movement and appeals to Willard's audience, fellow prohibitionists.

## Essential Themes

Frances Willard emphasizes the value of versatility in order to advance her "Do Everything" policy. At one point she explicitly mentions the labor and women's suffrage movements as akin to the temperance movement; however, the majority of this excerpt sees Willard not discussing the specifics of these other movements nor their policy intricacies but instead trying to win her audience over to the general concept of versatility. "Virtues, like hounds, hunt in packs," she argues, and it behooves the prohibitionists to widen their agenda and their ranks. "Everything is not in the Temperance Reform," she adds later, "but the Temperance Reform should be in everything." Willard and her audience were in agreement over the endgame of the temperance movement: prohibition. There were disagree-ments over the path to get there, and Willard's call for versatility attempts to persuade those in favor of a narrower focus on temperance alone to engage with a broader swath of issues.

—*Anthony Vivian, PhD*

## Bibliography and Additional Reading

Bordin, Ruth. *Frances Willard: A Biography*. Chapel Hill: University of North Carolina Press, 1986.

Gifford, Carolyn, ed. *Writing Out My Heart: Selections from the Journal of Frances E. Willard, 1855–96*. Champaign: University of Illinois Press, 1995.

Gifford, Carolyn, and Amy R. Slagell, eds. *Let Something Good Be Said: Speeches and Writings of Frances E. Willard*. Champaign: University of Illinois Press, 2007.

Gusfield, Joseph R. *Symbolic Crusade: Status Politics and the American Temperance Movement*. Champaign: University of Illinois Press, 1986.

*Francis Burton Harrison (1873–1957), American politician*

# ■ Harrison Narcotic Act

**Date:** December 1914
**Author:** Francis Burton Harrison
**Genre:** Legislation

## Summary Overview

This legislation was one of the first federal laws to regulate the nonmedicinal use of narcotic drugs, and dealt primarily with opium and drugs derived from coca leaves (primarily cocaine). This bill limited access to these drugs to distributors who were registered with the federal government, physicians and other medical professionals, and patients who had a valid doctor's prescription for the drugs. Passage of the Harrison Act was prompted by the increasing visibility of narcotic use in the late 1800s and early 1900s. The bill provided for the licensing of suppliers to the medical professions, and required strict record keeping along with payment of a minimal tax. Products that had only minimal amounts of certain narcotics were exempted from this legislation, and government officials making legitimate purchases for government agencies were also exempted.

## Defining Moment

The forces behind the passage of the Harrison Act included domestic concerns about drug abuse, foreign policy concerns, and some blatantly racist stereotypes about ethnic minorities. Nonmedicinal use of drugs such as opium or cocaine was relatively rare in pre-Civil War America. There was no federal legislation dealing with such drugs, and many were sold openly, and small amounts of such drugs were used in a variety of patent medicines and other products. As physicians began to prescribe these drugs for legitimate medical treatments, people became familiar with the effects produced, and some turned to these drugs for nonmedicinal use. By the end of the 1800s, medical writers and popular journalists had convinced many Americans that the nation had a significant and growing drug problem, and the public came to associate such illicit usage with the poor and with foreign immigrants and ethnic minorities.

Foreign policy issues which influenced the passage of this legislation included the wide-spread use of opium among the people of the Philippines, which had come under U.S. control as a result of the Spanish-American War in 1898. Government officials, especially in the State Department, also believed that the United States had to address domestic drug use because the nation was involved in international efforts to combat the trade in opium. In 1906, President Theodore Roosevelt called for an international conference to address the opium trade. The first such meeting was held in Shanghai, China, in 1909. Dr. Hamilton Kemp Wright, who influenced the drafting of the Harrison Act, was one of the U.S. representatives to this conference. A second conference was held at The Hague in the Netherlands in 1912, and resulted in The Hague Convention, a treaty that aimed to address the sale of cocaine in the Far East. American policy makers were embarrassed that while the United States was a signatory to this agreement, it had no domestic regulations on the use of opium and other narcotics. When Congress debated the Harrison Act over the course of several days, more attention was paid to the international issues than to domestic drug abuse.

Support for the Harrison Act was also created by the use of brazenly racist stereotypes that played on the fear of the behavior of Chinese immigrants, blacks, and other minorities when under the influence of illicit drugs. Journalists and even some renowned medical spokesmen made fantastic charges, such as suggesting that African Americans exhibited "superhuman" strength after taking such drugs and were not only difficult to control but virtually impervious to the effects of shots from police handguns. It was not only fringe, extremist journals that printed such charges; examples appeared in professional medical journals and in the *New York Times*.

## Author Biography

The sponsor of this bill was Francis Burton Harrison, a congressman from New York who served in the House of Representatives from 1903 to 1905, and from 1907 to 1913. He was born in New York City on December 18, 1873. He graduated from Yale University in 1895, and from the New York Law School in 1897. He served in the U.S. Army during the Spanish-American War. After leaving Congress, he served as the governor-general of the Philippines until the outbreak of World War II. Harrison died in Flemington, New Jersey, on November 21, 1957.

Much of what is included in the Harrison Act was based on a previous bill that was never adopted. David Foster (1857–1912), a Republican member of the House from Vermont and chair of the House Committee on Foreign Affairs, introduced a bill in April, 1910, that had many of the same provisions of the Harrison Act. However, extensive opposition from the medical community and the pharmaceutical industry kept this bill from being passed. Foster had been encouraged to write this bill by Dr. Hamilton Wright (1867–1917), a physician who had become a prominent advocate of regulations on the nonmedicinal use of drugs. Wright had been appointed by President Theodore Roosevelt to serve on the U.S. Opium Commission. When Foster's bill was rejected by Congress, Wright encouraged Harrison to draft a new bill, removing some of the parts that had caused the failure of Foster's bill.

Advertisement for curing morphine addiction, ca. 1900

## HISTORICAL DOCUMENT: Harrison Narcotic Act

AN ACT To provide for the registration of, with collectors of internal revenue, and to impose a special tax on all persons who produce, import, manufacture, compound, deal in, dispense, sell, distribute, or give away opium or coca leaves, their salts, derivatives, or preparations, and for other purposes.

Be it enacted by the Senate and House of Representatives of the United States of America in Congress assembled, that on and after the first day of March, nineteen hundred and fifteen, every person who produces, imports, manufactures, compounds, deals in, dispenses, distributes, or gives away opium or coca leaves or any compound, manufacture, salt, derivative, or preparation thereof, shall register with the collector of internal revenue of the district, his name or style, place of business, and place or places where such business is to be carried on: Provided, that the office, or if none, then the residence of any person shall be considered for purposes of this Act to be his place of business. At the time of such registry and on or before the first of July annually thereafter, every person who produces, imports, manufactures, compounds, deals in, dispenses, distributes, or gives away any of the aforesaid drugs shall pay to the said collector a special tax at the rate of $1 per annum: Provided, that no employee of any person who produces, imports, manufactures, compounds, deals in, dispenses, distributes, or gives away any of the aforesaid drugs, acting within the scope of his employment, shall be required to register or to pay the special tax provided by this section: Provided further, That officers of the United States Government who are lawfully engaged in making purchases of the above-named drugs for the various departments of the Army and Navy, the Public Health Service, and for Government hospitals and prisons, and officers of State governments or any municipality therein, who are lawfully engaged in making purchases of the above-named drugs for State, county, or municipal hospitals or prisons, and officials of any Territory or insular possession, or the District of Columbia or of the United States who are lawfully engaged in making purchases of the above-named drugs for hospitals or prisons therein shall not be required to register and pay the special tax as herein required.

It shall be unlawful for any person required to register under the terms of this Act to produce, import, manufacture, compound, deal in, dispense, sell, distribute, any of the aforesaid drugs without having registered and paid the special tax provided for in this section.

That the word "person" in this Act shall be construed to mean and include a partnership, association, company, or corporation, as well as a natural person; and all provisions of existing law relating to special taxes, so far as applicable, including the provisions of section thirty-two hundred and forty of the Revised Statutes of the United States are hereby extended to the special tax herein imposed.

That the Commissioner of Internal Revenue, with the approval of the Secretary of the Treasury, shall make all needful rules and regulations for carrying the provisions of this Act into effect.

Sec 2.—That it shall be unlawful for any person to sell, barter, exchange, or give away any of the aforesaid drugs except in pursuance of a written order of the person to whom such article is sold, bartered, exchanged, or given, on a form to be issued in blank for that purpose by the Commissioner of Internal Revenue. Every person who shall accept any such order, and in pursuance thereof shall sell, barter, exchange, or give away any of the aforesaid drugs shall preserve such order for a period of two years in such a way as to be readily accessible to inspection by any officer, agent, or employee of the Treasury Department duly authorized for that purpose, and the State, Territorial, district, municipal and insular officials named in Section five of this Act. Every person who shall give an order as herein provided to any other person for any of the aforesaid drugs shall, at or before the time of giving of such order, make or cause to be made, a duplicate thereof on a form to be issued in blank for that purpose by the Commissioner of Internal Revenue, and in the case of the acceptance of such order, shall preserve such duplicate for said period of two years in such a way as to be readily accessible to inspection by the officers, agents, employees, and officials herein mentioned. Nothing contained in this section shall apply—

(a) To the dispensing or distribution of any of the aforesaid drugs to a patient by a physician, dentist, or veterinary surgeon registered under this Act in the course of his professional practice only: Provided, That such physician, dentist, or veterinary surgeon shall keep a record of all such drugs dispensed or distributed, showing the amount dispensed or distributed, the date, and the name and address of the person to whom such drugs are dispensed or distributed; except such as may be dispensed or distributed to a patient upon whom such physician, dentist, or veterinary surgeon shall personally attend; and such record shall be kept for a period of two years from the date of dispensing or distributing such drugs, subject to inspection, as provided in this Act.

(b) To the sale, dispensing, or distributing of any of the aforesaid drugs by a dealer to a consumer under and in pursuance of a written prescription issued by a physician, dentist, or veterinary surgeon registered under this Act. Provided, however, That such prescription shall be dated as of the day on which signed and shall be signed by the physician, dentist, or veterinary surgeon who shall have issued the same: And provided further, That such dealer shall preserve such prescription for a period of two years from the day on which such prescription is filled in such a way as to be readily accessible by the officers, agents, employees, and officials hereinbefore mentioned.

(c) To the sale, exportation, shipment, or delivery of any of the aforesaid drugs by any person within the United States or any Territory or the District of Columbia or any of the insular possessions of the United States to any person in any foreign country, regulating their entry in accordance with such regulations for importation thereof into such foreign country as are prescribed by said country, such regulations to be promulgated from time to time by the Secretary of State of the United States.

(d)   To the sale, barter, exchange, or giving away of any of the aforesaid drugs to any officer of the United States Government, or any State, territorial, district, county, or municipal or insular government lawfully engaged in making purchases thereof for various departments of the Army and Navy, the Public Health Service, and for Government, State, territorial, district, county, or municipal, or insular hospitals and prisons.

The Commissioner of Internal Revenue, with the approval of the Secretary of the Treasury, shall cause suitable forms to be prepared for the purposes mentioned above, and shall cause the same to be distributed to collectors of internal revenue for sale by them to those persons who shall have registered and paid the special tax as required by section one of this Act, in their districts, respectively; and no collector shall sell any of such forms to any persons other than a person who has registered and paid the special tax as required by section one of this Act in his district. The price at which said forms shall be sold by collectors shall be fixed by the Commissioner of Internal Revenue with the approval of the Secretary of the Treasury, but shall not exceed the sum of $1 per hundred. Every collector shall keep an account of the number of forms sold by him, the names of the purchasers, and the number of forms sold to each of such purchasers. Whenever any collector shall sell any of such forms, he shall cause the name of the purchaser thereof to be plainly stamped thereon before delivering the same; and no person other than such purchaser shall use any of said forms bearing the name of such purchaser for the purpose of procuring any of the aforesaid drugs, or furnish any of the forms bearing the name of such purchaser to any person with intent thereby to procure the shipment or delivery of any of the aforesaid drugs. It shall be unlawful for any person to obtain by means of said order forms any of the aforesaid drugs for any purpose other than the use, sale, or distribution thereof by him in the conduct of a lawful business in said drugs or in the legitimate practice of his profession.

> "An act to prohibit the importation and use of opium for other than medicinal purposes.

The provisions of this Act shall apply to the United States, the District of Columbia, the Territory of Alaska, the Territory of Hawaii, the insular possessions of the United States, and the Canal Zone. In Porto Rico and the Philippine Islands the administration of this Act, the collection of said special tax, and the issuance of the order forms specified in section two shall be performed by the appropriate internal revenue officers of these governments, and all revenues collected hereunder in Porto Rico and the Philippine Islands shall accrue intact to the governments thereof, respectively. The courts of first instance in the Philippine Islands shall possess and exercise jurisdiction in all cases arising under this Act in said islands. The President is authorized and directed to issue such executive orders as will carry into effect in the Canal Zone the intent and purpose of this Act by providing for the registration and the imposition of a special tax upon all persons in the Canal Zone who produce, import, compound, deal in, dispense, sell, distribute, or give away opium or coca leaves, their salts, derivatives, or preparations.

Sec 3.—That any person who shall be registered in any internal revenue district under the provisions of section one of this Act shall, whenever required to do so by the collector of the district, render to the said collector a true and correct statement or return, verified by affadavit, setting forth the quantity of aforesaid drugs received by him in said internal revenue district during such period immediately preceding the demand of the collector, not exceeding three months, as the said collector may fix and determine; the names of the persons from whom said drugs were received; the quantity in each instance of the quantity received from each of such persons, and the date received.

Sec 4.—That it shall be unlawful for any person who shall not have registered and paid the special tax as required by section one of this Act to send, ship, carry, or deliver any of the aforesaid drugs from any State or Territory or the District of Columbia, or any insular possession of the United States, to any person in any other State or Territory or the District of Columbia or any insular possession of the United States: Provided, that nothing contained in this section shall apply to common carriers engaged in transporting the aforesaid drugs, or to any employee acting within the scope of his employment, of any person who shall have registered and paid the special tax as required by section one of this Act, or to any person who shall deliver such drug which has been prescribed or dispensed by a physician, dentist, or veterinary surgeon required to register under the terms of this Act, who has been employed to prescribe for the particular patient receiving such drug, or to any United States, State, county, municipal, District, territorial, or insular officer or official acting within the scope of his official duties.

Sec 5.—That the duplicate-order forms and the prescriptions required to be preserved under the provisions of section two of this Act, and the statements or returns filed in the office of the collector of the district, under the provisions of section three of this Act, shall be open to inspection by officers, agents, and employees of the Treasury Department duly authorized for that purpose; and such officials of any State or Territory, or of any organized municipality therein, or of the District of Columbia, or any insular possession of the United States as shall be charged with the enforcement of any law or municipal ordinance regulating the sale, prescribing, dispensing, dealing in, or distribution of the aforesaid drugs. Each collector of internal revenue is hereby authorized to furnish, upon written request, certified copies of any of the said statements or returns filed in his office to any of such officials of any State or Territory, or organized municipality therein, or of the District of Columbia, or any insular possession of the United States, as shall be entitled to inspect said statements or returns filed in the office of the said collector, upon the payment of a fee of $1 for each one hundred words in the copy or copies so requested. Any person who shall disclose the information contained in the said statements or returns or in the said duplicate-order forms, except as herein expressly provided, and except for the purpose of enforcing the provisions of this Act, or for the purpose of enforcing any law of any State or Territory, or the District of Columbia, or any insular possession of the United States, or ordinance of any organization or municipality therein, regulating the sale, prescribing, dispensing, dealing in, or distribution of the aforesaid drugs shall, on conviction, be fined or imprisoned as provided by section nine of this Act. And collectors of internal revenue are hereby authorized to furnish upon written request, to any person, a certified copy of the names of any and all persons who may be listed in their respective collection district as special tax-payers under the provisions of this Act, upon payment of a fee of $1 per hundred names or fraction thereof in the copy so requested.

Sec 6.—That the provisions of this Act shall not be construed to apply to the sale, distribution, or giving away, dispensing, or possession of preparations and remedies which do not contain more than two grains of opium, or more than one-fourth of a grain of morphine, or more than one-eighth of grain of heroin, or more than one grain of codeine, or any salt or derivative of them in one fluid ounce, or, if a solid or semi-solid preparation, in one avoirdupois ounce, or to liniments, ointments, and other preparations which contain cocaine or any of its salts or alpha or beta eucaine or any of their salts or any synthetic substitute for them: Provided, that such remedies and preparations are sold, distributed, given away, dispensed, or possessed as medicines and not for the purpose of evading the intentions and provisions of this Act. The provisions of this Act shall not apply to decocainized coca leaves or preparations made therefrom, or to other preparations of coca leaves which do not contain cocaine.

Sec 7.—That all laws relating to the assessment, collection, remission, and refund of internal revenue taxes, including section thirty-two hundred and twenty-nine of the Revised Statutes of the United States, so far as applicable to and not inconsistent with the provisions of this Act, are hereby extended and made applicable to the special taxes imposed by this Act.

Sec 8.—That it shall be unlawful for any person not registered under the provisions of this Act, and who has not paid the special tax provided for by this Act, to have in his possession or under his control any of the aforesaid drugs; and such possession or control shall be presumptive evidence of a violation of this section, and also a violation of the provisions of section one of this Act: Provided, That this section shall not apply to any employee of a registered person, or to a nurse under the supervision of a physician, dentist, or veterinary surgeon registered under this Act, having such possession or control by virtue of his employment or occupation and not on his own account; or to the possession of any of the aforesaid drugs which has or have been prescribed in good faith by a physician, dentist, or veterinary surgeon registered under this Act; or to any United States, State, county, municipal, district, Territorial or insular officer or official who has possession of any of said drugs, by reason of his official duties, or to a warehouseman holding possession for a person registered and who has paid taxes under this Act; or to common carriers engaged in transporting such drugs; Provided further, that it shall not be necessary to negative any of the aforesaid exemptions in any complaint, information, indictment or other writ or proceeding laid or brought under this Act; and the burden of proof of any such exemption shall be upon the defendant.

Sec 9.—That any person who violates or fails to comply with any of the requirements of this Act shall, on conviction, be fined not more than $2,000 or be imprisoned not more than five years, or both, in the discretion of the court.

Sec 10.—That the Commissioner of Internal Revenue, with the approval of the Secretary of the Treasury, is authorized to appoint such agents, deputy collectors, inspectors, chemists, assistant chemists, clerks, and messengers in the field and in the Bureau of Internal Revenue in the District of Columbia as may be necessary to enforce the provisions of this Act.

Sec 11.—That the sum of $150,000, or so much thereof as may be necessary, be, and hereby is, appropriated, out of any moneys in the Treasury not otherwise appropriated, for the purpose of carrying into effect the provisions of this Act.

Sec 12.—That nothing contained in this Act shall be construed to impair, alter, amend, or repeal any of the provisions of the Act of Congress approved June thirtieth, nineteen hundred and six entitled "An act for preventing the manufacture, sale, or transportation of adulterated, or misbranded, or poisonous, or deleterious foods, drugs, medicines, and liquors, and for regulating traffic therein, and for other purposes" and any amendment thereof, or of the Act approved February ninth, nineteen hundred and nine entitled, "An act to prohibit the importation and use of opium for other than medicinal purposes" and any amendment thereof.

*Approved, December 17, 1914*

## Document Analysis

The most significant thing to note in the long official title of this legislation at the beginning of the text is that it is a tax act. It does not prohibit the sale or distribution of any of the drugs covered (primarily opium and derivatives of the coca plant such as cocaine) but simply requires that all those that selling or distributing such products pay a tax to the federal government and be registered with the collectors of federal revenue, and keep detailed records of all transactions.

The tax required by this bill was minimal—only $1 per year for any registered dealer or dispenser. The federal government would sell the forms required for the record keeping, but the charge for these was also minimal. Thus, while this bill was technically a tax, it is evident that generating revenue was not the real purpose. The main purpose of the bill was to provide a means of registering those involved in the production, sale or distribution of these drugs, and to establish a system of detailed record keeping for such transactions, with special federal agents authorized to inspect these records.

While the taxes and the costs of maintaining these records might not have been burdensome, the penalties for violations of the Harrison Act were significant—a fine of up to $2,000, and imprisonment for up to five years—or both, according to the discretion of the judge. The point of the legislation was to restrict distribution of these drugs to known, registered producers and dispensers, who would be required to record all transactions. One significant question was not addressed in this bill: What constitutes a valid medical use of these drugs, which would justify a doctor issuing a legitimate prescription?

## Essential Themes

The Harrison Act was the first federal law to address the nonmedicinal use of opium and cocaine, and its passage was a sign of a growing concern about illicit drug use in the United States. While drug control and the movement to outlaw the manufacture of alcoholic beverages were two different issues, it is interesting to note that the amendment to prohibit the manufacture and sale of "intoxicating liquors" was passed by Congress and sent to the states for ratification just three years after the passage of the Harrison Act. Both were products of a Progressive Era desire to bring order and stability to American society.

A significant theme in the agitation leading up to the passage of this bill is how foreign policy and domestic politics are often closely intertwined. When the United States took control of the Philippines, it had to face the issue of the widespread use of opium among the Filipino people. The United States was also involved in international efforts to control the trade in opium, and many who backed the Harrison Act believed the United States needed to show it was addressing such issues at home, so that its international efforts would seem sincere.

While the Harrison Act did not make the illicit use of drugs a crime, it was intended to prevent such use by limiting unrestricted access to opium and cocaine, and to ensure that these drugs were used only under proper medical supervision. In practice, government agents enforcing the law often arrested physicians for issuing prescriptions to people addicted to the use of opium or cocaine. The medical profession saw this as treatment, but the government saw addiction as a behavioral issue and not a treatable disease. When such arrests went to court, the courts often upheld the government's position. In *Jin Fuey Moy v. U.S.*, 1920, the Supreme Court ruled that a doctor could be prosecuted for prescribing drugs for the purpose of "satisfying the cravings of an addict." However, *Linder v. U.S.*, 1925, the court reversed itself and limited the government's ability to prosecute doctors for such actions.

—*Mark S. Joy, PhD*

## Bibliography and Additional Reading

Courtwright, David T. *Dark Paradise: A History of Opiate Addiction in America.* Cambridge, MA: Harvard University Press, 2012.

Faupel, Charles E., and Alan M. Horowitz, and Greg S. Wever. *The Sociology of American Drug Use.* 2nd ed. New York: Oxford University Press, 2010.

Jonnes, Jill. *Hep-Cats, Narcs, and Pipe Dreams: A History of America's Romance with Illegal Drugs.* Baltimore: Johns Hopkins University Press, 1999.

Musto, David F. *The American Disease: Origins of Narcotic Control.* New York: Oxford University Press, 1999.

# ■ Volstead Act

**Date:** 1919
**Author:** United States Congress, written by Wayne Wheeler
**Genre:** law

## Summary Overview

The Volstead Act was the enabling legislation for the Eighteenth Amendment to the US Constitution, which prohibited the "manufacture, sale, or transportation of intoxicating liquors"—that is, Prohibition. The act was named for its author, Andrew Volstead, a Republican congressman from Minnesota. The formal name of the Volstead Act, passed over the veto of President Woodrow Wilson on October 28, 1919, was the National Prohibition Act.

The Prohibition movement had begun in the nineteenth century when reformers, many of them motivated by religious beliefs and by the conviction that many of the nation's social ills could be tied to drinking, tried to reduce the demand for alcohol by persuading people to give up drinking. Early in the twentieth century, these reformers shifted their focus to curtailing the supply of alcohol by supporting passage of state laws that restricted the sale of alcohol and that shut down bars and taverns. By 1914 numerous states were "dry," meaning that they had adopted some form of prohibition; among them were Maine, Kansas, North Dakota, Georgia, Oklahoma, Mississippi, North Carolina, Tennessee, and West Virginia. Many counties throughout the nation also went "dry"; to this day, it remains illegal to drink Jack Daniel's whiskey in the Tennessee county where it is distilled. Over the next five years the number of dry states continued to rise, and by 1919 the number of congressional representatives from dry states outnumbered those from "wet" states by a significant margin. Meanwhile, in 1917, Congress had approved a resolution containing the basic wording of the Eighteenth Amendment, which was in the process of ratification by the states.

During World War I, reformers were able to pass federal laws restricting alcohol, in an effort to preserve the morals of servicemen and to conserve grain for the war effort. One of their arguments was that the consumption of German beer was sapping the will of American servicemen to fight. Chief among these laws was the Wartime Prohibition Act of 1918, which is referred to in Title I of the Volstead Act; ironically, this act was not actually passed until after the armistice that ended the fighting went into effect.

The Wartime Prohibition Act law prohibited the manufacture and sale of all beverages—including beer and wine—that contained more than 2.75 percent alcohol. The Volstead Act, which in large measure was a revision of the Wartime Prohibition Act, was more restrictive, banning the manufacture and sale of "beverages which contain one-half of 1 per centum or more of alcohol by volume." Wilson vetoed the bill because he believed that it was too severe in banning beer and because he objected to the continuation of wartime prohibition after the cessation of hostilities.

Prohibition was generally regarded as a failure, and throughout the 1920s calls rose for repealing the Eighteenth Amendment. Those calls were answered in 1933 with the ratification of the Twenty-First Amendment, repealing the Eighteenth Amendment. The Volstead Act had been modified that year to allow the manufacture and sale of 3.2 percent beer, but the Twenty-First Amendment rendered the Volstead Act moot.

## Defining Moment

The primary audience for the Volstead act was, on the surface, the American people. On the one hand the law was meant to placate the growing bloc of "dries," especially the vocal activists of the suffrage movement, whose progressive-minded agenda included the absolute ban on alcohol, and the unified front of teetotalers, represented by the act's primary author Wayne Wheeler and his powerful Ant-Saloon League. On the other hand, the act was a repudiation of immigrant groups, highest among them the European communities clustered in urban centers such as Chicago, New York, and Milwaukee, for whom the consumption of alcohol was tied to cultural identity.

## Author Biography

Wayne Wheeler, the principal author of what became known as the Volstead Act, was born in Ohio on November, 10, 1869. Wheeler's anti-alcohol stance developed early; as a boy he was injured by a drunken pitch-fork wielding farm-hand. After attending college, Wheeler worked various odd jobs before becoming an organizer for the newly established Anti-Saloon League (ASL), a special interest group devoted to one issue: the absolute ban on alcohol. After receiving his law degree, Wheeler threw himself into temperance work, rising through the ranks of the ASL, while mastering the manipulation of media to drive his political agenda. With Wheeler at the helm, the ASL won several crucial victories, in the first decade of the twentieth century, including unseating several powerful "wet" politicians. With pressure on both major parties and a single-issue platform, Wheeler's ASL was able to push the Volstead Act, which Wheeler penned himself, through Congress and dozens of state legislatures to become the Eighteenth Amendment in late 1919. After his successes, Wheeler's opinions on alcohol and how to cure people of alcohol's evils became increasingly extreme, at one point going so far as to advocate that poison be added so as to dissuade drinkers. Under pressure, Wheeler stepped down from his position at the ASL in the summer of 1927 and died soon afterward. He was fifty-seven.

## HISTORICAL DOCUMENT

### AN ACT

To prohibit intoxicating beverages, and to regulate the manufacture, production, use, and sale of high-proof spirits for other than beverage purposes, and to insure an ample supply of alcohol and promote its use in scientific research and in the development of fuel, dye, and other lawful industries.

  Be it enacted by the Senate and House of Representatives of the United States of America in Congress assembled, That the short title of this Act shall be the "National Prohibition Act."

### TITLE I.

### TO PROVIDE FOR THE ENFORCEMENT OF WAR PROHIBITION.

The term "War Prohibition Act" used in this Act shall mean the provisions of any Act or Acts prohibiting the sale and manufacture of intoxicating liquors until the conclusion of the present war and thereafter until the termination of demobilization, the date of which shall be determined and proclaimed by the President of the United States. The words "beer, wine, or other intoxicating malt or vinous liquors" in the War Prohibition Act shall be hereafter construed to mean any such beverages which contain one-half of 1 per centum or more of alcohol by volume: Provided, That the foregoing definition shall not extend to dealcoholized wine nor to any beverage or liquid produced by the process by which beer, ale, porter or wine is produced, if it contains less than one-half of 1 per centum of alcohol by volume, and is made as prescribed in section 37 of Title II of this Act, and is otherwise denominated than as beer, ale, or porter, and is contained and sold in, or from, such sealed and labeled bottles, casks, or containers as the commissioner may by regulation prescribe.

SEC. 2. The Commissioner of Internal Revenue, his assistants, agents, and inspectors, shall investigate and report violations of the War Prohibition Act to the United States attorney for the district in which committed, who shall be charged with the duty of prosecuting, subject to the direction of the Attorney General, the offenders as in the case of other offense against laws of the United States; and such Commissioner of Internal Revenue, his assistants, agents, and inspectors may swear out warrants before United States commissioners or other officers or courts authorized to issue the same for the apprehension of such offenders, and may, subject to the control of the said United States attorney, conduct the prosecution at the...trial for the purpose of having the offenders held for the action of a grand jury.

SEC. 3. Any room, house, building, boat, vehicle, structure, or place of any kind where intoxicating liquor is sold, manufactured, kept for sale, or bartered in violation of the War Prohibition Act, and all intoxicating liquor and all property kept and used in maintaining such a place, is hereby declared to be a public and common nuisance, and any person who maintains or assists in maintaining such public and common nuisance shall be guilty of a misdemeanor, and upon conviction thereof shall be fined not less than $100 nor more than $1,000, or be imprisoned for not less than thirty days or more than one year, or both. If a person has knowledge that his property is occupied or used in violation of the provisions of the War Prohibition Act and suffers the same to be so used, such property shall be subject to a lien for, and may be sold to pay, all fines and costs assessed against the occupant of such building or property for any violation of the War Prohibition Act occurring after the passage hereof, which said lien shall attach from the time of the filing of notice of the commencement of the suit in the office where the records of the transfer of real estate are kept; and any such lien may be established and enforced by legal action instituted for that purpose in any court having jurisdic-

*Prohibiting the sale and manufacture of intoxicating liquors until the conclusion of the present war.*

tion. Any violation of this title upon any leased premises by the lessee or occupant thereof shall, at the option of the lessor, work a forfeiture of the lease.

SEC. 4. The United States attorney for the district where such nuisance as is defined in this Act exists, or any officer designated by him or the Attorney General of the United States, may prosecute a suit in equity in the name of the United States to abate and enjoin the same. Actions in equity to enjoin and abate such nuisances may be brought in any court having jurisdiction to hear and determine equity causes. The jurisdiction of the courts of the United States under this section shall be concurrent with that of the courts of the several States.

If it be made to appear by affidavit, or other evidence under oath, to the satisfaction of the court, or judge in vacation, that the nuisance complained of exists, a temporary writ of injunction shall forthwith issue restraining the defendant or defendants from conducting or permitting the continuance of such nuisance until the conclusion of the trial. Where a temporary injunction is prayed for, the court may issue an order restraining the defendants and all other persons from removing or in any way interfering with the liquor or fixtures, or other things used in connection with the violation constituting the nuisance. No bond shall be required as a condition for making any order or issuing any writ of injunction under this Act. If the court shall find the property involved was being unlawfully used as aforesaid at or about the time alleged in the petition, the court shall order that no liquors shall be manufactured, sold, bartered, or stored in such room, house, building, boat, vehicle, structure, or places of any kind, for a period of not exceeding one year, or during the war and the period of demobilization. Whenever an action to enjoin a nuisance shall have been brought pursuant to the provisions of this Act, if the owner, lessee, tenant, or occupant appears and pays all costs of the proceedings and files a bond, with sureties to be approved by the clerk of the court in which the action is brought, in the liquidated sum of not less than $500 nor more than $1,000, conditioned that he will immediately abate said nuisance and prevent the same from being established or kept therein a period of one year thereafter, or during the war and period of demobilization, the court, or in vacation the judge, may, if satisfied of his good faith, direct by appropriate order that the property, if already closed or held under the order of abatement, be delivered to said owner, and said order of abatement canceled, so far as the same may relate to said property; or if said bond be given and costs therein paid before judgment on an order of abatement, the action shall be thereby abated as to said room, house, building, boat, vehicle, structure, or place only. The release of the property under the provisions of this section shall not release it from any judgment, lien, penalty, or liability to which it may be subject by law.

In the case of the violation of any injunction, temporary or permanent, granted pursuant to the provisions of this Title, the court, or in vacation a judge thereof, may summarily try and punish the defendant. The proceedings for punishment for contempt shall be commenced by filing with the clerk of the court from which such injunction issued information under oath setting out the alleged facts constituting the violation, whereupon the court or judge shall forthwith cause a warrant to issue under which the defendant shall be arrested. The trial may be had upon affidavits, or either party may demand the production and oral examination of the witnesses. Any person found guilty of contempt under the provisions of this section shall be punished by a fine of not less than $500 nor more than $1,000, or by imprisonment of not less than thirty days nor more than twelve months, or by both fine and imprisonment.

SEC. 5. The Commissioner of Internal Revenue, his assistants, agents, and inspectors, and all other officers of the United States whose duty it is to enforce criminal laws, shall have all the power for the enforcement of the War Prohibition Act or any provisions thereof which is conferred by law for the enforcement of existing laws relating to the manufacture or sale of intoxicating liquors under the laws of the United States.

SEC. 6. If any section or provision of this Act shall be held to be invalid, it is hereby provided that all other provisions of this Act which are not expressly held to be invalid shall continue in full force and effect.

SEC. 7. None of the provisions of this Act shall be construed to repeal any of the provisions of the "War Prohibition Act," or to limit or annul any order or regulation prohibiting the manufacture, sale, or disposition of intoxicating liquors within certain prescribed zones or districts, nor shall the provisions of this Act be construed to prohibit the use of the power of the military or naval authorities to enforce the regulations of the President or Secretary of War or Navy issued in pursuance of law, prohibiting the manufacture, use, possession, sale, or other disposition of intoxicating liquors during the period of the war and demobilization thereafter.

## GLOSSARY

**centum:** Latin for hundred.

**lien:** right to confiscate property until debt is paid.

**abate:** lessen, reduce, or remove.

**enjoin:** prohibit by issuing injunction.

**abatement:** ending or lessening of something.

## Document Analysis

The purpose of the Volstead Act is to "prohibit intoxicating beverages, and to regulate the manufacture, production, use, and sale of high-proof spirits for other than beverage purposes." In Title I of the act, "To Provide for the Enforcement of War Prohibition," Congress defines terms and outlines enforcement provisions for the "War Prohibition Act," which banned the "sale and manufacture of intoxicating liquors until the conclusion of the present war and thereafter until the termination of demobilization."

Congress turns to enforcement of the act beginning with section 2 of Title I. In this section, the Internal Revenue Service is authorized to investigate and report violations of the act. Section 3 states that any place where intoxicating liquors are "sold, manufactured, kept for sale, or bartered" is in violation of the act, and its liquor and property are "hereby declared to be a public and common nuisance." Section 3 also specifies fines. Section 4 authorizes the US attorney general and US attorneys to file suit against violators of the act and outlines procedures to be followed to issue an injunction "restraining the defendant or defendants from conducting or permitting the continuance of such nuisance." Any person who violates the injunction can be summarily tried and punished. Section 5 extends enforcement authority to "other officers of the United States whose duty it is to enforce criminal laws." Section 6 is a standard provision that states that if any portion of the act is invalidated, the rest of the act remains in force, and section 7 states that none of the provisions of the Volstead Act are to be construed to repeal any provisions contained in the "War Prohibition Act." Section 7 also states that the act does not prohibit military or naval authorities from enforcing regulations having to do with the disposition of liquor during the war or demobilization after the war.

## Essential Themes

Americans always drank. Drinks such as beer, hard cider, and mead had long been staples of frontier and farming culture. But with the introduction of hard spirits, such as vodka and whiskey, in the nineteenth century, the relationship between society and alcohol began to change drastically. As the alcohol content rose, drinking became a contentious issue, with many reformers, especially suffragists and the emerging progressives, claiming that alcohol, now with substantially more powerful intoxicating effects, was eroding the foundations of society. Women most notably, believing that only female purity could cleanse social ills, argued that alcohol and alcoholism were primarily responsible for marital abuse and the breakdown of the family unit. If men were sober, the common wisdom held, they could more easily follow a moral path and thus preserve the nation. While temperance was a major plank of both the suffrage movement —most exemplified by the work of Francis Willard and her Woman's Christian Temperance Union—and abolition—championed by the likes of Frederick Douglass, it was not until the formation of the Anti-Saloon League that prohibition became a serious national issue. By the turn of the nineteenth century, after scoring several successes, and coming under the determined leadership of Wayne Wheeler, the ASL became a major political force. Wheeler understood that to maximize success, the ASL had to be a single-issue lobbying organization, working with political leaders across party lines to introduce temperance legislation and work actively against the election or reelection of anti-prohibition candidates. Employing a modern media strategy that relied heavily on sensational stories linking alcohol to crime, poverty, and immigration, Wheeler was able push several cities and states to pass limited anti-alcohol legislation and drum out of office many prominent "wets," including the governor of his home state of Ohio.

With World War I came a sharp rise in anti-German sentiment, which Wheeler and the ASL were able to exploit with an effective ad campaign against powerful German brewers such as Adolphus Busch and Frederick Pabst. Once hostilities ended, prohibition, along with suffrage and a host of other progressive laws, were introduced to Congress as war measures, laws necessary to the preservation of peace. Despite being largely unpopular, the Volstead Act, under pressure from the ASL, made its way through Congress and was rapidly ratified by the states, officially added as the Eighteenth Amendment to the Constitution in 1919 and 1920.

Perhaps no other piece of American legislation had a more negative impact than the Volstead Act. With alcohol becoming illegal, but public demand remaining as high as ever, what had once been the purview of legitimate businesses was quickly taken over by criminal gangs. Gangsters such as Al Capone and Lucky Luciano, who may have otherwise faded into obscurity, became masters of an ever growing criminal empire, and began to organize their rackets, centered around alcohol, in the form of a corporation that became known as the Syndicate. With the price of alcohol skyrocketing, bootleggers, as they came to be known, became incredibly rich, spending much of their money not only to import and brew ever increasing quantities of alcohol, but also to bribe local and federal officials from beat cops to the highest reaches of the executive branch. Within a few years, while imports of cocktail shakers boomed, speakeasies and other illegal saloons began to pop up across the nation. Soon, disagreement over price and territory amongst bootleggers led to all-out gang wars that rocked cities such as New York, Boston, and Chicago. All the while the hapless federal government, and most notably the Treasury Department, charged with enforcing Prohibition, faced a hostile public and little or no funding to do its job. Finally, the many exceptions in the law, including allotments of alcohol for medical purposes and religious uses, allowed for a thriving independent black market. Things came to a head in 1929 with the onset of the Great Depression, as thousands of desperate, jobless men flooded into the illegal rackets. Violence soared and for several years criminals became the biggest celebrities of the day. These tribulations, caused by Prohibition, would be felt for decades, in the form of organized crime and the relationship between the government and the citizenry, as millions of ordinary Americans became lawbreakers. In 1933, under overwhelming public pressure, Congress repealed the Eighteenth Amendment, making alcohol legal once again, and undoing, what many came to consider, as America's greatest legislative mistake.

—*K.P. Dawes, MA, and Michael J. O'Neal, PhD*

## Bibliography and Additional Reading

Bergreen, Laurence. *Capone: The Man and the Era*. Simon and Schuster, 2013.

Blumenthal, Karen. *Bootleg: Murder, Moonshine, and the Lawless Years of Prohibition*. Flash Point, 2011.

Clark, Norman H. *Deliver Us from Evil: An Interpretation of American Prohibition*. W.W. Norton and Company, 1976.

McGirr, Lisa. *The War on Alcohol: Prohibition and the Rise of the American State*. W.W. Norton and Company, 2015.

Okrent, Daniel. *Last Call: The Rise and Fall of Prohibition*. Simon and Schuster, 2010.

Raab, Selwyn. *Five Families: The Rise, Decline, and Resurgence of America's Most Powerful Mafia Empires*. Thomas Dunne Books, 2014.

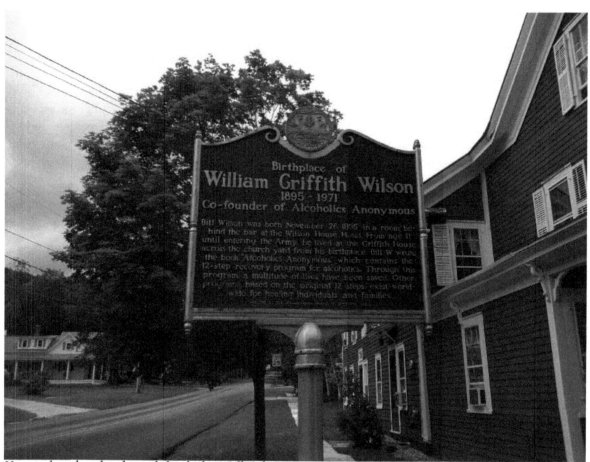

*Historical marker placed outside hotel where Bill Wilson, co-founder of Alcoholics Anonymous, was born in East Dorset, Vermont*

# ■ Alcoholics Anonymous "Big Book"

**Date:** 1939
**Author:** Bill Wilson
**Genre:** Self-help book

## Summary Overview

The Alcoholics Anonymous (AA) organization is known around the world for its work helping those addicted to alcohol. Its core beliefs, history, and program are contained within *Alcoholics Anonymous: The Story of How Many Thousands of Men and Women Have Recovered from Alcoholism*—usually known as the Big Book. Crucial to the creation of both Alcoholics Anonymous and the Big Book was Bill Wilson or, Bill W. The foreword to the original 1939 edition of the book and the original 12 steps in the recovery process represent the emergence of a powerful force in the battle against alcoholism. They also indicate the very small scale on which the original organization operated.

## Defining Moment

Medical treatment for alcohol addiction in the early twentieth century was largely restricted to those who were able to afford hospitalization. Often, however, the treatment consisted of using drugs for purging in the event of alcohol poisoning. For the most part, many medical professionals considered chronic alcoholism an incurable, fatal disease. The emergence of Alcoholics Anonymous in the 1930s and the publication of the Big Book in 1939 was the result of a confluence of several events and trends. One of these was the emergence of a movement known as the Oxford Group. The other was the psychological theories of Carl Jung.

The Oxford Group began in England in 1921 as "A First Century Christian Fellowship" (the Oxford Group name would emerge in the early 1930s). This was a Christian religious fellowship organization that had a simple outlook that could be summarized very briefly. Some of its principles would later be reflected in the 12 Steps of AA, such as "all people are sinners," "all sinners can be changed," and "confession is a pre-requisite to change." The group encouraged practices such as sharing sins and temptations with other members of the group and making restitution to everyone whom they had wronged.

Carl Jung's role in the development of Alcoholics Anonymous came through a man named Rowland Hazard III. Hazard saw the famed psychiatrist for help with his alcoholism. Jung declared that Hazard's alcoholism was not able to be treated through medical means. What he needed was a profound spiritual experience. This advice led Hazard to discover the Oxford Group. The group's commitment to personal change and reform were applied to the "sinful" condition of alcoholism. Hazard became acquainted with Ebby Thatcher, who would later play a role in Bill Wilson's sobriety. Wilson joined the Oxford Group but, later, he and Dr. Bob Smith would break away from the group and establish a new method based on mutual support among alcoholics and recovering alcoholics. This culminated in the publication of the Big Book in 1939. While Bill Wilson was the primary author, Bob Smith contributed as well and many alcoholics' personal experiences were included in the book.

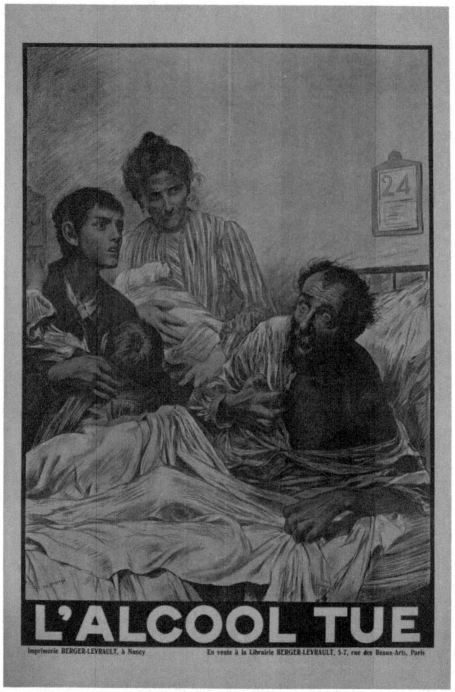

*An alcoholic man with delirium tremens on his deathbed, surrounded by his terrified family. The writing on the bottom of the image says "alcohol kills."*

## Author Biography

Bill W.—the suitably anonymous cofounder of Alcoholics Anonymous—was born William Griffith Wilson in 1895. Wilson was born at the inn his parents owned and operated in East Dorset, Vermont, but as a young child his parents abandoned him, with Bill being raised by his grandparents. Biographers describe Wilson as a rebellious child who eventually settled down, becoming active in school athletic and music programs. Wilson also suffered from depression and anxiety from an early age.

Bill Wilson's struggle with alcohol abuse began while he was serving in the Army; he found that the intoxicating effects of alcohol alleviated his social anxiety. He married Lois Burnham in 1918. Following service in the First World War, the Wilsons lived in New York. Biographer Susan Cheever recounts that Wilson was prevented from graduating law school because he failed to pick up his diploma due to drunkenness. Wilson turned to stock speculation and investment advising, but his alcoholism led to his failure in that field as well.

After medical treatment for his alcoholism failed, Wilson came into contact with Ebby Thatcher, who had gotten sober via his work with the Oxford Group and who urged Wilson to place his trust in God and turn away from drinking. Wilson attempted a medical solution for his alcoholism one last time, and while in the hospital claimed to have experienced a religious conversion and never again drank alcohol.

Wilson became acquainted with another member of the Oxford Group, Dr. Bob Smith, and together they began working with other alcoholics—an effort that would culminate in the establishment of Alcoholics Anonymous. Wilson died from complications of emphysema on January 24, 1971.

## HISTORICAL DOCUMENT

### Foreword to First Edition

We, of Alcoholics Anonymous, are more than one hundred men and women who have recovered from a seemingly hopeless state of mind and body. To show other alcoholics PRECISELY HOW THEY CAN RECOVER is the main purpose of this book. For them, we think these pages will prove so convincing that no further authentication will be necessary. We hope this account of our experiences will help everyone to better understand the alcoholic. Many do not yet comprehend that he is a very sick person. And besides, we are sure that our new way of living has its advantages for all.

It is important that we remain anonymous because we are too few, at present, to handle the overwhelming number of personal appeals which will result from this publication. Being mostly business or professional folk we could not well carry on our occupations in such an event. We would like it clearly understood that our alcoholic work is an avocation only, so that when writing or speaking publicly about alcoholism, we urge each of our Fellowship to omit his personal name, designating himself instead as "A Member of Alcoholics Anonymous."

Very earnestly we ask the press also, to observe this request, for otherwise we shall be greatly handicapped.

We are not an organization in the conventional sense of the word. There are no fees nor dues whatsoever. The only requirement for membership is an honest desire to stop drinking. We are not allied with any particular faith, sect or denomination, nor do we oppose anyone. We simply wish to be helpful to those who are afflicted.

We shall be interested to hear from those who are getting results from this book, particularly from those who have commenced work with other alcoholics. We shall try to contact such cases.

Inquiry by scientific, medical and religious societies will be welcomed.

*ALCOHOLICS ANONYMOUS*

### Original Twelve Steps

Here are the steps we took, which are suggested as a program of recovery:

1. We admitted we were powerless over alcohol, that our lives had become unmanageable.
2. Came to believe that a Power greater than ourselves could restore us to sanity.
3. Made a decision to turn our will and our lives over to the care of God as we understood Him.
4. Made a searching and fearless moral inventory of ourselves.
5. Admitted to God, to ourselves, and to another human being the exact nature of our wrongs.
6. Were entirely ready to have God remove all these defects of character.
7. Humbly asked Him to remove our shortcomings.
8. Made a list of all persons we had harmed, and became willing to make amends to them all.
9. Made direct amends to such people wherever possible, except when to do so would injure them or others.
10. Continued to take personal inventory and when we were wrong promptly admitted it.
11. Sought through prayer and meditation to improve our conscious contact with God as we understood Him, praying only for knowledge of His will for us and the power to carry that out.

---

## GLOSSARY

**avocation:** an activity that one regularly engages in that is not their way of making a living

**fellowship:** a group of likeminded people with a similar goal, organized more loosely than a business or other formal organization

**make amends:** to provide a solution to a mistake that has caused some issue or problem; particularly interpersonal issues

---

## Document Analysis

The foreword begins with an explanation of what—or, rather, who—Alcoholics Anonymous is. They are over a hundred people who had been alcoholics but who had "recovered from a seemingly hopeless state of mind and body." This is a significant phrasing. They do not say they have recovered from alcohol addiction, but rather the emphasis is on recovering from both the physical and mental effects of alcohol abuse. The purpose of the book is to illustrate the ways in which these alcoholics have recovered and to provide examples that other alcoholics can follow and that will help people understand those who struggle with alcohol addiction. The first paragraph of the foreword concludes with the suggestion that the principles upon which Alcoholics Anonymous is based have application beyond the treatment of alcoholism.

Next, the author addresses the importance of anonymity. While personal privacy is certainly a consideration, at this early stage in the organization's existence, they did not want to create a situation where the hundred members would be subjected to "overwhelming" demand for help. The work undertaken by the members of the organization is "an avocation," meaning it is not meant to be done as a voluntary activity, is not a way to make a living. Later in the organi-

zational development of Alcoholics Anonymous this notion was codified as one of the "Twelve Traditions" that would guide the organization ("Alcoholics Anonymous should remain forever nonprofessional, but our service centers may employ special workers.") The author requests that members remain anonymous when talking to the press and that the press respect the AA members' need to remain anonymous. Again, the author alludes to the danger of the volunteer group being overwhelmed with demands on their time that they would not be able to accommodate.

The next paragraph discusses the extremely decentralized nature of the group and highlights the fact that there is no financial burden for those who wish to become members. The only requirement for joining is "an honest desire to stop drinking." Despite the religious nature of the initial twelve steps, they emphasized that AA is not a sectarian organization; it welcomed all and only wanted to help those afflicted with alcoholism.

The foreword closes with a request for feedback from those who have been helped by the material contained in the book—a reminder to those of us reading in the present day that at this point in 1939, Alcoholics Anonymous was in its nascent stages and very much an experiment.

*Henrietta Buckler Sieberling (1888-1979) was born in Kentucky, raised in El Paso, Texas. She attended Vassar and in 1917 married John Frederick Sieberling. They had three children together and lived in Ohio. She credited with being one of the founders of Alcoholics Anonymous; she was the one who set up the meeting of the co-founders of Alcoholics Anonymous, Bill Wilson and Dr. Bob Smith, on Mother's Day 1935. (She was not known to have a drinking problem.)*

The original twelve steps were described as a "program of recovery." They were meant to be followed in order, each step building on the one preceding it. The first step, admitting powerlessness over alcohol, is in many ways parallel to the Oxford Group's maxim that "confession is a pre-requisite to change." The alcoholic can expect no improvement until he is willing to acknowledge his condition.

The second and third steps are crucial to subsequent steps and to the understanding of the whole enterprise: believing that a "power greater" than the alcoholic existed and could "restore" the alcoholic to "sanity," and surrendering to this power, were important. While, in the foreword, the author denied that the organization represented or endorsed any specific religious group, sect, or denomination, it *is* a theistic group that dictates a dependence on a divine being. Steps five, six, and seven also rely on the alcoholic's acceptance of God. Steps eight, nine, and ten involve the ongoing work of repairing the relationships that have been broken by alcoholism and require the alcoholic to commit to further soul searching and repentance. Step eleven again invokes God, requiring active prayer and meditation to discern God's will.

The final step recalls the origins of the group—the work of the Oxford Group and Jung's advice to Rowland Hazard. Completion of the program represented a spiritual awakening; a transformational experience that restored mental and physical health. Having received this awakening, the members share the benefits of this message and practices to others who may be suffering.

## Essential Themes

Both the foreword and the Twelve Steps themselves embody some of the essential themes of the Alcoholics Anonymous movement. The first of these is the decentralized, volunteer-based nature of the organization. The impetus for the creation of the organization was Bill Wilson's realization that alcoholics in conversation and relationships with other alcoholics was a necessary part of the recovery process. By the time the Big Book emerged in 1939, that conversation had grown to encompass over one hundred persons.

The other theme is the spiritual nature of the twelve steps. While there was—and continues to be—a dictate that the organization remain nonsectarian, the wording of the steps clearly reflects a western, monotheistic vision of the deity.

—*Aaron John Gulyas, MA*

## Bibliography and Additional Reading

Cheever, Susan. *My Name Is Bill—Bill Wilson: His Life and the Creation of Alcoholics Anonymous.* New York: Washington Square Press, 2004.

Kurtz, Ernest. *Not God: A History of Alcoholics Anonymous.* Center City, MN: Hazelden, 1991.

McGowan, Philip. "AA and the Redeployment of Temperance Literature." *Journal of American Studies* 48, no. 1 (2014): 51–78.

Schaberg, William H. *Writing the Big Book: The Creation of A.A.* Las Vegas: Central Recovery Press, 2018.

Tieman, John Samuel. "The Origins of Twelve-Step Spirituality: Bill W. and Edward Dowling, S. J." *U.S. Catholic Historian* 13, no. 3 (1995): 121–35.

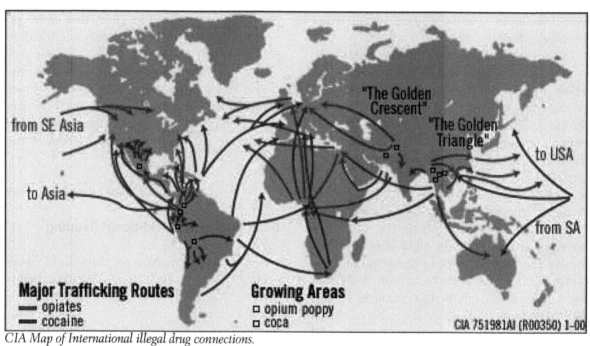

*CIA Map of International illegal drug connections.*

# ■ Report of the Joint Committee of the American Bar Association and the American Medical Association on Narcotic Drugs

**Date:** 1958
**Authors:** American Bar Association and the American Medical Association Joint Committee
**Genre:** Report

## Summary Overview

During the 1950s, political leaders in the United States were aggressively attempting to control the rise of narcotic drug use. Most of the attempts to regulate the use of these drugs was to create mandatory minimum sentences for drug-related crimes. In 1958, the American Bar Association (ABA) and the American Medical Association (AMA) developed a joint committee to examine alternative ways to address the emerging drug crisis the country was facing. The report included five major areas that the committee wanted to explore and conduct research on. The report was met with great criticism from the Federal Bureau of Narcotics (FBN), headed by Harry Anslinger. Ultimately, the committee was dissolved and the report itself had no significant impact on the drug crisis at the time.

## Defining Moment

Sparked by public fear over the popularization of drug use spreading throughout the United States, the government began to find solutions to the problem—often by developing strict punishments for crimes relating to illegal drugs. A series of laws were passed in the 1950s to restrict access to powerful narcotic drugs and to enact minimum sentences for possession of certain types of drugs. As prison populations began to rise dramatically, and without any solid evidence that these laws were successful in deterring drug use, organizations such as the American Bar Association and the American Medical Association began to consider their role in helping to deal with this pressing and important issue. While the medical profession had been concerned with narcotic drugs and opioids since the Civil War, it had not actively participated in trying to influence lawmakers to examine the issue (except for taking a stance on legislation that emerged in the early 1920s). A spokesperson from the American Bar Association approached the AMA and proposed that the two groups join forces to undertake a joint study that could help guide the actions of lawmakers.

The Eighty-Fifth Congress was in place from January 1957 to January 1959, during the fifth and sixth years of Dwight D. Eisenhower's presidency. Democrats held a majority in both chambers, and much of the legislature's focus was on the civil rights issues of the time. However, some of the legislation passed in the preceding Eighty-Fourth Congress had focused heavily on how to handle drug-related crimes in America and, therefore, the Eighty-Fifth Congress was faced with the ramifications of those policies.

## Author Biography

The American Bar Association (ABA) was founded in 1878; it is a voluntary association made up of lawyers and law students in America. The ABA cites its most important activities as setting academic standards for law schools and developing a sound model to formulate ethical codes for the legal profession. The ABA began focusing on narcotic drug laws following the passage of the 1952 Boggs Act, which outlined mandatory minimum sentencing for drug crimes.

The American Medical Association (AMA) was founded in 1847 and is the largest association of physicians in the United States. The stated goal of the AMA is to "promote the art of science and medicine and the betterment of public health." While the AMA had not taken a formal position on narcotics laws since 1924, it did have a significant interest in addressing addiction issues and by 1956 had designated alcoholism as an illness calling for medical treatment.

## HISTORICAL DOCUMENT

### DRUG ADDICTION, CRIME OR DISEASE?

#### Interim Report

For the last half-century public authorities in the United States have been wrestling with the problem of controlling addiction to narcotic drugs. Since the twenties, legislation and enforcement policies have aimed at total repression, with criminal sanctions of notable severity attaching to every transaction connected with the non-medical use of drugs. Drug-law enforcement has become a major police activity of federal, state and local governments; the threat of long imprisonment, even of death penalties, hangs over not only the smuggler and the peddler, but the addict-victim of the illicit traffic.

Addiction to narcotic substances has been recognized as a health problem for a long time and in many different countries. It has also in our times and in our national community, emerged as a criminal law problem of distressing magnitude and persistency. The fields of medicine and law are thus equally affected, and the Joint Committee which offers this report has undertaken its assignment with enthusiasm at the prospect of uniting its parent organizations in a common effort centered in an area where the concerns of each overlap and largely coincide. If the Joint Committee can contribute something towards mutual enlightenment and ultimate agreement between the medical and legal professions regarding the drug problem, it may clear the way for desirable reforms. But regardless of the final outcome, its work to date has been highly gratifying to those engaged in it simply by virtue of its resounding success as an experiment in close cooperation between the American Medical Association and the American Bar Association.

The Joint Committee warmly acknowledges the participation of another cooperating partner, the Russell Sage Foundation, which contributed substantial material aid to finance the Joint Committee's work. We wish particularly to express our appreciation to Dr. Donald Young and Dr. Leonard S. Cottrell, Jr., of the Foundation, who have followed the Joint Committee's work closely, contributing invaluably from their broad wisdom and experience in the field of social science research.

## Background

The medical profession in this country was widely concerned about the use and abuse of opiate preparations at least as long ago as the Civil War era. The American Medical Association supported the enactment of regulatory legislation before the Harrison Act (1914) became law, and its House of Delegates gave active consideration to the development of the federal regulatory pattern in the formulative period 1919–23. A Special Committee on the Narcotic Drug Situation in the United States, appointed pursuant to a resolution of the A. M. A. House of Delegates in June, 1919, studied the situation and submitted an edifying report the following year. A standing Committee on Narcotic Drugs, of the A. M. A. Council on Health and Public Instruction, served actively thereafter. But except for expressing its position on various matters of administrative detail, the A. M. A. has taken no formal position with regard to the operation of the country's narcotics laws since the adoption, in June, 1924, of a resolution on so-called ambulatory treatment proposed by its Committee on Narcotic Drugs.

In 1954, interest was reawakened by the submission of a proposal from the New York State Medical Society for the legalization of the distribution of narcotics to addicts. The proposal was referred by the A. M. A. House of Delegates to its Council on Pharmacy and Chemistry and Council on Mental Health, and in April, 1955, the latter body appointed a special Committee on Narcotic Addiction, charged with the responsibility of making a thorough study of the matter. Dr. Felix, an A. M. A. member of the Joint Committee, served as chairman of the special committee, which has recently completed its work with a report concluding that the advisability of free distribution cannot be settled on the basis of objective facts at hand, recommending further study and research, and suggesting that the 1924 resolution of the House of Delegates should be revised.

The American Bar Association first concerned itself with narcotic drug laws when its Commission on Organized Crime considered (and disapproved) the mandatory minimum sentences and minimum penalties provided in the first Boggs Act, endorsed by the Kefauver Committee, which became law in 1952. As a result of interest developed in its consideration of these provisions, the A. B. A.'s Section of Criminal Law created a standing Committee on Narcotics and Alcohol. The latter committee, after a survey of federal and state legislation on the subject, proposed a three-part resolution which was passed by the A. B. A. House of Delegates in February, 1955: "Resolved, That the Section of Criminal Law, through its Chairman or other such appropriate representative as he may appoint, be and it is hereby authorized:

(1)   To explore with the American Medical Association the possibilities of a jointly conducted study of the narcotic drug traffic and related problems, by and on behalf of the organizations through their own research facilities or in collaboration with other interested persons or organizations.

(2)   To investigate through the American Bar Foundation the availability of funds from sources outside the Association in aid of the study described in the preceding paragraph, and with the approval of the American Bar Foundation to utilize such funds as may be found to be available for that purpose.

(3)   To urge the Congress of the United States to undertake a re-examination of the Harrison Act, its amendments and related enforcement and treatment policies and problems."

It is of interest to note with respect to part (3) of the A. B. A. resolution that the adoption of Senate Resolution 67, authorizing the Daniels Committee study, followed it within a month (84th Congress, Ist Session, March 18, 1955).

Overtures to the American Medical Association through the A. B. A.'s Section of Criminal Law evoked a cordial response, and the project became a truly joint undertaking from the outset. The original appointees to the Joint Committee, Drs. Felix and Starr and Mr. Stetler for the A. M. A., Judge Dimock and Messrs. Fortas and King for the A. B. A., have continued to serve. In the matters of seeking resources for research and organizing its program, the American Bar Foundation, while not participating directly because the subject matter includes non-legal areas, has given the Joint Committee valued guidance and assistance.

### Work of the Joint Committee

At its first meeting (Washington, March, 1956) the Joint Committee established as its ultimate purpose "to determine whether the two Associations can or should agree upon common principles or a common course of action" with respect to the subject of narcotic drugs. It was decided that the barbiturates, though similar to opiates in some respects, should not be included in the studies at this time. The Joint Committee outlined a number of areas and problems about which factual data seemed lacking, and noted that a considerable amount of research might be required before final conclusions could safely be reached. During the Summer of 1956, a number of research foundations were approached in quest of advice and support with respect to the Joint Committee's studies. Without exception the responses were approbative, but it was suggested that before seeking any substantial grant of funds, the areas of inquiry ought to be carefully analyzed and reduced to proposals for specific research activity in each case; in the convincing words of one foundation spokesman, "We cannot finance problems—only projects." Thus it was decided to commence on a modest scale with a survey of existing data, an analysis of present conditions and the preparation of one or more specific "project designs." For assistance in making this start, the Joint Committee was most fortunate in being able to reach an agreement with the Russell Sage Foundation of New York.

> **W**e cannot finance problems—only projects.

The Russell Sage Foundation is dedicated to "the improvement of social and living conditions in the United States," differing from many of its counterparts in that it maintains its own research staff and participates directly in many of the undertakings it supports. Its work in recent years has many times entailed cooperation with professional groups, particularly in law, medicine, psychology and psychiatry. Its own general program is currently aimed at increasing the utilization of the social sciences in professional practice.

In October, 1956 a formal application was made to the Russell Sage Foundation for a grant of $15,000 to be used in study of existing data and the preparation of one or more project designs. This application was approved, and the grant made, on November 8, 1956. The Foundation offered the cooperation of its staff, offered to provide office space for the Joint Committee at its headquarters, and undertook to handle all administrative details.

With approval from the A. M. A. Board of Directors and the American Bar Foundation, the Joint Committee accepted these arrangements. At its next meeting (Washington, December, 1956) a representative of the Russell Sage Foundation assisted in reviewing the areas to be studied in preparation of the project designs, and the details of procedure were worked out. The Joint Committee next addressed itself to the task of finding a qualified director—a task most fortunately concluded when Judge Morris Ploscowe, formerly director of the A. B. A. Commission on Organized Crime and well known for his studies in the field of crime and criminal law administration, agreed to serve. An important factor in the Joint Committee's selection of Judge Ploscowe was that the Report of the A. M. A. Council on Mental Health on Narcotic Addiction, then just submitted, contained so much excellent material on the medical aspects of addiction that the need for medical research appeared limited and a larger part of the Joint Committee's own work could, it believed, be concentrated on legal, administrative and sociological aspects. The Joint Committee met again (Philadelphia, March, 1957) With Judge Ploscowe to discuss his undertaking, and at this time, partly in view of the A. M. A. report mentioned above, it was suggested that in some aspects, at least, enough reliable data might be found already available to enable him to reach conclusions in the course of his analysis. Agreement was reached that the work would thus keep three aims in view: (1) To survey existing sources to find out how much already existing material was available and could be relied upon; (2) To determine what experiments and research projects ought to be sponsored by the Joint Committee to remedy deficiencies in present knowledge of the field; and (3) To draw conclusions, where possible from existing sources, as to any areas which appeared capable of accurate analysis without further study.

## Reports and Recommendations

With the foregoing aims in view, a study of the drug addiction problem has gone forward, making use of all available sources and resulting in the report, by Judge Ploscowe, "Some Basic Problems in Drug Addiction and Suggestions for Research," appended hereto as Appendix A. We commend the thoughtful, realistic appraisal of the problems of drug addiction and the critical analysis of present policies toward drug addicts contained in Judge Ploscowe's report. He has clearly spelled out the need for a revision of present attitudes toward and present approaches to drug addicts and drug addiction.

In July-August, 1957, the drug laws and enforcement policies of England and certain European countries were examined, for comparative purposes, by Rufus King, resulting in the report appended hereto as Appendix B.

At its most recent meeting (Washington, November 18, 1957) the Joint Committee considered the aforementioned reports. It approved the substance of the report of Judge Ploscowe without formally adopting its language or specific appraisals. It agreed to go forward with the preparation of projects in the five specific areas suggested therein, namely:

(1)  An Outpatient Experimental Clinic for the Treatment of Drug Addicts (Appendix A, p. 103) Although it is clear, as the report sets forth, that the so-called clinic approach to drug addiction is the subject of much controversy, the Joint Committee feels that the possibilities of trying some such outpatient facility, on a controlled experimental basis, should be explored, since it can make an invaluable contribution to our knowledge of how to deal with drug addicts in a community, rather than on an institutional basis. It has been suggested that the District of Columbia, being an exclusively federal jurisdiction and immediately accessible to both law-enforcement and public health agencies, might be an advantageous locus for this experiment.

(2)  A Study of Relapse and Causative Factors (Appendix A, p. 108) It is not possible to fully measure the worth of treatment and rehabilitation measures without more data than has yet been accumulated on the rate of relapse, and on the causative factors underlying both addiction and successful rehabilitation. The Joint Committee feels that large scale research in this area (complementing several limited studies which are already under way) would be highly desirable. Such research is absolutely indispensable to any thorough-going evaluation of present policies in dealing with narcotic addiction, as well as to the formulation of new approaches in dealing with this difficult problem.

(3)  Educational and Preventative Research (Appendix A, p. 109) The dissemination of accurate information about narcotic addiction has been neglected and even discouraged by some enforcement authorities. The Joint Committee feels that this

matter should be studied critically, to determine whether a campaign of enlightenment might not produce good results. The Joint Committee also feels that other preventative techniques can be devised which can aid materially in lowering the incidence of drug addiction.

(4)  Legal Research (Appendix A, p. 113) There is uncertainty at present both in
the ambiguous provisions of some of our narcotic drug statutes and in the court decisions through which they have been applied. There is also doubt as to whether the
premises on which our present narcotic laws rest are sound and validly conceived. A
critical study in this area would make possible a thorough evaluation of present legal
approaches to narcotic addiction. It should result in the formulation of better methods for dealing with the addict and more realistic and sounder means for controlling
the illicit drug traffic.

(5)  Research in the Administration of Present Laws (Appendix A, p. 115) There
is considerable uncertainty and confusion in the enforcement of existing drug laws.
This may be inherent in the nature of the laws, procedures or administrative and judicial machinery which seeks to enforce them. A careful study of how existing laws are
operating should provide invaluable guides for a rational drug control program in this
country.

## The Program Ahead

The five areas described above are those in which the Joint Committee intends to
develop specific project designs for its research. This step, to be taken next, is still
within the compass of the Russell Sage Foundation grant, and will occupy the Joint
Committee's director and cooperating staff until completed. When the designs are
complete, additional funds will be sought to carry them out. In some cases, they may
appropriately be turned over to other organizations and agencies; for example, it is
contemplated that the resources of the American Bar Foundation could be utilized for
the legal-research projects.

It is anticipated that another work of value will be completed while the research
projects are being developed: a selected bibliography of current material on narcotic
drugs has been collected for the Joint Committee and this, plus a carefully edited set
of selected readings, will be submitted for publication, if approved, by the Russell
Sage Foundation.

The Joint Committee still holds its basic aim, namely, to determine whether
the two Associations can agree upon common principles, or a common course of
action, with respect to the narcotic drug problem. Its final report will contain its
conclusions on this subject as well as its statement of principles and recommended
action. But until more is learned about the narcotic problem—until at least some
of the proposed research is completed—the Joint Committee believes it should
proceed slowly. No final conclusions are therefore offered at this time and no time-
table of future progress is attempted. Unless otherwise directed, the Joint Commit-

tee will carry on at its present pace until it is satisfied that the assignment given to it has been fully carried out.

RUFUS KING, Chairman
JUDGE EDWARD J. DIMOCK
ABE FORTAS
DR. ROBERT H. FELIX
DR. ISAAC STARR
C. JOSEPH STETLER

## GLOSSARY

**narcotics:** substances used to treat moderate to severe pain; narcotics bind to opioid receptors in the central nervous system; used in moderation these drugs dull the senses, relieve pain, and induce profound sleep, but in excessive doses they can cause stupor, coma, convulsions, and in some cases death

## Document Analysis

The document cites the nature of the problem as being related to the addictive nature of narcotic drugs and that relationship of drug use to law enforcement of the drugs. The committee notes that drug law enforcement is the major focus of law enforcement officials at all levels of government: local, state, and federal, which the committee states can become very confusing; and the committee makes note of the heavy legal penalties assigned to drug-related crimes. The committee is reticent to make the outright claim that this law enforcement focus and the penalties for drug crimes is wrong, but instead states by uniting medicine and law important reforms could be made to existing policy that might better address the drug problem in the United States. So, while the language in the actual report is somewhat vague, it is clear the committee is not convinced that policies designed to be strictly punitive in nature are the best solution to the problem.

In particular, Congress is encouraged by the joint committee to reconsider the Harrison Act, which included legal language outlining who could be supplied with narcotics. This law placed significant restrictions on whom doctors were allowed to give narcotic medications to, and in reality resulted in the arrest in occasional imprisonment of doctors. Through a $15,000 grant from the Russell Sage Foundation the committee moved forward with research in five areas they felt could offer insight in how to best address the drug epidemic. The committee planned to examine an experimental clinic for treating addicts that focused on outpatient rehabilitation, why people tended to relapse, the feasibility of educating the public on the harmful nature of these drugs, and whether or not preventative measures could be effective, as well as a study to determine how well current punitive laws are working.

## Essential Themes

The ABA-AMA report was met with serious criticism and was blatantly attacked by an advisory committee to the Federal Bureau of Narcotics, which was comprised of individuals who were known to side with the firm punitive law stance of Harry Anslinger (the head of the Federal Bureau of Narcotics). Because the committee did not take a particularly clear or bold stance on any of the issues it brought up in the report, and Congress had not weighed in, Anslinger was not restricted in his mission to crack down on drug use in the nation, although he often used fear tactics to frighten the public into accepting his aggressive penalties. Anslinger at no time endorsed the committee's recommendations and went so far as to claim that the report was not accurate and was inconsistent and ambiguous if not outright false.

The committee also faced financing challenges and the inability to secure steady funding for research plans. Combined with the attack from Anslinger's agency, the ABA-AMA committee inevitably disbanded. Years later, the ABA had a staff member evaluate the joint committee's report and the staffer reported that it was difficult to truly determine the intent of the committee. Since then, America has witnessed a consistent war on drugs that still focuses on punitive measures but has incorporated, to a certain degree, the concept of rehabilitation and the recognition that addiction may be akin to disease. Currently, the opioid crisis in America is the most serious public health issue; it claimed the lives of over 70,000 citizens from 2018–2019 alone. More people die from opioid overdoses in American than car crashes, and the government seems to be at a loss for how to appropriately address this devastating phenomenon.

—*Amber R. Dickinson, PhD*

## Bibliography and Additional Reading

Erlen, Jonathon, Joseph F. Spillane, and Rebecca Carroll. *Federal Drug Control: The Evolution of Policy and Practice.* New York: Pharmaceutical Products Press, 2004.

"The Early Years." *The Drug Enforcement Administration,* May 2018. www.dea.gov/sites/default/files/2018–05/Early Years p 12–29.pdf.

Institute of Medicine (US) Committee for the Substance Abuse Coverage Study; Gerstein D.R., Harwood H.J., eds. *Treating Drug Problems: Volume 2: Commissioned Papers on Historical, Institutional, and Economic Contexts of Drug Treatment.* A Century of American Narcotic Policy. Washington, DC: National Academies Press, 1992.

Jepsen, Jorgen. Reviewed Work: "Drug Addiction—Crime or Disease? By the ABA and the AMA Joint Committee on Narcotic Drugs." *The Journal of Criminal Law, Criminology, and Police Science* 53. no. 1 (1962): 76–78.

McGreal, Chris. *American Overdose: The Opioid Tragedy in Three Acts.* New York: PublicAffairs, 2018.

Pembleton, Matthew R. *Containing Addiction: The Federal Bureau of Narcotics and the Origins of America's Global Drug War.* Amherst: University of Massachusetts Press, 2017.

# ■ *Special Report: Smoking and Health*

**Date:** January 11, 1964
**Authors:** Luther Terry
**Genre:** Report

## Summary Overview

Tobacco has been a ubiquitous part of American culture since before the nation's founding. Links had long been made between smoking tobacco and adverse health effects; however, the large and growing tobacco industry and smokers themselves had largely looked past these connections. Surgeon General Luther Terry oversaw the 1964 report featured in this chapter, Smoking and Health. The report compiled the previous medical studies detailing the harmful effects of smoking and categorically established a causal role between smoking and various diseases and cancers. The adverse health effects are so great, the document concludes, that they lead to a substantially higher death rate. The report estimates an increased death rate of 70 percent among male cigarette smokers, with female smokers experiencing a less pronounced but still significant increase. Smoking remains a persistent part of American culture but has seen a decline over recent decades, in part from the details of this 1964 report.

## Defining Moment

Tobacco cultivation and usage has been engrained in American society and culture since before the country's founding. The drug was used widely throughout the Americas before 1492. The arrival of European colonists brought it global. Settlers in Jamestown, Virginia, cultivated tobacco in the early seventeenth century, and the crop quickly became popular among European settlers throughout what is today the continental United States. As a labor-intensive cash crop, it accelerated early America's reliance on slavery. Smoking likewise became embedded in American culture. Despite its ballooning global popularity, tobacco faced its early critics. King James I detested the drug and bore witness to early awareness of its detrimental health effects. His 1604 Counterblaste to Tobacco called tobacco usage "a custome lothsome to the eye, hatefull to the Nose, harmefull to the braine, dangerous to the Lungs, and in the blacke stinking fume thereof, neerest resembling the hor-rible Stigian smoke of the pit that is bottome-lesse."

Tobacco cultivation and usage continued to soar in the twentieth century. Its detractors also continued to expound its harmfulness. Dr. Alton Ochsner, interviewed in this document, formed the Ochsner Clinic with associates in 1942 Louisiana. This clinic became a nationwide force in the fight against the spread of tobacco usage. In the United Kingdom, Sir Richard Doll and Sir Austin Bradford Hill began the landmark British Doctors Study in 1951. The study tracked the health effects of smoking on patients for five decades and eventually revealed in stark terms the dangers of this drug. In the United States, anti-smoking advocates united and formed Tobacco Institute Incorporated in 1958. Surgeon General Leroy E. Burney began studying the issue in earnest in the 1950s. His successor, surgeon general Luther L. Terry, released the report Smoking and Health—Report of the Advisory Committee of the Surgeon General of the Public Health Service on January 11, 1964. The report unequivocally detailed the links smoking has to specific cancers and diseases.

By the time of the Surgeon General's report of early 1964, the tobacco industry had become big business in the United States, and the tobacco corporations went to great lengths to protect their business model in the face of this damning report. Well-funded tobacco lobbyists flooded Capitol Hill to fight off legislation. Tobacco marketing departments, meanwhile, advertised cigarettes with better filters and lower tar levels. If this seemed like a concession to the medical consensus, it was limited: Tobacco corporations banded together, denied the settled science, and fought to undermine public trust in the medical conclusions. As decades of additional medical studies bolstered the findings of the 1964 report, the tobacco industry only hardened its stance. In a congressional hearing before the Energy and Commerce Subcommittee on Health and the Environment in 1994, the CEOs of the seven largest American tobacco corporations all flatly denied a link between smoking and negative health defects under oath.

## Author Biography

Luther Terry was a physician and a U.S. Surgeon General. Born on September 15, 1911, in Red Level, Alabama, Terry followed his father, Red Level's town doctor, into the medical field. He graduated with a bachelor's degree from Birmingham-Southern College and a medical degree from Tulane University. Following stints as a doctor and instructor, Terry became the Chief of Medical Services at the Public Health Service Hospital in Baltimore, Maryland. From there he transitioned to roles at the National Institutes of Health (NIH) and Johns Hopkins University. He rose in the ranks of the NIH to become Assistant Director. In 1961 President John F. Kennedy appointed him to become the ninth Surgeon General of the United States. His time as Surgeon General is remembered mostly for the report on smoking featured in this chapter. He continued to campaign against smoking after leaving the government and served as a professor at the University of Pennsylvania. He died on March 29, 1985, of heart failure.

---

## HISTORICAL DOCUMENT: REPORT OF THE ADVISORY COMMITTEE TO THE SURGEON GENERAL OF THE PUBLIC HEALTH SERVICE U.S DEPARTMENT OF HEALTH, EDUCATION, AND WELFARE

Public Health Service

Public Health Service Publication No. 1103

Foreword

Since the turn of the century, scientists have become increasingly interested in the effects of tobacco on health. Only within the past few decades, however, has a broad experimental and clinical approach to the subject been manifest; within this period the most extensive and definitive studies have been undertaken since 1950.

Few medical questions have stirred such public interest or created more scientific debate than the tobacco-health controversy. The interrelationships of smoking and health undoubtedly are complex. The subject does not lend itself to easy answers. Nevertheless, it has been increasingly apparent that answers must be found.

As the principal Federal agency concerned broadly with the health of the American people, the Public Health Service has been conscious of its deep responsibility for seeking these answers. As steps in that direction it has seemed necessary to determine, as precisely as possible, the direction of scientific evidence and to act in accordance with that evidence for the benefit of the people of the United States. In 1959, the Public Health Service assessed the then available evidence linking smoking with health and made its findings known to the professions and the public. The Service's review of the evidence and its statement at that time was largely focused on the relationship of cigarette smoking to lung cancer. Since 1959 much additional data has accumulated on the whole subject.

Accordingly, I appointed a committee, drawn from all the pertinent scientific disciplines, to review and evaluate both-this new and older data and, if possible, to reach some definitive conclusions on the relationship between smoking and health in general. The results of the Committee's study and evaluation are contained in this Report.

I pledge that the Public Health Service will undertake a prompt and thorough review of the Report to determine what action may be appropriate and necessary. I am confident that other Federal agencies and nonofficial agencies will do the same.

The Committee's assignment has been most difficult. The subject is complicated and the pressures of time on eminent men busy with many other duties has been great. I am aware of the difficulty in writing an involved technical report requiring evaluations and judgments from many different professional and technical points of view. The completion of the Committee's task has required the exercise of great professional skill and dedication of the highest order. I acknowledge a profound debt of gratitude to the Committee, the many consultants who have given their assistance, and the members of the staff. In doing so, I extend thanks not only for the Service but for the Nation as a whole.

*SURGEON GENERAL*

## Introduction

## Chapter 1

Realizing that for the convenience of all types of serious readers it would be desirable to simplify language, condense chapters and bring opinions to the forefront, the Committee offers Part I as such a presentation. This Part includes: (a) an introduction comprising, among other items, a chronology especially pertinent to the subject of this study and to the establishment and activities of the Committee, (h) a short account of how the study was conducted, (c) the chief criteria used in making judgments, and (d) a brief overview of the entire Report....

The modern period of investigation of smoking and health is included within the past sixty-three years. In 1900 an increase in cancer of the lung was noted particularly by vital statisticians, and their data are usually taken as the starting point for studies on the possible relationship of smoking and other uses of tobacco to cancer of the lung and of certain other organs, to diseases of the heart and blood vessels, and cardiovascular diseases in general; coronary artery disease in particular), and to the non-cancerous (non-neoplastic) diseases of the lower respiratory tract (especially chronic bronchitis and emphysema). The next important basic date for starting comparisons is 1930, when the definite trends in mortality and disease-incidence considered in this Report became more conspicuous. Since then a great variety of investigations have been carried out. Many of the chemical compounds in tobacco and in tobacco smoke have been isolated and tested. Numerous experimental studies in lower animals have been made by exposing them to smoke and to tars, gases and various constituents in tobacco and tobacco smoke. It is not feasible to submit human beings to experiments that might produce cancers or other serious damage, or to expose them to possibly noxious agents over the prolonged periods under strictly controlled conditions that would be necessary for a valid test. Therefore, the main evidence of the effects of smoking and other uses of tobacco upon the health of human beings has been secured through clinical and pathological observations of conditions occurring in men, women and children in the course of their lives, and by the application of epidemiological and statistical methods by which a vast array of information has been assembled and analyzed.

Among the epidemiological methods which have been used in attempts to determine whether smoking and other uses of tobacco affect the health of man, two types have been particularly useful and have furnished information of the greatest value for the work of this Committee. These are (1) retrospective studies which deal with data from the personal histories and medical and mortality records of human individuals in groups; and (2) prospective studies, in which men and women are chosen randomly or from some special group, such as a profession, and are followed from the time of their entry into the study for an indefinite period, or until they die or are lost on account of other events.

Since 1939 there have been 29 retrospective studies of lung cancer alone which have varying degrees of completeness and validity. Following the publication of several notable retrospective studies in the years 1952-1956, the medical evidence tending to link cigarette smoking to cancer of the lung received particularly widespread attention. At this time, also, the critical counterattack upon retrospective studies and upon conclusions drawn from them was launched by unconvinced individuals and groups. The same types of criticism and skepticism have been, and are, marshaled against the methods, findings, and conclusions of the later prospective studies. They will be discussed further in Chapter 3, Criteria for Judgment, and in other chapters, especially Chapter 8, Mortality, and Chapter 9, Cancer.

During the decade 1950–1960, at various dates, statements based upon the accumulated evidence were issued by a number of organizations. These included the British Medical Research Council: the cancer societies of Denmark, Norway, Sweden, Finland, and the Netherlands: the American Cancer Society: the American Heart Association: the Joint Tuberculosis Council of Great Britain: and the Canadian National Department of Health and Welfare. The consensus, publicly declared, was that smoking is an important health hazard, particularly with respect to lung cancer and cardiovascular disease.

> *In general, the greater the number of cigarettes smoked daily, the higher the death rate.*

Early in 1954, the Tobacco Industry Research Committee (T.I-R.C.) was established by representatives of tobacco manufacturers, growers, and warehousemen to sponsor a program of research into questions of tobacco use and health. Since then, under a Scientific Director and a Scientific Advisory Board composed of nine scientists who maintain their respective institutional affiliations, the Tobacco Industry Research Committee has conducted a grants-in-aid program, collected information, and issued reports.

The U.S. Public Health Service first became officially engaged in an appraisal of the available data on smoking and health in June 1956, when, under the instigation of the Surgeon General, a scientific Study Group on the subject was established jointly by the National Cancer Institute, the National Heart Institute, the American Cancer Society, and the American Heart Association. After appraising sixteen independent studies carried on in five countries over a period of 18 years, this group concluded that there is a causal relationship between excessive smoking of cigarettes and lung cancer.

Impressed by the report of the Study Committee and by other new evidence. Surgeon General Leroy E. Burney issued a statement on July 12, 1957, reviewing the matter and declaring that: "The Public Health Service feels the weight of the evidence is increasingly pointing in one direction: that excessive smoking is one of the causative factors in lung cancer." Again, in a special article entitled "Smoking and Lung Cancer—A Statement of the Public Health Service," published in the Journal of the American Medical Association on November 28, 1959, Surgeon General Burney referred to his statement issued in 1957 and reiterated the belief of the Public Health Service that: "The weight of evidence at present implicates smoking as the principal factor in the increased incidence of lung cancer," and that: "Cigarette smoking particularly is associated with an increased chance of developing lung cancer." These quotations state the position of the Public Health

Service taken in 1957 and 1959 on the question of smoking and health. That position has not changed in the succeeding years, during which several units of the Service conducted extensive investigations on smoking and air pollution, and the Service maintained a constant scrutiny of reports and publications in this field....

## Chapter 4

Summaries and Conclusions

[....]

This chapter is presented in two sections. Section A contains background information, the gist of the Committee's findings and conclusions on tobacco and health, and an assessment of the nature and magnitude of the health hazard. Section B presents all formal conclusions adopted by the Committee and selected comments abridged from the detailed Summaries that appear in each chapter of Part IT of the Report. The full scope and depth of the Committee's inquiry may be comprehended only by study of the complete Report.

## A. BACKGROUND AND HIGHLIGHTS

In previous studies, the use of tobacco, especially cigarette smoking, has been causally linked to several diseases. Such use has been associated with increased deaths from lung cancer and other diseases, notably coronary artery disease, chronic bronchitis, and emphysema. These widely reported findings, which have been the cause of much public concern over the past decade, have been accepted in many countries by official health agencies, medical associations, and voluntary health organizations.

The potential hazard is great because these diseases are major causes of death and disability. In 1962, over 500,000 people in the United States died of arteriosclerotic heart disease (principally coronary artery disease), 41,000 died of lung cancer, and 15,000 died of bronchitis and emphysema....

Another cause for concern is that deaths from some of these diseases have been increasing with great rapidity over the past few decades.

Lung cancer deaths, less than 3,000 in 1930, increased to 18,000 in 1950. In the short period since 1955, deaths from lung cancer rose from less than 27,000 to the 1962 total of 41,000. This extraordinary rise has not been recorded for cancer of any other site. While part of the rising trend for lung cancer is attributable to improvements in diagnosis and the changing 4ge-composition and size of the population, the evidence leaves little doubt that a true increase in lung cancer has taken place.

Deaths from arteriosclerotic, coronary, and degenerative heart disease rose from 273,000 in 1940, to 396,000 in 1950, and to 578,000 in 1962.

Reported deaths from chronic bronchitis and emphysema rose from 2,300 in 1945 to 15,000 in 1962.

The changing patterns and extent of tobacco use are a pertinent aspect of the tobacco-health problem.

[. . . .]

Nearly 70 million people in the United States consume tobacco regularly. Cigarette consumption in the United States has increased markedly since the turn of the Century, when per capita consumption was less than 50 cigarettes a year. Since 1910, when cigarette consumption per person (15 years and older) was 138, it rose to 1,365 in 1930, to 1,828 in 1940, to 3,322 in 1950, and to a peak of 3,986 in 1961. The 1955 Current Population Survey showed that 68 percent of the male population and 32.4 percent of the female population 18 years of age and over were regular smokers of cigarettes.

In contrast with this sharp increase in cigarette smoking, per capita use of tobacco in other forms has gone down. Per capita consumption of cigars declined from 117 in 1920 to 55 in 1962. Consumption of pipe tobacco, which reached a peak of 2½ lbs. per person in 1910, fell to a little more than half a pound per person in 1962. Use of chewing tobacco has declined from about four pounds per person in 1900 to half a pound in 1962.

The background for the Committee's study thus included much general information and findings from previous investigations which associated the increase in cigarette smoking with increased deaths in a number of major disease categories. It was in this setting that the Committee began its work to assess the nature and magnitude of the health hazard attributable to smoking.

Kinds of Evidence

In order to judge whether smoking and other tobacco uses are injurious to health or related to specific diseases, the Committee evaluated three main kinds of scientific evidence:

1. *Animal experiments.* In numerous studies, animals have been exposed to tobacco smoke and tars, and to the various chemical compounds they contain. Seven of these compounds (polycyclic aromatic compounds) have been established as cancer-producing (carcinogenic). Other substances in tobacco and smoke, though not carcinogenic themselves, promote cancer production or lower the threshold to a known carcinogen. Several toxic or irritant gases contained in tobacco smoke produce experimentally the kinds of non-cancerous damage seen in the tissues and cells of heavy smokers. This includes suppression of ciliary action that normally cleanses the trachea and bronchi, damage to the lung air sacs, and to mucous glands and goblet cells which produce mucus.

2. *Clinical and autopsy studies.* Observations of thousands of patients and autopsy studies of smokers and non-smokers show that many kinds of damage to body

functions and to organs, cells, and tissues occur more frequently and severely in smokers. Three kinds of cellular changes—loss of ciliated cells, thickening (more than two layers of basal cells), and presence of atypical cells—are much more common in the lining layer (epithelium)of the trachea and bronchi of cigarette smokers than of non-smokers. Some of the advanced lesions seen in the bronchi of cigarette smokers are probably premalignant. Cellular changes regularly found at autopsy in patients with chronic bronchitis are more often present in the bronchi of smokers than non-smokers. Pathological changes in the air sacs and other functional tissue of the lung (parenchyma) have a remarkably close association with past history of cigarette smoking.

3. *Population studies.* Another kind of evidence regarding an association between smoking and disease comes from epidemiological studies.

In retrospective studies, the smoking histories of persons with a specified disease (for example, lung cancer) are compared with those of appropriate control groups without the disease. For lung cancer alone, 29 such retrospective studies have been made in recent years. Despite many variations in design and method, all but one (which dealt with females) showed that proportionately more cigarette smokers are found among the lung cancer patients than in the control populations without lung cancer.

Extensive retrospective studies of the prevalence of specific symptoms and signs of chronic cough, sputum production, breathlessness, chest illness, and decreased lung functioning consistently show that these occur more often in cigarette smokers than in non-smokers. Some of these signs and symptoms are the clinical expressions of chronic bronchitis, and some are associated more with emphysema; in general, they increase with amount of smoking and decrease after cessation of smoking.

Another type of epidemiological evidence on the relation of smoking and mortality comes from seven prospective studies which have been conducted since 1951. In these studies, large numbers of men answered questions about their smoking or non-smoking habits. Death certificates have been obtained for those who died since entering the studies, permitting total death rates and death rates by cause to be computed for smokers of various types as well as for non-smokers. The prospective studies thus add several important dimensions to information on the smoking-health problem. Their data permit direct comparisons of the death rates of smokers and non-smokers, both overall and for individual causes of death, and indicate the Strength of the association between smoking and specific diseases.

Each of these three lines of evidence was evaluated and then considered together in drawing conclusions. The Committee was aware that the mere establishment of a statistical association between the use of tobacco and a disease is not enough. The causal significance of the use of tobacco in relation to the disease is the crucial question. For such judgments all three lines of evidence are essential, as discussed in more detail on pages 26-27 of this Chapter, and in Chapter 3.

The experimental, clinical, and pathological evidence, as well as data from population studies, is highlighted in Section B of this Chapter, which in turn refers the reader to specific places in Part II of the Report where this evidence is presented in detail.

In the paragraphs which follow, the Committee has chosen to summarize the results of the seven prospective population studies which, as noted above, constitute only one type of evidence. They illustrate the nature and potential magnitude of the smoking-health problem, and bring out a number of factors which are involved.

EVIDENCE FROM THE COMBINED RESULTS OF PROSPECTIVE STUDIES
The Committee examined the seven prospective studies separately as well as their combined results. Considerable weight was attached to the consistency of findings among the several studies. However, to simplify presentation, only the combined results are highlighted here.

Of the 1,123,000 men who entered the seven prospective studies and who provided usable histories of smoking habits (and other characteristics such as age), 37,391 men died during the subsequent months or years of the studies. No analyses of data for females from prospective studies are presently available.

To permit ready comparison of the mortality experience of smokers and non-smokers, two concepts are widely used in the studies—excess deaths of smokers compared with non-smokers, and mortality ratio. After adjustments for differences in age and the number of cigarette smokers and non-smokers, an expected number of deaths of smokers is derived on the basis of deaths among non-smokers. Excess deaths are thus the number of actual (observed) deaths among smokers in excess of the number expected. The mortality ratio, for which the method of computation is described in Chapter 8, measures the relative death rates of smokers and non-smokers. If the age-adjusted death rates are the same, the mortality ratio will be 1.0; if the death rates of smokers are double those of non-smokers, the mortality ratio will be 2.0. (Expressed as a percentage, this example would be equivalent to a 100 percent increase....

The mortality ratio for male cigarette smokers compared with non-smokers, for all causes of death taken together, is 1.68, representing a total death rate nearly 70 percent higher than for non-smokers....

In the combined results from the seven studies, the mortality ratio of cigarette smokers over non-smokers was particularly high for a number of diseases: cancer of the lung (10.8), bronchitis and emphysema (6.1), cancer of the larynx (5.4), oral cancer (4.1), cancer of the esophagus (3.4), peptic ulcer (2.8), and the group of other circulatory diseases (2.6). For coronary artery disease the mortality ratio was 1.7.

Expressed in percentage-form, this is equivalent to a statement that for coronary artery disease, the leading cause of death in this country, the death rate is 70 percent higher for cigarette smokers. For chronic bronchitis and emphysema, which are among the leading causes of severe disability, the death rate for cigarette smokers is 500 percent higher than for non-smokers. For lung cancer, the most frequent site of cancer in men, the death rate is nearly 1,000 percent higher.

Other Findings of the Prospective Studies
In general, the greater the number of cigarettes smoked daily, the higher the death rate. For men who smoke fewer than 10 cigarettes a day, according to the seven prospective studies, the death rate from all causes is about 40 percent higher than for non-smokers. For those who smoke from 10 to 19 cigarettes a day, it is about 70 percent higher than for non-smokers; for those who smoke 20 to 39 a day, 90 percent higher; and for those who smoke 40 or more, it is 120 percent higher.

Cigarette smokers who stopped smoking before enrolling in the seven studies have a death rate about 40 percent higher than non-smokers, as against 0 percent higher for current cigarette smokers. Men who began smoking before age 20 have a substantially higher death rate than those who began after age 25. Compared with non-smokers, the mortality risk of cigarette smokers, after adjustments for differences in age, increases with duration of smoking (number of years), and is higher in those who stopped after age 55 than for those who stopped at an earlier age. ...

Possible relationships of death rates and other forms of tobacco use were also investigated in the seven studies. The death rates for men smoking less than 5 cigars a day are about the same as for non-smokers. For men smoking more than 5 cigars daily, death rates are slightly higher. There is some indication that these higher death rates occur primarily in men who have been smoking more than 30 years and who inhale the smoke to some degree. The death rates for pipe smokers are little if at all higher than for non-smokers, even for men who smoke 10 or more pipefuls a day and for men who have smoked pipes more than 30 years.

Excess Mortality
Several of the reports previously published on the prospective studies included a table showing the distribution of the excess number of deaths of cigarette smokers among the principal causes of death. The hazard must be measured not only by the mortality ratio of deaths in smokers and non-smokers, but also by the importance of a particular disease as a cause of death.

In all seven studies, coronary artery disease is the chief contributor to the excess number of deaths of cigarette smokers over non-smokers, with lung cancer uniformly in second place. For all seven studies combined, coronary artery disease (with a mortality ratio of 1.7) accounts for 45 percent of the excess deaths among cigarette smokers, whereas lung cancer (with a ratio of 10.8) accounts for 16 percent.

Some of the other categories of diseases that contribute to the higher death rates for cigarette smokers over non-smokers are diseases of the heart and blood vessels, other than coronary artery disease, 14 percent; cancer sites other than lung, 8 percent; and chronic bronchitis and emphysema, 4 percent.

Since these diseases as a group are responsible for more than 85 percent of the higher death rate among cigarette smokers, they are of particular interest to public health authorities and the medical profession.

## ASSOCIATIONS AND CAUSALITY

The array of information from the prospective and retrospective studies of smokers and non-smokers clearly establishes an association between cigarette smoking and substantially higher death rates. The mortality ratios in Table 2 provide an approximate index of the relative strength of this association, for all causes of death and for 14 disease categories.

In this inquiry the epidemiologic method was used extensively in the assessment of causal factors in the relationship of smoking to health among human beings upon whom direct experimentation could not be imposed. Clinical, pathological, and experimental evidence was thoroughly considered and often served to suggest an hypothesis or confirm or contradict other findings. When coupled with the other data, results from the epidemiologic studies can provide the basis upon which judgments of causality may be made.

It is recognized that no simple cause-and-effect relationship is likely to exist between a complex product like tobacco smoke and a specific disease in the variable human organism. It is also recognized that often the coexistence of several factors is required for the occurrence of a disease, and that one of the factors may play a determinant role; that is, without it, the other factors (such as genetic susceptibility) seldom lead to the occurrence of the disease.

## THE EFFECTS OF SMOKING: PRINCIPAL FINDINGS

Cigarette smoking is associated with a 70 percent increase in the age-specific death rates of males, and to a lesser extent with increased death rates of females. The total number of excess deaths causally related to cigarette smoking in the U.S. population cannot be accurately estimated. In view of the continuing and mounting evidence from many sources, it is the judgment of the Committee that cigarette smoking contributes substantially to mortality from certain specific diseases and to the overall death rate.

### Lung Cancer

Cigarette smoking is causally related to lung cancer in men; the magnitude of the effect of cigarette smoking far outweighs all other factors. The data for women, though less extensive, point in the same direction.

The risk of developing lung cancer increases with duration of smoking and the number of cigarettes smoked per day, and is diminished by discontinuing smoking. In comparison with non-smokers, average male smokers of cigarettes have approximately a 9– to 10–fold risk of developing lung cancer and heavy smokers at least a 20–fold risk.

The risk of developing cancer of the lung for the combined group of pipe smokers, cigar smokers, and pipe and cigar smokers is greater than for non-smokers, but much less than for cigarette smokers.

Cigarette smoking is much more important than occupational exposures in the causation of lung cancer in the general population.

### Chronic Bronchitis and Emphysema

Cigarette smoking is the most important of the causes of chronic bronchitis in the United States, and increases the risk of dying from chronic bronchitis and emphysema. A relationship exists between cigarette smoking and emphysema but it has not been established that the relationship is causal. Studies demonstrate that fatalities from this disease are infrequent among non-smokers.

For the bulk of the population of the United States, the relative importance of cigarette smoking as a cause of chronic broncho-pulmonary disease is much greater than atmospheric pollution or occupational exposures.

### Cardiovascular Diseases

It is established that male cigarette smokers have a higher death rate from coronary artery disease than non-smoking males. Although the causative role of cigarette smoking in deaths from coronary disease is not proven, the Committee considers it more prudent from the public health viewpoint to assume that the established association has causative meaning than to suspend judgment until no uncertainty remains.

Although a causal relationship has not been established, higher mortality of cigarette smokers is associated with many other cardiovascular diseases, including miscellaneous circulatory diseases, other heart diseases, hypertensive heart disease, and general arteriosclerosis.

### Other Cancer Sites

Pipe smoking appears to be causally related to lip cancer. Cigarette smoking is a significant factor in the causation of cancer of the larynx. The evidence supports the belief that an association exists between tobacco use and cancer of the esophagus, and between cigarette smoking and cancer of the urinary bladder in men, but the data are not adequate to decide whether these relationships are causal. Data on an association between smoking and cancer of the stomach are contradictory and incomplete.

### The Tobacco Habit and Nicotine

The habitual use of tobacco is related primarily to psychological and social drives, reinforced and perpetuated by the pharmacological actions of nicotine.

Social stimulation appears to play a major role in a young person's early and first experiments with smoking. No scientific evidence supports the popular hypothesis that smoking among adolescents is an expression of rebellion against authority. Individual stress appears to be associated more with fluctuations in the amount of smoking than with the prevalence of smoking. The overwhelming evidence indicates that smoking at its beginning, habituation, and occasional discontinuation is to a very large extent psychologically and socially determined.

Nicotine is rapidly changed in the body to relatively inactive substances with low toxicity. The chronic toxicity of small doses of nicotine is low in experimental animals. These two facts, when taken in conjunction with the low mortality ratios of pipe and cigar smokers, indicate that the chronic toxicity of nicotine in quantities absorbed from smoking and other methods of tobacco use is very low and probably does not represent an important health hazard.

The significant beneficial effects of smoking occur primarily in the area of mental health, and the habit originates in a search for contentment. Since no means of measuring the quantity of these benefits is apparent, the Committee finds no basis for a judgment which would weigh benefits against hazards of smoking as it may apply to the general population.

The Committee's Judgment in Brief

On the basis of prolonged study and evaluation of many lines of converging evidence, the Committee makes the following judgment:

Cigarette smoking is a health hazard of sufficient importance in the United States to warrant appropriate remedial action.

[....]

## Document Analysis

Several excerpts from the 387-page *Surgeon General's Report Smoking and Health* make up this document, including parts of the foreword, chapter 1, and chapter 4. These excerpts lay out the background and conclusions of the report.

The foreword includes a little background before discussing the committee's appointment and introducing the report. It is not until chapters 1 and 4 that the author goes into detail on the background of the report. The first chapter begins with the "modern period of investigation of smoking and health," starting at the turn of the twentieth century. It covers the accelerating studies of the first half of the century, followed by the government's initial intervention: "The U.S. Public Health Service first became officially engaged in an appraisal of the available data on smoking and health in June, 1956, when, under the instigation of the Surgeon General, a scientific Study Group on the subject was established jointly by the National Cancer Institute, the National Heart Institute, the American Cancer Society, and the American Heart Association." Chapter 4 includes an entire subsection on "Background and Highlights" which outlines the more immediate backdrop of the comprehensive 1964 report. This includes the extensive and increasing use of tobacco products, in particular cigarettes: "Nearly 70 million people in the United States consume tobacco regularly." The contradictory trends of the increasing understanding of smoking's harms and the continually increasing usage provided an impetus for the committee's decisive report.

Chapter 4 summarizes the results of the report, introducing the findings that subsequent chapters handle in depth. It links tobacco smoking to a higher mortality rate. To explain this connection, it cites a higher probability for smokers of contracting specific ailments, namely lung cancer, chronic bronchitis, emphysema, cardiovascular diseases, and other cancers. The evidence leads the committee to assert its conclusion in brief: "Cigarette smoking is a health hazard of sufficient importance in the United States to warrant appropriate remedial action." Earlier medical reports had linked smoking and adverse health effects, yet the comprehensivity of this report and the backing of the United States federal government granted this report additional weight. The document increased the visibility of smoking's ill effects to the American public, yet the massive resources of the tobacco industry fought to limit the report's influence and preserve America's smoking habit.

## Essential Themes

The committee constructed the report to lay out categorically and comprehensively for the American public the dangers of smoking tobacco. The author dwells upon the theme of death to drive the point home. The excerpt from chapter 4 establishes the higher death rate associated with smoking: "In general, the greater the number of cigarettes smoked daily, the higher the death rate." Using the extensive evidence available to them, the committee calculates the specific increase in the death rate of smokers: "The mortality ratio for male cigarette smokers compared with non-smokers, for all causes of death taken together, is 1.68, representing a total death rate nearly 70 percent higher than for non-smokers...." The author offers the numbers for male smokers as these are the more pronounced figures. Women are not free from the ill effects of smoking, the committee concludes, but their numbers prove less stark. The author returns to the theme of death again and again: "The array of information from the prospective and retrospective studies of smokers and non-smokers clearly establishes an association between cigarette smoking and substantially higher death rates...Cigarette smoking is associated with a 70 percent increase in the age-specific death rates of males, and to a lesser extent with increased death rates of females." The ill health effects of smoking are numerous, yet death, the ultimate potential danger posed by smoking, provides the most direct message for the committee to get through to the American public.

—*Anthony Vivian, PhD*

### Bibliography and Additional Reading

Barnett, Ross, Graham Moon, Jamie Pearce, Lee Thompson, & Liz Twigg. *Smoking Geographies: Space, Place and Tobacco*. Hoboken, NJ: Wiley, 2017. Print.

Brandt, Allan. *The Cigarette Century: The Rise, Fall, and Deadly Persistence of the Product That Defined America*. New York: Basic Books, 2009. Print.

Gately, Iain. *Tobacco: A Cultural History of How an Exotic Plant Seduced Civilization*. New York: Grove Press, 2003. Print.

Milov, Sarah. *The Cigarette: A Political History*. Cambridge, MA: Harvard University Press, 2019. Print.

# ■ Controlled Substances Act—Section 202

**Date:** October 27, 1970
**Authors:** Harley O. Staggers, et al.
**Genre:** Law

## Summary Overview

American laws prohibiting or in other ways limiting narcotics have a long history. However, before 1970 these laws were implemented at the federal, state, and local levels in a haphazard manner, which left a patchwork of confusing and arbitrary discrepancies. Introduced by Democratic congressman Harley O. Staggers and signed by Republican president Richard Nixon, the Controlled Substance Act attempted to standardize federal treatment of all controlled substances. In doing so, the law established five hierarchical schedules for these substances based on three criteria. These same schedules persist today and remain controversial. The year after Nixon signed this act into law, he declared a "War on Drugs." This crusade intensified over the ensuing decades, leaving behind a broken approach to drug policy and notably high rates of incarceration.

## Defining Moment

Before the Controlled Substances Act, the United States federal government outlawed various drugs but in an ad hoc manner. The American tendency for drug laws to target immigrants and racial minorities began with the very first drug law passed in the United States. In 1875, San Francisco outlawed opium dens. Nearly forty years later, in 1914, President Woodrow Wilson signed the Harrison Act into law, which attempted to federalize various states' hodgepodge prohibitions against cocaine and opiates. Congress outlawed alcohol via the Eighteenth Amendment in 1917, but this prohibition was lifted in 1933 by the Twenty-First Amendment. In 1937, the Marihuana Tax Act became law. As the Harrison Act standardized state laws on cocaine and opiates, the Marihuana Tax Act federalized laws pertaining to cannabis, putting a $1 tax on the distribution of the drug.

In 1970, the Controlled Substances Act comprehensively regulated most known narcotics. Harley O. Staggers introduced the law

into the House of Representatives on September 10, 1970, and the bill passed both houses of Congress in less than two months. President Richard Nixon signed it into law on October 27, 1970, and it went into effect on May 1, 1971, the same year Nixon first declared a "War on Drugs." The Bureau of Narcotics and Dangerous Drugs was created to address the problem, which got subsumed by the Drug Enforcement Administration in 1973. The act played into Nixon's "tough on crime" posture, a central tenet of his Southern Strategy that helped him cruise to reelection in 1972 by winning former Democratic strongholds in the South. The act has undergirded the subsequent war on drugs. However, as initially passed, the Controlled Substances Act was far less draconian than later iterations. Only under the Nixon administration did more funding appropriated for the drug war go to treatment than law enforcement.

In the years since the passage of the Controlled Substance Act, Congress has passed various amendments to the law and additional laws to fuel an accelerating war on drugs. The

*U.S. Food and Drug Administration agents inspect packages for illegal drug shipments at an international mail facility in New York.*

double-digit amendments to the law tweak it to fit changing times. Many amendments added or upgraded the status of various narcotics, such as the 1990 Anabolic Steroids Act and 1993 Domestic Chemical Diversion and Control Act, which reacted to epidemics of anabolic steroids and methamphetamine, respectively. The war on drugs, under both Republican and moderate Democratic administrations, grew in size and scope. President Ronald Reagan imposed mandatory minimums for crack cocaine, used primarily in minority communities, with lesser penalties for powder cocaine, used primarily in white communities. President Bill Clinton intensified some of the tough-on-drug policies of his Republican predecessors and elevated the job of Drug Czar to a cabinet position.

## Author Biography

United States federal laws typically have multiple authors and editors. As the congressman who first introduced what would become the Controlled Substances Act to the House of Representatives, Harley Orrin Staggers is most responsible for its contents. Born on August 3, 1907, in Keyser, West Virginia, Staggers attended Emory and Henry College and Duke University. He worked as a sheriff in Mineral County, West Virginia before serving in the Navy during the Second World War. After returning to West Virginia, he won a seat in the U.S. House of Representatives as a Democrat in 1948, a seat he would hold for over three decades. The longevity of his tenure allowed him to rise in the ranks of the influential House Committee on Interstate and Foreign Commerce, which he chaired from 1966 until 1981. As chair of this committee, Staggers introduced the act featured in this chapter. He likewise oversaw a committee investigation into drug use among professional athletes in 1973. He was an ardent supporter of the railroad industry and as such championed what became known as the Staggers Rail Act. Harley Staggers died on August 20, 1991.

## HISTORICAL DOCUMENT: Schedules of Controlled Substances

SEC. 202.

(a)   There are established five schedules of controlled substances, to be known as schedules I, II, III, IV, and V. Such schedules shall initially consist of the substances listed in this section. The schedules established by this section shall be updated and republished on a semiannual basis during the two-year period beginning one year after the date of enactment of this title and shall be updated and republished on an annual basis thereafter.

(b)   Except where control is required by United States obligations under an international treaty, convention, or protocol, in effect on the effective date of this part, and except in the case of an immediate precursor, a drug or other substance may not be placed in any schedule unless the findings required for such schedule are made with respect to such drug or other substance. The findings required for each of the schedules are as follows:

SCHEDULE I.—
(A)   The drug or other substance has a high potential for abuse.

(B)   The drug or other substance has no currently accepted medical use in treatment in the United States.

(C)   There is a lack of accepted safety for use of the drug or other substance under medical supervision.

SCHEDULE II.—
(A)   The drug or other substance has a high potential for abuse.

(B)   The drug or other substance has a currently accepted medical use in treatment in the United States or a currently accepted medical use with severe restrictions.

(C)   Abuse of the drug or other substances may lead to severe psychological or physical dependence.

SCHEDULE III.—
(A)   The drug or other substance has a potential for abuse less than the drugs or other substances in schedules I and II.

(B)   The drug or other substance has a currently accepted medical use in treatment in the United States.

(C)   Abuse of the drug or other substance may lead to moderate or low physical dependence or high psychological dependence.

SCHEDULE IV.—
(A)   The drug or other substance has a low potential for abuse relative to the drugs or other substances in schedule III.

(B)   The drug or other substance has a currently accepted medical use in treatment in the United States.

(C)   Abuse of the drug or other substance may lead to limited physical dependence or psychological dependence relative to the drugs or other substances in schedule III.

SCHEDULE V.—

(A)   The drug or other substance has a low potential for abuse relative to the drugs or other substances in schedule IV.

(B)   The drug or other substance has a currently accepted medical use in treatment in the United States.

(C)   Abuse of the drug or other substance may lead to limited physical dependence or psychological dependence relative to the drugs or other substances in schedule IV.

(c)   Schedules I, II, III, IV, and V shall, unless and until amended pursuant to section 201, consist of the following drugs or other substances, by whatever official name, common or usual name, chemical name, or brand name designated:

SCHEDULE I—
Opiates. Unless specifically excepted or unless listed in another schedule, any of the following opiates, including their isomers, esters, ethers, salts, and salts of isomers, esters, and ethers, whenever the existence of such isomers, esters, ethers, and salts is possible within the specific chemical designation:
(1) Acetylmethadol.
(2) Allylprodine.

(3) Alphacetylmathadol.
(4) Alphameprodine.
(5) Alphamethadol.
(6) Benzethidine.
(7) Betacetylmethadol.
(8) Betameprodine.
(9) Betamethadol.
(10) Betaprodine.
(11) Clonitazene.
(12) Dextromoramide.
(13) Dextrorphan.
(14) Diampromide.
(15) DiethyIthiambutene.
(16) Dimenoxadol.
(17) Dimepheptanol.
(18) Dimethylthiambutene.
(19) Dioxaphetyl bulyrate.
(20) Dipipanone.
(21) Ethylmethylthiambutene.
(22) Etonitazene.
(23) Etoxeridine.
(24) Furethidine.
(25) Hydroxy pethidine.
(26) Ketobemidone.
(27) Levomoramide.
(28) Levophenacylmorphan.
(29) Morpheridine.
(30) Noracymethadol.
(31) Norlevorphanol.
(32) Normethadone.
(33) Norpipanone.
(34) Phenadoxone.
(35) Phenampromide.
(36) Phenomorphan.
(37) Phenoperidine.
(38) Piritramide.
(39) Proheptazine.
(40) Properidine.
(41) Racemoramide.
(42) Trimeperidine.

*Opiate derivatives.* Unless specifically excepted or unless listed in another schedule, any of the following opium derivatives, their salts, isomers, and salts of isomers whenever the existence of such salts, isomers, and salts of isomers is possible within the specific chemical designation: (1) Acetorphine. (2) Acetyldihydrocodeine. (3) Benzylmorphine. (4) Codeine methylbromide. (5) Codeine-N-Oxide. (6) Gyprenorphine. (7) Desomorphine. (8) Dihydromorphine. (9) Etorphine. (10) Heroin. (11) Hydromorphinol. (12) Methyldesorphine. (13) Methylhydromorphine. (14) Morphine methylbromide. (15) Morphine methylsulfonate. (16) Morphine-N-Oxide. (17) Myrophine. (18) Nicocodeine. (19) Nicomorphine. (20) Normorphine. (21) Pholcodine. (22) Thebacon.

*Hallucinogenic substances.* Unless specifically excepted or unless listed in another schedule, any material, compound, mixture, or preparation, which contains any quantity of the following hallucinogenic substances, or which contains any of their salts, isomers, and salts of isomers whenever the existence of such salts, isomers, and salts of isomers is possible within the specific chemical designation: (1) 3,4-methylenedioxy amphetamine. (2) 5-methoxy-3,4-methylenedioxy amphetamine. (3) 3,4,5-trimethoxy amphetamine. (4) Bufotenine. (5) Diethyltryptamine. (6) Dimethyltryptamine. (7) 4-methyl-2,5-dimethoxyamphetamine. (8) Ibogaine. (9) Lysergic acid diethylamide. (10) Marihuana. (11) Mescaline. (12) Peyote. (13) N-ethyl-3-piperidyl benzilate. (14) N-methyl-3-piperidyl benzilate. (15) Psilocybin. (16) Psilocyn. (17) Tetrahydrocannabinols.

## SCHEDULE II
Substances, vegetable origin or chemical synthesis. Unless specifically excepted or unless listed in another schedule, any of the following substances whether produced directly or indirectly by extraction from substances of vegetable origin, or independently by means of chemical synthesis, or by a combination of extraction and chemical synthesis:

(1)  Opium and opiate, and any salt, compound, derivative, or preparation of opium or opiate.

(2)  Any salt, compound, derivative, or preparation thereof which is chemically equivalent or identical with any of the substances referred to in clause (1), except that these substances shall not include the isoquinoline alkaloids of opium.

(3)  Opium poppy and poppy straw.

(4)  Coca leaves and any salt, compound, derivative, or preparation of coca leaves, and any salt, compound, derivative, or preparation thereof which is chemically

equivalent or identical with any of these substances, except that the substances shall not include decocainized coca leaves or extraction of coca leaves, which extractions do not contain cocaine or ecgonine.

*Opiates.* Unless specifically excepted or unless listed in another schedule, any of the following opiates, including their isomers, esters, ethers, salts, and salts of isomers, esters and ethers, whenever the existence of such isomers, esters, ethers, and salts is possible within the specific chemical designation: (I) Alphaprodine. (2) Anileridine. (3) Bezitramide. (4) Dihydrocodeine. (5) Diphenoxylate. (6) Fentanyl. (7) Isomethadone. (8) Levomethorphan. (9) Levorphanol. (10) Metazocine. (11) Methadone. (12) Methadone-Intermediate, 4-cyano—2—dimethylamino-4,4-diphenyl butane. (13) Moramide-Intermediate, 2—methyl—3—morpholino-1, 1-diphenylpropane-carboxylic acid. (14) Pethidine. (15) Pethidine-Intermediate-A, 4—cyano-l-methyl-4- phenylpiperidine. (16) Pethidine-Intermediate-B, ethyl—4-phenylpiperidine-4-carboxylate. (17) Pethidine-Intermediate-C, 1-methyl—4—phenylpiperidine-4-carboxylic acid. (18) Phenazocine. (19) Piminodine. (20) Eacemethorphan. (21) Racemorphan.

*Methamphetamine.* Unless specifically excepted or unless listed in another schedule, any injectable liquid which contains any quantity of methamphetamine, including its salts, isomers, and salts of isomers.

## SCHEDULE III

(a)    Stimulants. Unless specifically excepted or unless listed in another schedule, any material, compound, mixture, or preparation which contains any quantity of the following substances having a stimulant effect on the central nervous system:

(1) Amphetamine, its salts, optical isomers, and salts of its optical isomers.

(2) Phenmetrazine and its salts.

(3) Any substance (except an injectable liquid) which contains any quantity of methamphetamine, including its salts, isomers, and salts of isomers.

(4) Methylphenidate.

(b)    Depressants. Unless specifically excepted or unless listed in another schedule, any material, compound, mixture, or preparation which contains any quantity of the following substances having a depressant effect on the central nervous system: (1) Any substance which contains any quantity of a derivative of barbituric acid, or any salt of a derivative of barbituric acid. (2) Chorhexadol. (3) Glutethimide. (4)

Lysergic acid. (5) Lysergic acid amide. (6) Methyprylon. (7) Phencyclidine. (8) Sulfondiethylmethane. (9) Sulfonethylmethane. (10) Sulfonmethane.

(c)   Nalorphine.

(d)   Narcotic drugs. Unless specifically excepted or unless listed in another schedule, any material, compound, mixture, or preparation containing limited quantities of any of the following narcotic drugs, or any salts thereof: (1) Not more than 1.8 grams of codeine per 100 milliliters or not more than 90 milligrams per dosage unit, with an equal or greater quantity of an isoquinoline alkaloid of opium. (2) Not more than 1.8 grams of codeine per 100 milliliters or not more than 90 milligrams per dosage unit, with one or more active, nonnarcotic ingredients in recognized therapeutic amounts. (3) Not more than 300 milligrams of dihydrocodeinone per 100 milliliters or not more than 15 milligrams per dosage unit, with a fourfold or greater quantity of an isoquinoline alkaloid of opium. (4) Not more than 300 milligrams of dihydrocodeinone per 100 milliliters or not more than 15 milligrams per dosage unit, with one or more active, nonnarcotic ingredients in recognized therapeutic amounts. (5) Not more than 1.8 grams of dihydrocodeine per 100 milliliters or not more than 90 milligrams per dosage unit, with one or more active, nonnarcotic ingredients in recognized therapeutic amounts. (6) Not more than 300 milligrams of ethylmorphine per 100 milliliters or not more than 15 milligrams per dosage unit, with one or more active, nonnarcotic ingredients in recognized therapeutic amounts. (7) Not more than 600 milligrams of opium per 100 milliliters or per 100 grams, or not more than 25 milligrams per dosage unit, with one or more active, nonnarcotic ingredients in recognized therapeutic amounts. (8) Not more than 50 milligrams of morphine per 100 milliliters or per 100 grams with one or more active, nonnarcotic ingredients in recognized therapeutic amounts.

SCHEDULE IV
(1) Barbital. (2) Chloral betaine. (3) Chloral hydrate. (4) Ethchlorvynol. (5) Ethinamate. (6) Methohexital. (7) Meprobamate. (8) Methylphenobarbital. (9) Paraldehyde. (10) Petrichloral. (11) Phenobarbital.

SCHEDULE V
Narcotic drugs containing nonnarcotic active medicinal ingredients. Any compound, mixture, or preparation containing any of the following limited quantities of narcotic drugs, which shall include one or more nonnarcotic active medicinal ingredients in sufficient proportion to confer upon the compound, mixture, or preparation valuable medicinal qualities other than those possessed by the narcotic drug alone: (1) Not more than 200 milligrams of codeine per 100 milliliters or per 100 grams. (2) Not more than 100 milligrams of dihydrocodeine per 100 milliliters or per 100 grams. (3)

Not more than 100 milligrams of ethylmorphine per 100 milliliters or per 100 grams. (4) Not more than 2.5 milligrams of diphenoxylate and not less than 25 micrograms of atropine sulfate per dosage unit. (5) Not more than 100 milligrams of opium per 100 milliliters or per 100 grams.

(d) Stimulants or depressants containing active medicinal ingredients, exception. The Attorney General may by regulation except any compound, mixture, or preparation containing any depressant or stimulant substance in paragraph (a) or (b) of schedule II I or in schedule IV or V from the application of all or any part of this title if (1) the compound, mixture, or preparation contains one or more active medicinal ingredients not having a depressant or stimulant effect on the central nervous system, and (2) such ingredients are included therein in such combinations, quantity, proportion, or concentration as to vitiate the potential for abuse of the substances which do have a depressant or stimulant effect on the central nervous system.

## Document Analysis

This document, Section 202 of the Controlled Substances Act of 1970, covers the schedules of controlled substances. After two paragraphs of introduction, the section details the criteria of the schedules and then lists the drugs in each one. This analysis examines what distinguishes the five schedules and discusses how circumstances have evolved since this document was composed.

The law categorizes all controlled substances in five schedules based on three criteria, A, B, and C. The criteria look at the potential for abuse, the medical usage, and the potential for dependency. The first two schedules both have "a high potential for abuse," separating them off from the lower three schedules. What distinguishes schedule I drugs from schedule II drugs are their accepted medical usages. If they do not have any accepted medical usage, they are schedule I; if they have "a currently accepted medical use in treatment in the United States or a currently accepted medical use with severe restrictions," they are schedule II. The lower three tiers all possess "a low potential for abuse"

and have an accepted medical usage; they differ among themselves in their potential for dependency. Schedule III drugs "may lead to moderate or low physical dependence or high psychological dependence," already a step down from the possibility of "severe" physical or psychological dependence caused by schedule II substances. The final two categories base their dependency criteria on the schedules above them. Schedule IV substances "may lead to limited physical dependence or psychological dependence relative to the drugs or other substances in schedule III." The text delineating schedule V drugs reads the same but for substances "limited…relative to… schedule IV" drugs. One shortcoming of this hierarchy is that there is no space for substances that have no accepted medical usage but less than "high potential for abuse."

American society's perspective on drug usage in general and on particular drugs has evolved a great deal since 1970. The lawmakers anticipated a need for flexibility, qualifying the drugs listed as those "known" at the time and labeling the lists "initial." The law further stipulates a regimented process in which the schedules can be updated to match the evolving times.

In the years since 1970, with the war on drugs intensifying and new drugs becoming isolated and/or popularized, lawmakers have added and upgraded drugs. For example, in 1990, anabolic steroids were added to schedule III, after their proliferation among professional and nonprofessional athletes. Critics have argued that while lawmakers are responsive in adding and upgrading drugs, they are less so in downgrading substance to meet circumstances. The case of cannabis, or marijuana, marks one high-profile point of critique. Medical usages of cannabis have become better understood since 1970, including treatments for chronic seizures, glaucoma, and posttraumatic stress disorder (PTSD). However, cannabis remains a schedule I substance in its federal designation despite it being legalized in some capacity in a rapidly growing majority of states. Critics have pointed to cannabis' placement ahead of cocaine, a schedule II drug, as particularly telling. Contrary to common misconception, it is not cannabis' and cocaine's potentials for abuse or dependency that cause this but their accepted medical usages. Nevertheless, with the medical usages of cannabis listed above and medicinal cocaine relegated to the folklore and history of the early twentieth century, the discrepancy remains problematic.

## Essential Themes

Two themes developed in this text are hierarchy and adjustability, both of which prove relatively straightforward. The hierarchy becomes necessary given the attempted comprehensivity of the law. By trying to regulate and standardize the federal government's treatment of all controlled substances, lawmakers are forced to deal with a wide range of drugs from potentially harmful to extremely deadly. With such a broad spectrum, a hierarchy becomes advantageous. The question of whether the law's particular hierarchy—five schedules based on three criteria—is the most effective remains hotly debated. Since the law does develop a rigid hierarchy, it incorporates the concept of adjustability in order to reserve the right to change the categorization of any given drug in future. The document even sets a regimented plan for when the lists of drugs are to be updated: "The schedules established by this section shall be updated and republished on a semiannual basis during the two-year period beginning one year after the date of enactment of this title and shall be updated and republished on an annual basis thereafter." Despite the incorporation of this amendability, the text does not directly allow for changes to the number of schedules nor their criteria; only changes to the placement of specific drugs within the given schedule system are allowed.

—*Anthony Vivian, PhD*

## Bibliography and Additional Reading

Mallea, Paula. *The War on Drugs: A Failed Experiment*. Toronto: Dundurn Press, 2014.

Provine, Doris Marie. *Unequal under Law: Race in the War on Drugs*. Chicago: University of Chicago Press, 2007.

Thompson, Hunter S. *Fear and Loathing on the Campaign Trail '72*. New York: Simon & Schuster, 2012.

White, Christopher. *The War on Drugs in the Americas*. New York: Routledge, 2020.

# ■ Nancy Reagan's "Just Say No" Message to the Nation

**Date:** September 14, 1986
**Author:** Nancy Reagan
**Genre:** Televised speech; address to the nation

## Summary Overview

The "Just Say No" campaign, launched by First Lady Nancy Reagan in the early years of the Reagan administration, was the public face of a massive antidrug program aimed at curbing the drug use that had become common in American society since the 1970s. Alongside Ronald Reagan's "War on Drugs," Nancy Reagan launched a massive initiative telling kids to "just say no" if offered drugs. "Just Say No" spawned a nationwide antidrug grassroots campaign and is still remembered today for its effect on American drug policy.

However, the "Just Say No" campaign is often criticized for a variety of reasons. Its simplistic message motivated the antidrug movement through fear, suggesting that drug users were dangerous to vulnerable children. It also has been criticized for the way it conflated all types of drugs, and in so doing ended up punishing minor drug offenders out of proportion to their crimes. The "Just Say No" campaign influences how the U.S. government responds to drug use to this day; and in an era where marijuana legalization is becoming more widespread, this campaign helps us understand the motivations behind current antidrug policies.

## Defining Moment

During the 1960s, drug use had become closely identified with the counterculture and the youth movements; as those movements gained momentum in the climate of the late sixties, many drugs began to lose their radical connotations. By the 1970s, drug use was widespread, and often tolerated in mainstream culture: television shows such as *Taxi* and *Saturday Night Live* made numerous references to drug use, and films such as *Annie Hall, Airplane,* and *Up in Smoke* depicted drug use as humorous. In a study in 1977, about a quarter of Americans admitted to using marijuana, and 10 percent admitted to currently using it; by 1979, 54 percent of Americans reported using an illegal drug in the past twelve months and 12 percent admitted to using cocaine.

During the mid-1970s, experts and government officials generally agreed that the dangers

of drug use were either not a priority, or impractical to combat. By the end of the seventies, eleven states had decriminalized marijuana, and President Jimmy Carter had argued for lighter drug laws when he said that "penalties against possession of a drug should not be more damaging ... than the use of the drug itself." Even First Lady Betty Ford said in an interview on the *60 Minutes* TV show that she was sure her children "have probably tried marijuana." She admitted that, were she their age, she too probably would try it; trying marijuana was like having "your first beer or cigarette."

However, despite this growing acceptance of drug usage, the late 1970s also witnessed a widespread moral panic over child safety. From about 1977 onwards, awareness of child abuse grew and concerns over the phenomenon became more widespread. Stories about serial killers and sexual predators came to dominate the news, and the conservative activist Anita Bryant's "Save Our Children" campaign demonized gay men and women as predators who preyed on young children. Around this time, Ron and Marsha Keith Schuchard formed Families in Action, the country's first antidrug parent group, after the Schuchards witnessed an unwelcome transformation in their thirteen-year-old daughter that they attributed to marijuana use. Drug use now became increasingly scrutinized and villainized in American culture.

In the early 1980s, news that Colombian drug cartels were smuggling mass quantities of cocaine into South Florida was circulated by the press. In response to these developments, President Ronald Reagan launched a renewed "War on Drugs" to combat the threat of illegal narcotics. Focusing on foreign drug trafficking, the U.S. government used military measures to crack down on drug cartels and put pressure on South American governments to stem drug importation into the United States. Meanwhile, the president's wife, Nancy Reagan, started a domestic crusade against drug use by young people. Dubbed "Just Say No," after Mrs. Reagan told a group of high school girls in California that if anyone offered them drugs, they should "just say no," the movement won nation-

al popularity and became the centerpiece of the Reagan-era domestic drug policy. The first lady toured the country, explaining to children and young people the dangers of drug use.

## Author Biography

Nancy Davis was born July 6, 1921. She attended Smith College and then landed a part in a Broadway musical, which subsequently turned into a career as a minor actress in Hollywood. In the early 1950s, she met Ronald Reagan, then head of the Screen Actors' Guild. The two married in 1952 and she began devoting herself to domestic life. When her husband ran for the Republican presidential nomination in 1976, and when he won the presidency four later, Nancy Reagan served as his trusted advisor and was privy to many of his most important decisions.

By playing the part of a "traditional" woman who sacrificed her career to her family, she helped Ronald Reagan cultivate his image within the emerging conservative movement. The "Just Say No" campaign was an example of how Nancy Reagan managed to balance her education and activism with the docile role that social conservatism expected of her.

## HISTORICAL DOCUMENT: Nancy Reagan's "Just Say No" Message

As a mother, I've always thought of September as a special month, a time when we bundled our children off to school, to the warmth of an environment in which they could fulfill the promise and hope in those restless minds. But so much has happened over these last years, so much to shake the foundations of all that we know and all that we believe in. Today there's a drug and alcohol abuse epidemic in this country, and no one is safe from it—not you, not me, and certainly not our children, because this epidemic has their names written on it. Many of you may be thinking: "Well, drugs don't concern me." But it does concern you. It concerns us all because of the way it tears at our lives and because it's aimed at destroying the brightness and life of the sons and daughters of the United States.

For 5 years I've been traveling across the country—learning and listening. And one of the most hopeful signs I've seen is the building of an essential, new awareness of how terrible and threatening drug abuse is to our society. This was one of the main purposes when I started, so of course it makes me happy that that's been accomplished. But each time I meet with someone new or receive another letter from a troubled person on drugs, I yearn to find a way to help share the message that cries out from them. As a parent, I'm especially concerned about what drugs are doing to young mothers and

> *Life can be great, but not when you can't see it.*

their newborn children. Listen to this news account from a hospital in Florida of a child born to a mother with a cocaine habit: "Nearby, a baby named Paul lies motionless in an incubator, feeding tubes riddling his tiny body. He needs a respirator to breathe and a daily spinal tap to relieve fluid buildup on his brain. Only 1 month old, he's already suffered 2 strokes."

Now you can see why drug abuse concerns every one of us—all the American family. Drugs steal away so much. They take and take, until finally every time a drug goes into a child, something else is forced out—like love and hope and trust and confidence. Drugs take away the dream from every child's heart and replace it with a nightmare, and it's time we in America stand up and replace those dreams. Each of us has to put our principles and consciences on the line, whether in social settings or in the workplace, to set forth solid standards and stick to them. There's no moral middle ground. Indifference is not an option. We want you to help us create an outspoken intolerance for drug use. For the sake of our children, I implore each of you to be unyielding and inflexible in your opposition to drugs.

Our young people are helping us lead the way. Not long ago, in Oakland, California, I was asked by a group of children what to do if they were offered drugs, and I answered, "Just say no." Soon after that, those children in Oakland formed a Just Say No club, and now there are over 10,000 such clubs all over the country. Well, their participation and their courage in saying no needs our encouragement. We can help by using every opportunity to force the issue of not using drugs to the point of making others uncomfortable, even if it means making ourselves unpopular.

Our job is never easy because drug criminals are ingenious. They work every day to plot a new and better way to steal our children's lives, just as they've done by developing this new drug, crack. For every door that we close, they open a new door to death. They prosper on our unwillingness to act. So, we must be smarter and stronger and tougher than they are. It's up to us to change attitudes and just simply dry up their markets.

And finally, to young people watching or listening, I have a very personal message for you: There's a big, wonderful world out there for you. It belongs to you. It's exciting and stimulating and rewarding. Don't cheat yourselves out of this promise. Our country needs you, but it needs you to be clear-eyed and clear-minded. I recently read one teenager's story. She's now determined to stay clean but was once strung out on several drugs. What she remembered most clearly about her recovery was that during the time she was on drugs everything appeared to her in shades of black and gray and after her treatment she was able to see colors again.

So, to my young friends out there: Life can be great, but not when you can't see it. So, open your eyes to life: to see it in the vivid colors that God gave us as a precious gift to His children, to enjoy life to the fullest, and to make it count. Say yes to your life. And when it comes to drugs and alcohol just say no.

## Document Analysis

This speech, given by Nancy Reagan in 1986, demonstrates many of the consistent themes that Reagan stressed while serving as first lady. The "Just Say No" campaign's main argument was that drugs were dangerous because they threatened to do irreparable harm to families and especially to American children. Nancy Reagan closely connects drug use to family life from the beginning, especially by opening her speech by presenting herself as "a mother." The rest of the speech is targeted particularly to parents and children, noting that "drugs concern all of us," because they "destroy[] the brightness and life of [our] sons and daughters."

By focusing on drugs' effects on children, Nancy Reagan was able to connect drugs to the ongoing moral panics about children already present in the 1970s. This also gave drug use a moral component: while drugs had been linked to crime or to college dropouts in the 1960s, Reagan focused on protecting child victims of the drug crisis. To do so she used horror stories about "crack babies," or newborn children who suffered debilitating health defects because of the drug abuses of their parents. Similar stories were becoming more common in this era. During an appearance she made on the television sitcom *Diff'rent Strokes*, the first lady told the

"true" story of a boy named Charlie who violently beat his little sister after she refused to give him money for drugs. These stories, while they may have had some basis in truth, were manipulated and sensationalist, thereby creating a black-and-white image regarding drug use: drugs led directly to child abuse, and drug use within a family was inevitably a sign of the presence of an abusive parent or family member.

The "Just Say No" campaign also differed from previous programs by making no distinction between types of drugs. Importantly, throughout her speech Reagan refers only to "drugs," mentioning only one (cocaine) by name a single time. This was a conscious choice; one of the points of the "Just Say No" campaign was to attack the prevailing notion that "soft" drugs like marijuana were safer than "hard" drugs like cocaine or phencyclidine (PCP). In her appearance on *Diff'rent Strokes*, Reagan stated, "the real truth is, there's no such thing as soft drugs or hard drugs; all drugs are dumb." By conflating all drugs, the "Just Say No" campaign oversimplified the subject and made all substance use socially and morally suspect or even criminal. Drug users were depicted as dangerous to children in the same way that sexual predators were, and drug use was conflated with immorality regardless of the type of drug. Instead of approaching drug use as a societal problem, and presenting drug users as victims or as persons facing troubled circumstances, the campaign condemned drug use as an individual failing and depicted drug users as evil beings responsible for harming others.

## Essential Themes

The "Just Say No" campaign became a central part of the Reagan administration's larger war on drugs and led to a much larger crackdown on recreational drugs during the 1980s. In 1983, the Drug Abuse Resistance Education (D.A.R.E.) program put police officers into schools to explain to students the dangers of drug use. In 1986, Congress passed the Anti-Drug Abuse Act, which promoted a "zero-tolerance" policy for drug use, treating users as criminals for possession and use rather than promoting treatment and counseling services. By 1995, random drug-testing by companies was near universal, and Americans had gotten used to companies regularly violating their privacy to check for illicit substances. Culturally, Americans had also embraced the drug war: rather than the comical presentations of drug users common in the media in the 1970s, television shows such as *Family Ties* now depicted drug users as weak, immoral, and morally deviant.

There are some indicators that the war on drugs was successful. In 1981, 12.4 percent of high school seniors admitted to using cocaine in the past twelve months, while by 1992 only 3.1 say they had. On the other hand, evidence shows that the legacy of the "Just Say No" campaign is more complicated. A 2009 study demonstrated that kids who grew up with the D.A.R.E. program were just as likely to use drugs as those who had not, and a 2008 study indicated that drug prevention programs of the 1980s and '90s might have actually encouraged children to experiment with drugs. Furthermore, the campaign led to increased incarceration for drug use, creating a large expansion of the prison system in the United States. This disproportionately affected Black and Latino Americans: the drug that was most vilified during the eighties was "crack cocaine," commonly found in black, urban communities; and the increased police presence in schools promoted by the D.A.R.E. program led to Hispanic and Black students disproportionately being arrested for minor behavioral offenses.

By focusing on the immorality of drug use and on the victimhood of children, the "Just Say No" campaign created a simplistic message that ignored the effects of race, poverty, and lack of opportunity in influencing drug-related crimes. By treating all drugs as equally offensive, it also led minor drug offenses, such as possession of marijuana, being punished with reactionary mandatory long-term sentences. Furthermore, by ignoring the complicated nature of drug use and instead vilifying the users, the campaign effectively replaced treatment programs, which could have helped many of these users, with prisons.

The legacy of the "Just Say No" campaign asks us to think hard about how we treat drug use in our society. Should antidrug programs treat drug use as a moral evil? How should we treat users as persons struggling to overcome problems facing them? Are all drugs the same? And are incarceration or other punishments the best way to dissuade people from using them?

—*Aaron George, PhD*

## Bibliography and Additional Reading

Philip Jenkins. *Decade of Nightmares: The End of the Sixties and the Making of Eighties America.* New York: Oxford University Press, 2006.

John Hudak. *Marijuana: A Short History.* Washington, DC: Brookings Institute Press, 2016.

Kenneth B. Nunn. "Race, Crime and the Pool of Surplus Criminality: Or Why the War on Drugs Was a War on Blacks," *Journal of*

*Gender, Race and Justice* 381 (2002). https://scholarship.law.ufl.edu/facultypub/107/.

# ■ George Bush's Address to the Nation on National Drug Control Strategy

**Date:** September 5, 1989
**Author:** George H. W. Bush
**Genre:** Speech

## Summary Overview

As noted in the text of the speech reproduced here, this was the first major address of President George H.W. Bush's administration that was broadcast to American homes in prime time and geared for consumption by the general public. The speech demonstrated that policies against recreational drug use were going to be a focal point of Bush's domestic policy. Having been vice president in the Ronald Reagan administration, this speech demonstrated that Bush's drug policy was going to be a continuation, basically, of Reagan's hardline approach.

Making this speech eight months into his term as president, Bush sought to quickly increase the amount of funds available to various antidrug programs. With the new fiscal year only days away, he hoped the speech would create pressure on Congress to adopt his policy and fund the plans to implement it. While there were no strong groups fighting against his drug policy at this time, he knew that there would be some who would be skeptical of the need, or perhaps the effectiveness, of increasing funding for antidrug programs by more than a third, to about $8 billion. Ultimately, Bush was correct in his assessment that the autumn of 1989 would prove an opportune moment for advancing his policy.

## Defining Moment

As with all televised presidential speeches, Bush's drug policy speech was an effort to rally support for the goals he outlined. A strong stand against drugs had been a hallmark of his Republican predecessors, Richard Nixon and Ronald Reagan, with Democratic president Jimmy Carter taking a different approach to problems related to drug usage in the United States. Ultimately, the Republican effort to demonize drugs as a criminal activity (rather than as a societal problem involving physical dependence) was successful. While the percentage of Americans polled who called drug use the biggest problem for the United States was in the single digits in the early 1980s, after this speech it reached its peak at 64 percent. The speech by itself did not produce the change in attitude, but it did mark a rise in support for strong federal antidrug policies.

Bush's push for strong enforcement of drug laws by massively increasing the availability of federal funds to police departments meant, in turn, a dramatic increase in the number of people incarcerated for drug-related offenses. (It was generally easier to arrest and convict users than dealers or traffickers.) As a continuation of Reagan's strong antidrug stance, Bush had relatively small amounts of money allocated to the prevention of drug use among the populace and the treatment of drug users. The result was that by the time Bush left office in 1993, there were more individuals in federal prisons convicted on drug charges than what had been the total population of the federal prisons at the beginning of Reagan's presidency. During his tenure, Bush faced a Congress controlled by Democrats. However, at this time, there was a broad consensus on the antidrug efforts. In fact, the Democratic response to this speech, given by Sen. Joe Biden, called Bush's proposals too weak to be successful and advocated increased action against those involved in the drug trade.

## Author Biography

George Herbert Walker Bush (1924–2018), the forty-first president of the United States, was born in Massachusetts, although his family moved to Connecticut the year after his birth. His was a wealthy family, and their summer home in the resort town of Kennebunkport, Maine, became a second home for Bush throughout his life. Upon his 1942 graduation from high school (Phillips Academy) he enlisted in the Naval Aviation Corps, eventually serving in the Pacific Theater. During his time of military service, Bush met and married Barbara Pierce. Leaving the Navy after the end of the war, Bush attended Yale University, graduating in 1948. He and Barbara had six children (including George W., who became the forty-third president). His early career was in the oil business in Texas. Moving into government service, Bush was a member of the House of Representatives, ambassador to the United Nations, chair of the Republican National Committee, chief of the U.S. Mission to China (PRC), director of the Central Intelligence Agency, vice president, and then president (1989–1993). During his presidency, the Cold War came to an end, Iraq was defeated in the first Gulf War, and the framework of the North American Free Trade Agreement (NAFTA) was signed (although the final version was not ratified until after he had left office). After a disappointing loss to Bill Clinton in the 1992 election, Bush essentially retired from politics, allowing the younger generation to take up the reins. He died on November 30, 2018.

## HISTORICAL DOCUMENT

Good evening. This is the first time since taking the oath of office that I felt an issue was so important, so threatening, that it warranted talking directly with you, the American people. All of us agree that the gravest domestic threat facing our nation today is drugs. Drugs have strained our faith in our system of justice. Our courts, our prisons, our legal system, are stretched to the breaking point. The social costs of drugs are mounting. In short, drugs are sapping our strength as a nation. Turn on the evening news or pick up the morning paper and you'll see what some Americans know just by stepping out their front door: Our most serious problem today is cocaine, and in particular, crack.

Who's responsible? Let me tell you straight out—everyone who uses drugs, everyone who sells drugs, and everyone who looks the other way.

Tonight, I'll tell you how many Americans are using illegal drugs. I will present to you our national strategy to deal with every aspect of this threat. And I will ask you to get involved in what promises to be a very difficult fight.

This is crack cocaine seized a few days ago by Drug Enforcement agents in a park just across the street from the White House. It could easily have been heroin or PCP.

It's as innocent-looking as candy, but it's turning our cities into battle zones, and it's murdering our children. Let there be no mistake: This stuff is poison. Some used to call drugs harmless recreation; they're not. Drugs are a real and terribly dangerous threat to our neighborhoods, our friends, and our families.

No one among us is out of harm's way. When 4-year-olds play in playgrounds strewn with discarded hypodermic needles and crack vials, it breaks my heart. When cocaine, one of the most deadly and addictive illegal drugs, is available to school kids—school kids—it's an outrage. And when hundreds of thousands of babies are born each year to mothers who use drugs—premature babies born desperately sick—then even the most defenseless among us are at risk.

These are the tragedies behind the statistics, but the numbers also have quite a story to tell. Let me share with you the results of the recently completed household survey of the National Institute on Drug Abuse. It compares recent drug use to 3 years ago. It tells us some good news and some very bad news. First, the good. As you can see in the chart, in 1985 the Government estimated that 23 million Americans were using drugs on a "current" basis; that is, at least once in the preceding month. Last year that number fell by more than a third. That means almost 9 million fewer Americans are casual drug users. Good news.

Because we changed our national attitude toward drugs, casual drug use has declined. We have many to thank: our brave law enforcement officers, religious leaders, teachers, community activists, and leaders of business and labor. We should also thank the media for their exhaustive news and editorial coverage and for their air time and space for antidrug messages. And finally, I want to thank President and Mrs. Reagan for their leadership. All of these good people told the truth: that drug use is wrong and dangerous.

But as much comfort as we can draw from these dramatic reductions, there is also bad news, very bad news. Roughly 8 million people have used cocaine in the past year. Almost 1 million of them used it frequently—once a week or more. What this means is that, in spite of the fact that overall cocaine use is down, frequent use has almost doubled in the last few years. And that's why habitual cocaine users, especially crack users, are the most pressing, immediate drug problem.

> *Let there be no mistake. This stuff is poison.*

What, then, is our plan? To begin with, I trust the lesson of experience: No single policy will cut it, no matter how glamorous or magical it may sound. To win the war against addictive drugs like crack will take more than just a Federal strategy: It will take a national strategy, one that reaches into every school, every workplace, involving every family.

Earlier today, I sent this document, our first such national strategy, to the Congress. It was developed with the hard work of our nation's first Drug Policy Director, Bill

Bennett. In preparing this plan, we talked with State, local, and community leaders, law enforcement officials, and experts in education, drug prevention, and rehabilitation. We talked with parents and kids. We took a long, hard look at all that the Federal Government has done about drugs in the past—what's worked and, let's be honest, what hasn't. Too often, people in government acted as if their part of the problem—whether fighting drug production or drug smuggling or drug demand—was the only problem. But turf battles won't win this war; teamwork will.

Tonight, I'm announcing a strategy that reflects the coordinated, cooperative commitment of all our Federal agencies. In short, this plan is as comprehensive as the problem. With this strategy, we now finally have a plan that coordinates our resources, our programs, and the people who run them. Our weapons in this strategy are the law and criminal justice system, our foreign policy, our treatment systems, and our schools and drug prevention programs. So, the basic weapons we need are the ones we already have. What's been lacking is a strategy to effectively use them.

Let me address four of the major elements of our strategy. First, we are determined to enforce the law, to make our streets and neighborhoods safe. So, to start, I'm proposing that we more than double Federal assistance to State and local law enforcement. Americans have a right to safety in and around their homes. And we won't have safe neighborhoods unless we're tough on drug criminals—much tougher than we are now. Sometimes that means tougher penalties, but more often it just means punishment that is swift and certain. We've all heard stories about drug dealers who are caught and arrested again and again but never punished. Well, here the rules have changed: If you sell drugs, you will be caught. And when you're caught, you will be prosecuted. And once you're convicted, you will do time. Caught—prosecuted—punished.

I'm also proposing that we enlarge our criminal justice system across the board—at the local, State, and Federal levels alike. We need more prisons, more jails, more courts, more prosecutors. So, tonight I'm requesting—all together—an almost $1.5 billion increase in drug-related Federal spending on law enforcement.

And while illegal drug use is found in every community, nowhere is it worse than in our public housing projects. You know, the poor have never had it easy in this world. But in the past, they weren't mugged on the way home from work by crack gangs. And their children didn't have to dodge bullets on the way to school. And that's why I'm targeting $50 million to fight crime in public housing projects—to help restore order and to kick out the dealers for good.

The second element of our strategy looks beyond our borders, where the cocaine and crack bought on America's streets is grown and processed. In Colombia alone, cocaine killers have gunned down a leading statesman, murdered almost 200 judges and 7 members of their supreme court. The besieged governments of the drug-producing countries are fighting back, fighting to break the international drug rings. But you and I agree with the courageous President of Colombia, Virgilio Barco, who said that if

Americans use cocaine, then Americans are paying for murder. American cocaine users need to understand that our nation has zero tolerance for casual drug use. We have a responsibility not to leave our brave friends in Colombia to fight alone.

The $65 million emergency assistance announced 2 weeks ago was just our first step in assisting the Andean nations in their fight against the cocaine cartels. Colombia has already arrested suppliers, seized tons of cocaine, and confiscated palatial homes of drug lords. But Colombia faces a long, uphill battle, so we must be ready to do more. Our strategy allocates more than a quarter of a billion dollars for next year in military and law enforcement assistance for the three Andean nations of Colombia, Bolivia, and Peru. This will be the first part of a 5-year, $2 billion program to counter the producers, the traffickers, and the smugglers.

I spoke with President Barco just last week, and we hope to meet with the leaders of affected countries in an unprecedented drug summit, all to coordinate an inter-American strategy against the cartels. We will work with our allies and friends, especially our economic summit partners, to do more in the fight against drugs. I'm also asking the Senate to ratify the United Nations antidrug convention concluded last December.

To stop those drugs on the way to America, I propose that we spend more than a billion and a half dollars on interdiction. Greater interagency cooperation, combined with sophisticated intelligence-gathering and Defense Department technology, can help stop drugs at our borders.

And our message to the drug cartels is this: The rules have changed. We will help any government that wants our help. When requested, we will for the first time make available the appropriate resources of America's Armed Forces. We will intensify our efforts against drug smugglers on the high seas, in international airspace, and at our borders. We will stop the flow of chemicals from the United States used to process drugs. We will pursue and enforce international agreements to track drug money to the front men and financiers. And then we will handcuff these money launderers and jail them, just like any street dealer. And for the drug kingpins: the death penalty.

The third part of our strategy concerns drug treatment. Experts believe that there are 2 million American drug users who may be able to get off drugs with proper treatment, but right now only 40 percent of them are actually getting help. This is simply not good enough. Many people who need treatment won't seek it on their own, and some who do seek it are put on a waiting list. Most programs were set up to deal with heroin addicts, but today the major problem is cocaine users. It's time we expand our treatment systems and do a better job of providing services to those who need them.

And so, tonight I'm proposing an increase of $321 million in Federal spending on drug treatment. With this strategy, we will do more. We will work with the States. We will encourage employers to establish employee assistance programs to cope with drug use; and because addiction is such a cruel inheritance, we will intensify our search for ways to help expectant mothers who use drugs.

Fourth, we must stop illegal drug use before it starts. Unfortunately, it begins early—for many kids, before their teens. But it doesn't start the way you might think, from a dealer or an addict hanging around a school playground. More often, our kids first get their drugs free, from friends or even from older brothers or sisters. Peer pressure spreads drug use; peer pressure can help stop it. I am proposing a quarter-of-a-billion-dollar increase in Federal funds for school and community prevention programs that help young people and adults reject enticements to try drugs. And I'm proposing something else. Every school, college, and university, and every workplace must adopt tough but fair policies about drug use by students and employees. And those that will not adopt such policies will not get Federal funds—period!

The private sector also has an important role to play. I spoke with a businessman named Jim Burke who said he was haunted by the thought—a nightmare, really—that somewhere in America, at any given moment, there is a teenage girl who should be in school instead of giving birth to a child addicted to cocaine. So, Jim did something. He led an antidrug partnership, financed by private funds, to work with advertisers and media firms. Their partnership is now determined to work with our strategy by generating educational messages worth a million dollars a day every day for the next 3 years—a billion dollars worth of advertising, all to promote the antidrug message.

As President, one of my first missions is to keep the national focus on our offensive against drugs. And so, next week I will take the antidrug message to the classrooms of America in a special television address, one that I hope will reach every school, every young American. But drug education doesn't begin in class or on TV. It must begin at home and in the neighborhood. Parents and families must set the first example of a drug-free life. And when families are broken, caring friends and neighbors must step in.

These are the most important elements in our strategy to fight drugs. They are all designed to reinforce one another, to mesh into a powerful whole, to mount an aggressive attack on the problem from every angle. This is the first time in the history of our country that we truly have a comprehensive strategy. As you can tell, such an approach will not come cheaply. Last February I asked for a $700 million increase in the drug budget for the coming year.

And now, over the past 6 months of careful study, we have found an immediate need for another billion and a half dollars. With this added $2.2 billion, our 1990 drug budget totals almost $8 billion, the largest increase in history. We need this program fully implemented—right away. The next fiscal year begins just 26 days from now. So, tonight I'm asking the Congress, which has helped us formulate this strategy, to help us move it forward immediately. We can pay for this fight against drugs without raising taxes or adding to the budget deficit. We have submitted our plan to Congress that shows just how to fund it within the limits of our bipartisan budget agreement.

Now, I know some will still say that we're not spending enough money, but those who judge our strategy only by its pricetag simply don't understand the problem. Let's face it, we've all seen in the past that money alone won't solve our toughest problems. To be strong and efficient, our strategy needs these funds. But there is no match for a united America, a determined America, an angry America. Our outrage against drugs unites us, brings us together behind this one plan of action—an assault on every front.

This is the toughest domestic challenge we've faced in decades. And it's a challenge we must face not as Democrats or Republicans, liberals or conservatives, but as Americans. The key is a coordinated, united effort. We've responded faithfully to the request of the Congress to produce our nation's first national drug strategy. I'll be looking to the Democratic majority and our Republicans in Congress for leadership and bipartisan support. And our citizens deserve cooperation, not competition; a national effort, not a partisan bidding war. To start, Congress needs not only to act on this national drug strategy but also to act on our crime package announced last May, a package to toughen sentences, beef up law enforcement, and build new prison space for 24,000 inmates.

You and I both know the Federal Government can't do it alone. The States need to match tougher Federal laws with tougher laws of their own: stiffer bail, probation, parole, and sentencing. And we need your help. If people you know are users, help them—help them get off drugs. If you're a parent, talk to your kids about drugs—tonight. Call your local drug prevention program; be a Big Brother or Sister to a child in need; pitch in with your local Neighborhood Watch program. Whether you give your time or talent, everyone counts: every employer who bans drugs from the workplace; every school that's tough on drug use; every neighborhood in which drugs are not welcome; and most important, every one of you who refuses to look the other way. Every one of you counts. Of course, victory will take hard work and time, but together we will win. Too many young lives are at stake.

Not long ago, I read a newspaper story about a little boy named Dooney who, until recently, lived in a crack house in a suburb of Washington, DC. In Dooney's neighborhood, children don't flinch at the sound of gunfire. And when they play, they pretend to sell to each other small white rocks that they call crack. Life at home was so cruel that Dooney begged his teachers to let him sleep on the floor at school. And when asked about his future, 6-year-old Dooney answers, "I don't want to sell drugs, but I'll probably have to."

Well, Dooney does not have to sell drugs. No child in America should have to live like this. Together as a people we can save these kids. We've already transformed a national attitude of tolerance into one of condemnation. But the war on drugs will be hard-won, neighborhood by neighborhood, block by block, child by child.

If we fight this war as a divided nation, then the war is lost. But if we face this evil as a nation united, this will be nothing but a handful of useless chemicals. Victory—victory over drugs—is our cause, a just cause. And with your help, we are going to win.

Thank you, God bless you, and good night.

---

## GLOSSARY

**crack:** crystalized cocaine, which is smoked; developed during the cocaine glut of the 1970s to expand the market, it was initially marketed to people in inner cities

**crack vial:** a small glass "bottle" used to store/sell crack cocaine

**turf battles:** here, a power struggle in which one government agency tries to control budgets and activities in a specific policy area

---

### Document Analysis

President George H.W. Bush's speech on the drug crisis in the United States was about a real problem facing society. The increase in the use of crack cocaine during the 1980s was negatively impacting many people's lives. However, the solution that Bush chose to emphasize, increased policing and incarceration, would also negatively impact society, especially African Americans living in inner cities. The first of the four elements Bush believed could end the drug crisis, stronger enforcement of drug laws, funded with $1.5 billion in additional federal dollars, was the key to his drug initiative. It was also the part of the policy that stood to create the most favorable headlines for the administration and the statistics to show the policy's effectiveness. The other three elements, funded with the addition of about $636 million to the federal budget, were designed to assist interdiction efforts and to decrease demand. Both avenues held possibilities for lessening the drug crisis, although in a much less visible manner than arrests and trials.

Bush understood the impact that a televised speech from the Oval Office could have. In addition to the dramatic setting, he used a bag of crack as a prop to demonstrate its availability. (The drug buy in Lafayette Park was set up by the Drug Enforcement Administration, and the agent who bought the drug was behind the camera to verify that White House officials did not tamper with it, in case the material was needed for a trial.) Bush's charge that users, dealers, and "everyone who looks the other way" were jointly responsible for the problem was a major indictment of society. The change in cocaine usage, to which he referred in the speech, reflected the transition from powdered to crystallized cocaine. In the 1970s, powdered cocaine became a recreational (albeit illegal) drug for some in the middle and upper classes. For a variety of reasons, this declined in the 1980s. In order for the illegal drug industry to increase sales and profits, drug traffickers developed the crystallized form, "crack," and marketed it in major cities. As it caught on, this more addictive form spread throughout the United States, with many African American communities being intentionally targeted. Thus, when Bush proposed tougher enforcement of drug laws, this meant that African American communities were disproportionally affected. Stronger penalties were established for crack, as opposed to powdered cocaine, which made the effects of the strong antidrug campaign even greater for African Americans. This ultimately resulted in a federal incarceration rate for African Americans about five times that of white Americans.

Unlike the major push for increased aid to all aspects of law enforcement, the increase in funds for the treatment of drug addicts was a positive incentive for those who desired to overcome their addiction. While the associates of the drug cartels had made a major push to create a market for crack, treatment options were belatedly designed to decrease this market. The other step to decrease demand was by making educational institutions responsible for policing their students' use of drugs. Some funds were available for antidrug education, but Bush more ominously threatened to cut off federal student and federal funds to educational institutions that did not meet federal antidrug standards. Overall, these two elements did seem to have some impact on drug use. The other element, directed toward decreasing the supply, was a matter of assisting interdiction efforts of the South American countries in which the coca plant grew. Bush proposed increased foreign aid, although other factors within those countries kept this from being effective.

## Essential Themes

Although Bush's speech came at the high point of antidrug sentiment in the United States, its effects continued for decades. Building upon Reagan-era drug laws, Bush pushed for stronger enforcement and longer sentences for drug offenders, which continued long afterward to increase the prison population in the United States. Although Bush could only directly make changes in federal law enforcement, many states and cities not only accepted the funds for their police departments, but strengthened their drug laws. As the 1990s unfolded, sentiment regarding drug use moved toward greater acceptance and understanding of addiction and the social-structural factors involved in creating addicts. Although there was no move to decriminalize cocaine or opiates as there was for marijuana, the strong anticrack stance of the Reagan/Bush era diminished. President Clinton signed the law that made the penalties for possession of crack the same as for powdered cocaine. However, long prison sentences and the ramifications of being classified as an "ex-con" created devastation for many individuals and the communities to which they belonged. People of color, who seemed to have been especially targeted in this antidrug effort, still bear the brunt of the effects of hardline drug enforcement policies like those illustrated in Bush's speech.

Today, with the legalization of marijuana by many states, and the legalization of some other drugs by a few jurisdictions, some observers believe that a new era of recreational drug use has arrived. In addition, many individuals' perception of how drugs enter people's lives has been transformed by the opioid crisis of the early twenty-first century. For better or worse, the strong judicial push to control drugs has faded somewhat. At the same time, effective ways to deal with the negative effects of drugs on people and society continue to be explored.

—*Donald A. Watt, PhD*

## Bibliography and Additional Reading

Bennett, William J. "National Drug Control Strategy." *U.S. Department of Justice National Institute of Justice.* Washington, DC: The White House, 1990.

Bush, George H.W. "Presidential Address on National Drug Policy." C-SPAN. Washington, DC: National Cable Satellite Corporation, 2019.

Clark, Krissy with Kevin Sullivan, ed. "America's Drug War, Revealed." *Reveal: The Center for Investigative Reporting.* (Broadcast on Minnesota Public Radio's "The Uncertain Hour".) Emeryville, CA: The Center for Investigative Reporting, 2020.

Gonzenbach, William J. *The Media, the President and Public Opinion: A Longitudinal Analysis of the Drug Issue, 1984–1991.* (Routledge Communication Series.) Abingdon UK: Routledge, 2013.

Meacham, Jon. *Destiny and Power: The American Odyssey of George Herbert Walker Bush.* New York: Random House, 2015.

Moses, Catherine. "The Making of Drug Policy in the George H.W. Bush and William J. Clinton Administrations: The Pursuit of Failure." *Semanticscholar.org*. Athens, GA: The University of Georgia, 2004.

# ■ Testimony from the 1994 Tobacco Hearings

**Date:** April 14, 1994
**Authors:** Rep. Henry Waxman, et al.
**Genre:** Testimony

## Summary Overview

Tobacco proliferated in North America long before European colonists arrived; it has been infused into every era of the United States' history. As the harmfulness of the drug became more and more irrefutable across the twentieth century, the tobacco industry fought to protect its interests and undercut the overwhelming medical consensus. This document stands as a stark attestation of that process. The U.S. Congressional Energy and Commerce Subcommittee on Health and the Environment, chaired by Henry Waxman, called to testify before it the chief executive officers (CEOs) of the seven largest American tobacco companies. Waxman and other members of his committee asked the witnesses about nicotine's addictiveness and smoking's links to cancer and other diseases. To a man, the CEOs denied that nicotine was addictive and feigned ignorance regarding any negative health effects of tobacco.

## Defining Moment

Resistance to tobacco usage has a long tradition. In the early seventeenth century, King James I levied a high tariff on tobacco imports and published *A Counterblaste to Tobacco*, a screed against the drug. In it, he noted that tobacco is "hurtfull to the health of the whole body." Later in the text, he elaborated on this notion, calling tobacco "A custome lothsome to the eye, hatefull to the Nose, harmefull to the braine, dangerous to the Lungs, and in the blacke stinking fume thereof, neerest resembling the horrible Stigian smoke of the pit that is bottomelesse." This document confirms that there was early knowledge of tobacco's harmfulness despite its ballooning use and popularity. In the twentieth century, the government of Nazi Germany fought strongly against tobacco use, taxing it and legislating against it.

Stateside, Alton Ochsner cofounded the Ochsner Clinic along with four colleagues in Louisiana in 1942 and campaigned vehemently against America's entrenched tobacco culture.

In the late 1940s and early 1950s, Richard Doll of the United Kingdom linked tobacco smoking to lung cancer and other serious health conditions across numerous publications. Particularly notable among these was the British Doctors Study, which began in the early 1950s and carried on for half of a century. Following up on the 1957 Joint Report of Study Group on Smoking and Health, the United States Surgeon General more extensively connected smoking tobacco with health concerns and death in 1964. "The death rate for smokers of cigarettes only, who were smoking at the time of entry into particular prospective study, is about 70 percent higher than that for non-smokers," the 1964 report reads. It adds, "The death rates increase with the amount smoked." The report detailed specific cancers and other diseases linked to smoking and the extensive studies that underlay its findings.

In the late 1950s and early 1960s, tobacco companies raced to advertise their lower tar levels and superior filters. However, as the years went on and the medical consensus grew ever stronger, these corporations changed tack and banded together. In the mid-1970s, Tony Garrett, the CEO of Imperial Tobacco, convened a meeting of the CEOs of the seven largest international tobacco companies. In a scheme Garrett dubbed Operation Berkshire, the moguls agreed that they would not accede when asked about the science, would sue when nations attempted to legislate against them, and would work to rehabilitate smoking's faltering image.

The seven CEOs of American corporations who faced the House subcommittee in 1994 were different men than the seven convened by Garrett two decades earlier, but their tactics remained the same: circle the wagons, as it were, and resist. In 2003, 168 nations signed on to the World Health Organization's Framework Convention on Tobacco Control. In 2009, the Family Smoking Prevention and Tobacco Control Act first finally allowed the United States Food and Drug Administration to regulate tobacco.

## Author Biography

This document features several voices, the most prominent of which is that of Representative Henry Waxman, chair of the Energy and Commerce Subcommittee on Health and the Environment. Born on September 12, 1939 in Los Angeles, California, he earned his bachelor's degree and JD from the University of California, Los Angeles. He worked as a lawyer and elected official in the California Assembly before first being elected to the U.S. House of Representatives as a Democrat in 1974. He served twenty straight terms before retiring from Congress in January 2015. His heavily Democratic district in and around Los Angeles helped him secure such a long, consecutive tenure, which in turn allowed him to rise in the ranks in his committees. He served as the chair of the Energy and Commerce Subcommittee on Health and the Environment from 1979 to 1995, in which role he headed the hearing featured in this document. He also served as the chair of the House Oversight Committee from 2007 to 2009 and chair of the House Energy Committee from 2009 to 2011. Throughout his time in Congress, he focused especially on environmental and health issues as witnessed in this document. Waxman currently works as a lobbyist and chair of Waxman Strategies.

## HISTORICAL DOCUMENT

Witnesses:

William Campbell, President & CEO, Philip Morris, USA
James W. Johnston, Chairman and CEO, RJR Tobacco Company
Joseph Taddeo, President, U.S. Tobacco Company
Andrew H. Tisch, Chairman and CEO, Lorillard Tobacco Company
Edward A. Horrigan, Chairman and CEO, Liggett Group Inc.
Thomas E. Sandefur, Chairman and CEO, Brown and Williamson Tobacco Corp.
Donald S. Johnston, President and CEO, American Tobacco Company

Chaired by: Henry Waxman (D-CA)

REP. WAXMAN: The meeting of the subcommittee will come to order. I'd like to ask our guests to please take your seats. This is an historic hearing. For the first time ever, the chief executive officers of our nation's tobacco companies are testifying together before the United States Congress. They are here because this subcommittee has legislative jurisdiction over those issues that affect our health. And no health issue is as important as cigarette smoking....

When we hear about scientific disputes we have to listen to one expert versus another. But let me tell you there are some things that we know about from our own personal experience. I was a smoker and I know how addicted I was to smoking. I know how hard it was to quit, each and every time I did try to quit. And I had to do it a number of times before I was successful....

Mr. Johnson, I want to start with your testimony. You and your colleagues [based on their opening statements] seem to have almost a fanatical insistence that your products are the same as all these other products. This morning, in your written statement and your oral statement, you compared cigarettes to coffee, tea, sweets, sugar, warm milk, cheese, chocolate and Twinkies. That's quite a list. I'm struck by what I think is a calculated attempt to trivialize the devastating health impact of your product. You and I both know that Twinkies don't kill a single American a year. They may not add to a healthy diet, but they don't kill. The difference between cigarettes and Twinkies and the other products you mentioned is death. And I am sure you are aware that the Surgeon General and the American Medical Association estimate that cigarettes kill over 400,000 smokers every year. Putting aside your assertion that people accept this risk willingly, do you agree with this estimate?

MR. JOHNSTON: Do I agree with the estimate of 435,000 people? I've heard from this committee this morning three or four different numbers. My understanding of how that number is—

REP. WAXMAN: If you don't agree with the number, then give us your number. How many smokers die each year from smoking?

MR. JOHNSTON: I will explain.

REP. WAXMAN: No, I want your answer. We have a limited time.

MR. JOHNSTON: I do not know how many.

REP. WAXMAN: You disagree with the Surgeon General's opinion?

MR. JOHNSTON: It is a computer generated number that makes—

REP. WAXMAN: Mr. Johnston, I am going to have to ask you to respond to my question. Do you or do you not agree with the Surgeon General's estimate of over 400,000 smokers dying each year.

MR. JOHNSTON: I do not agree.

REP. WAXMAN: Okay. Do you know how many die each year?

MR. JOHNSTON: I do not know.

REP. WAXMAN: How can you as a chief executive officer of a company manufacturing a product that's been accused of killing so many people not know this information? How is it?

MR. JOHNSTON: I'm telling you that number is generated by a computer and it makes two important assumptions. The first that virtually everyone who smokes and dies, dies because they smoked, unless they got run over by a bus. And second, that model allows people to die one, two, three, four times. I don't know how that can happen, but that's what that model does.

REP. WAXMAN: Well, I'm struck by the overwhelming scientific agreement on the dangers of smoking. The U.S. Public Health Service, the Surgeon General, the Food and Drug Administration, the World Health Organization, the National Cancer Institute, the American Medical Association, I guess all these groups you would call the anti-tobacco industry. But they all say it is hazardous. The experts also agree that smoking causes heart disease. Do you agree that smoking causes heart disease?

MR. JOHNSTON: It may.

REP. WAXMAN: Okay. They agree that smoking causes lung cancer. Do you agree?

MR. JOHNSTON: It may.

REP. WAXMAN: Do you know whether it does?

MR. JOHNSTON: I do not know.

REP. WAXMAN: Why not?

MR. JOHNSTON: Because all of that is —

REP. WAXMAN: Proprietary?

MR. JOHNSTON:—statistically generated data. It is epidemiological as opposed to empirical. There have been no laboratory studies which have been able to confirm any statistics.

REP. WAXMAN: grandfather who smoked all of his life died of lung cancer. Do you think that lung cancer was caused by smoking?

MR. JOHNSTON: I don't know, Mr. Chairman.

REP. WAXMAN: The medical experts agree that smoking causes emphysema. Do you agree?

MR. JOHNSTON: It may.

REP. WAXMAN: They agree that smoking causes bladder cancer, stroke and low birth rate? Do you agree?

MR. JOHNSTON: It may.

REP. WAXMAN: Mr. Tisch, I want to move to you for a moment. In a deposition last year you were asked whether cigarette smoking causes cancer. Your answer was "I don't believe so." Do you stand by that answer today?

MR. TISCH: I do, sir.

REP. WAXMAN: Do you understand how isolated you are in the belief from the entire scientific community?

MR. TISCH: I do, sir.

REP. WAXMAN: You're the head of manufacturer of a product that's been accused by the overwhelming scientific community to cause cancer. You don't know? Do you have an interest in finding out?

MR. TISCH: I do, sir, yes.

REP. WAXMAN: And what have you done to pursue that interest?

MR. TISCH: We have looked at the data and the data that we have been able to see has all been statistical data that has not convinced me that smoking causes death.

> *"Cigarettes and nicotine clearly do not meet the classic definitions of addiction.*

REP. WAXMAN: Mr. Campbell, you were also deposed and you said "To my knowledge it has not been proven that cigarette smoking causes cancer." This is a rather passive and puzzling approach, especially in light of the consensus. Not by some, but all of the scientific community. Will you ever be convinced, and what evidence are you waiting for? And let's have the microphone passed over.

MR. CAMPBELL: Yes, I may be convinced. We don't know what causes cancer in general right now, so I think that we may find out what causes cancer and we may find out some relationship, which has yet to be proven.

REP. WAXMAN: Well you know I must say this is rather a passive approach. Don't you feel that you have an obligation, the same obligation that every other consumer company has, to determine whether you are causing harm and to take steps to minimize that harm? You're not meeting that responsibility, and it is clear your views on the health impacts of cigarettes are out of step with an overwhelming scientific evidence. If all the medical people who don't work for you say it causes cancer, what more do you need to understand that that's the case and to accept this, and then try to work constructively to try to see if we can avoid that terrible tragedy to so many people?

MR. CAMPBELL: Is there a question, sir?

REP. WAXMAN: That's a question.

MR. CAMPBELL: I'm sorry, it was too long for me to—

REP. WAXMAN: Well, I think that the point I am making is that all of you have some responsibility, not simply to say you don't know, even when this overwhelming weight of scientific evidence is against you. I think you have an obligation to know.

REP. RON WYDEN (D-OR): Thank you, Mr. Chairman. Just before we go to my questioning, I know that the witnesses want to turn this into the battle of the charts, I guess, with respect to Dr. Kessler and the FDA. We're going to get into it later, but we believe that the chart in question with respect to the FDA is an accurate one, and we'll get into it a little bit later. Let me begin my questioning on the matter of whether or not nicotine is addictive. Let me ask you first, and I'd like to just go down the row, whether each of you believes that nicotine is not addictive. I heard virtually all of you touch on it. Just yes or no. Do you believe nicotine is not addictive?

MR. CAMPBELL: (?) I believe nicotine is not addictive, yes.

REP. WYDEN: Mr. Johnston?

MR. JOHNSTON: Congressman, cigarettes and nicotine clearly do not meet the classic definitions of addiction. There is no intoxication.

REP. WYDEN: We'll take that as a no and, again, time is short. If you can just—I think each of you believe nicotine is not addictive. We just would like to have this for the record.

MR. TADDEO: (?) I don't believe that nicotine or our products are addictive.

MR. HORRIGAN (?) I believe nicotine is not addictive.

MR. TISCH: (?) I believe that nicotine is not addictive.

MR. SANDEFUR: (?) I believe that nicotine is not addictive.

MR. DONALD JOHNSTON: (?) And I, too, believe that nicotine is not addictive.

*Philip Morris advertisement, portrayed by Johnny Roventini. (Alexisrael)*

## Document Analysis

This document is an excerpt from the 1994 Energy and Commerce Subcommittee on Health and the Environment hearing on tobacco. House Representatives who sat on this committee asked the CEOs from the seven largest American tobacco companies questions under oath. This excerpt includes the questioning of Rep. Henry Waxman (D-CA) and the beginning of the questioning from Rep. Ron Wyden (D-OR). The two representatives attempt to get the CEOs to own up to the widespread harm that their product causes. Unsuccessful in that endeavor, they instead get the CEOs to obfuscate and lie under oath.

Waxman calls the meeting to order and gives an opening statement as chair of the committee. He establishes the importance of the hearing and the issue in general: "And no health issue is as important as cigarette smoking." He then tries to get individual CEOs to acknowledge and accede to the overwhelming evidence and medical consensus. For instance, he asks Mr. Johnston, "And I am sure you are aware that the Surgeon General and the American Medical Association estimate that cigarettes kill over 400,000 smokers every year… do you agree with this estimate?" The witness takes a while to answer before saying he does not agree and does not have a different estimate. He offers false information about how the estimate was formed: "Virtually everyone who smokes and dies, dies because they smoked, unless they got run over by a bus," and he otherwise misrepresents how the medical community arrives at its conclusions. Mr. Waxman moves on to other witnesses, Mr. Tisch and Mr. Campbell, and questions them about smoking's connection to diseases, particularly cancer. The witnesses likewise obfuscate and disagree with the medical consensus. To begin his own questioning, Rep. Wyden takes a different approach. Rather than address the witnesses one by one, he asks all the witnesses whether they believe nicotine is addictive or not. He explains why he is doing this: "I think each of you believe nicotine is not addictive. We just would like to have this for the record." He is right; to a man, they claim under oath that nicotine is not addictive.

Congressional hearings sometimes get dismissed as political theater and mere spectacle. However, some spectacles can be telling. Watching seven powerful CEOs clearly avoid the truth and outright lie under oath gives us an unmistakable sense of their businesses' priorities. This hearing showcases the disconnect that happens when businesses' commitment to their shareholders' profits comes in direct conflict with their customers' health.

## Essential Themes

The seven CEOs that appear as witnesses in this document use cohesion and ignorance as tools to get through the hearing. First, they band together, showing a united front and making their voices indistinguishable from one another. In times of trouble, adversaries can see advantages in joining forces to face a common threat. With the overwhelming medical consensus and a growing part of the American population against them, the CEOs have realized that their best chance of survival lies with one another. Dissension in their ranks would only further weaken their position. Second, the CEOs feign ignorance to the committee's questions. They repeatedly answer, "I don't know," and "It may." This ignorance has two main goals. On the one hand, the witnesses are trying to undercut the medical consensus by adding an element of doubt. The medical community is positive about smoking's connections to various health risks, but the witnesses want to give their audience permission to be less certain. Also, feigned ignorance is, legally speaking, much safer for the CEOs. It is much harder to convict someone of perjury who claims ignorance as opposed to someone who offers outright denials.

—*Anthony Vivian, PhD*

## Bibliography and Additional Reading

Barnett, Ross, Graham Moon, Jamie Pearce, Lee Thompson, and Liz Twigg. *Smoking Geographies: Space, Place and Tobacco.* Hoboken, NJ: Wiley, 2017.

Brandt, Allan. *The Cigarette Century: The Rise, Fall, and Deadly Persistence of the Product That Defined America.* New York: Basic Books, 2009.

Gately, Iain. *Tobacco: A Cultural History of How an Exotic Plant Seduced Civilization.* New York: Grove Press, 2003.

Milov, Sarah. *The Cigarette: A Political History.* Cambridge, MA: Harvard University Press, 2019.

# ■ Statement and News Release regarding Purdue OxyContin Case

**Date:** May 10, 2007
**Authors:** John L. Brownlee with Heidi Coy
**Genre:** Report

## Summary Overview

From the end of the 1990s into the early 2000s, opioid addiction skyrocketed in the United States, causing massive economic, social, and personal losses, including thousands of deaths. The change in the opioid addiction rate obviously had to do with greater access to opioids. The development of new prescription opioids, and their widespread use (and abuse) by prescribing physicians and their patients, was understood to lay at the heart of the problem. The results of the government's case against the drug manufacturer Purdue Pharma, along with several of its officers, was a major step toward possibly decreasing the availability of one of the most frequently used opioids, OxyContin. The decision by the company's owners and executives to plead guilty to the charges of misrepresenting the addictive qualities of the drug was the result of the strong case the government had assembled against them. The government's decision to push forward with the case demonstrated that pharmaceutical manufacturers not only had to satisfy the Food and Drug Administration (FDA) in terms of the manufacturing and marketing of a drug, they also had to keep abreast of and respond to data relating to the drug's actual use in the "real world" of the medical marketplace.

## Defining Moment

Relief from pain is sought by all who suffer it. However, some drugs for severe pain have properties that can create physical or psychological addiction among users. While relatively uncommon in drugs designed to relieve minor pain, these side effects are very common in pharmaceutical products designed to handle severe pain. Drugs obtained from the opium poppy (opioids), or chemically derived from the properties of the plant's seeds, depress the nervous system, decreasing the amount of stimulation received from the nerve endings that sense pain. These drugs, however, are generally addictive. For decades, companies have sought ways to obtain the positive (pain relief) properties of opioids while lessening the negative (addictive)

properties. OxyContin represents one such attempt at accomplishing this, and from the late 1990s it was marketed as one of the most successful attempts—even though circumstances came to prove that proposition false.

Many scientists working for Purdue Pharma had made a good faith effort to obtain favorable results, yet the level of nonaddictive properties claimed by the company to have been attained never matched the reality. The extended-release aspect of the drug was said to reduce both the euphoria that many opioid users experience (causing psychological addiction) as well as the level of physical dependence (chemical addiction). Both of these pronouncements proved to be incorrect. The number of people who became addicted to opioids via OxyContin soared in the drug's first decade of use. Purdue Pharma had made false statements to the FDA in its application process; documents showed that at least a year prior to the drug's approval, executives at Purdue Pharma understood that the claims were false. They nevertheless pressed forward with the application and included a statement on the drug's packaging suggesting how much safer OxyContin was than its competitors. This information was given to Purdue's sales force to encourage them to push the drug to health care providers.

As the use of OxyContin became more widespread, many health care providers saw that the results of its use did not match up with the company's claims. The resulting investigations were able to prove that the company had not been telling the truth about OxyContin. For the government to win its case against the company, however, it had to prove that the company knowingly provided false information to the FDA and made false statements in its sales pitch. Through diligent work, the incriminating documents were found, ultimately resulting in guilty pleas by several top executives and the company as a whole. The Justice Department's willingness to pursue the matter was a signal to all pharmaceutical companies that honesty was not just the best policy in drug research and marketing, it was the only acceptable one.

## Author Biography

John Leslie Brownlee (b. 1965) is a native of Wyoming. A graduate of Washington and Lee University, and later the William & Mary School of Law, Brownlee served in the Army Reserves' J.A.G. Corps from 1997 to 2007, having previously served in the infantry from 1987 to 1991. For four years, he was assistant U.S. attorney for the District of Columbia before being appointed the U.S. attorney for the Western District of Virginia in 2001. In that position, Brownlee oversaw several landmark investigations, including the Purdue Pharma case. Included on the second list, in 2006, of U.S. attorneys who should be fired (the Department of Justice said this was for mishandling a D-Day Memorial fraud case, while Brownlee asserted this was because he pressed the Purdue Pharma case), Brownlee left his position in 2008. Since then he has been in private practice.

Heidi Coy was the public affairs specialist for the U.S. Attorney's Office of the Western District Virginia for several years. She later served as a spokesperson for the Virginia Department of Transportation.

## HISTORICAL DOCUMENTS

U.S. Department of Justice
United States Attorney
Western District of Virginia

STATEMENT OF UNITED STATES ATTORNEY JOHN BROWNLEE ON THE GUILTY PLEA OF THE PURDUE FREDERICK COMPANY AND ITS EXECUTIVES FOR ILLEGALLY MISBRANDING OXYCONTIN

May 10, 2007

One of the oldest and most challenging medical mysteries is the treatment of pain. For centuries, scientists and doctors have searched for a drug that would safely relieve patients of their chronic pain without inflicting the dangerous side effects that routinely come from the use of addictive narcotics. The discovery of this "wonder" drug would bring hope and relief to millions of suffering patients and wealth beyond one's imagination to its creators.

In 1996, Purdue and its top executives claimed that they had developed such a drug; a safe drug that would help those suffering in pain. The name of that drug was OxyContin. Backed by an aggressive marketing campaign, Purdue's OxyContin became the new pain medication of choice for many doctors and patients. Purdue claimed it had created the miracle drug—a low risk drug that could provide long acting pain relief but was less addictive and less subject to abuse. Purdue's marketing campaign worked, and sales for OxyContin skyrocketed—making billions for Purdue and millions for its top executives.

But OxyContin offered no miracles to those suffering in pain. Purdue's claims that OxyContin was less addictive and less subject to abuse and diversion were false—and Purdue knew its claims were false. The result of their misrepresentations and crimes sparked one of our nation's greatest prescription drug failures. OxyContin is nothing more than pure oxycodone—a habit forming narcotic derived from the opium poppy. Purdue's OxyContin never lived up to its hype and never offered a low risk way of reducing pain as promised. Simply put, the genesis of OxyContin was not the result of good science or laboratory experiment. OxyContin was the child of marketeers and bottom line financial decision making.

Accordingly, this morning, in a federal courtroom in Abingdon, Virginia, the Purdue Frederick Company, the manufacturer and distributor of OxyContin, pleaded guilty to a felony charge of illegally misbranding OxyContin in an effort to mislead and defraud physicians and consumers. Purdue has agreed to pay over $600 million in criminal and civil penalties, fines and forfeitures, subjected itself to independent monitoring and an extensive remedial action program, and acknowledged that it illegally marketed and promoted OxyContin by falsely claiming that OxyContin was less addictive, less subject to abuse and diversion, and less likely to cause withdrawal symptoms than other pain medications—all in an effort to maximize its profits. Also, Purdue's Chief Executive Officer Michael Friedman, General Counsel Howard Udell, and former Chief Medical Officer Paul Goldenheim pleaded guilty to a misdemeanor charge of misbranding OxyContin and collectively agreed to pay $34.5 million in penalties. With its OxyContin, Purdue unleashed a highly abusable, addictive, and potentially dangerous drug on an unsuspecting and unknowing public. For these misrepresentations and crimes, Purdue and its executives have been brought to justice.

We have released a Criminal Information, Plea Agreements, a Corporate Integrity Agreement, a Statement of Facts, and a Complaint for Forfeiture that have been filed in U.S. District Court in Abingdon. Purdue and its top three executives have pleaded guilty to illegally misbranding OxyContin from 1996 thru 2001. The company has admitted that it misbranded OxyContin with the intent to defraud and mislead the public.

As part of this plea agreement, Purdue and its top three executives will pay $634.5 million in criminal and civil fines, penalties, and forfeitures, to be distributed as follows. First, Purdue will forfeit to the United States $276.1 million, a portion of which will be shared with the state and federal law enforcement agencies for their work during this investigation.

Second, Purdue will pay $130 million for compensation and settlement of private civil liabilities related to OxyContin. Any part of the $130 million that Purdue fails to distribute within two years will be immediately paid to the United States.

Third, Purdue will pay $100.6 million to the United States as reimbursement for payments made by government agencies for the settlement of false claims related to the misbranding of OxyContin. Those federal agencies include the Department of Health and Human Services, the Department of Labor, the Department of Defense, the Office Personnel Management, and the Veterans Administration.

Fourth, Purdue will pay $59.3 million to the State Medicaid programs as reimbursement for payments made by Medicaid for the settlement of false claims related to the misbranding of OxyContin. This money is available to any state to settle claims related to Purdue's criminal conduct.

Fifth, Purdue and its top three executives will pay $39.8 million to the Virginia Attorney General's Medicaid Fraud Control Unit Program Income fund. Virginia's MFCU is an important partner in our efforts to fight fraud against our medicaid programs.

Sixth, Purdue will pay $20 million to the Virginia Department of Health Professionals' operation of the Virginia Prescription Monitoring Program. The prescription monitoring program was initiated in part because of the big spike in prescription drug abuse that accompanied the illegal marketing of OxyContin. Currently, the program is largely funded by the Virginia taxpayers, and the $20 million payment by Purdue should endow the program for the foreseeable future.

Seventh, Purdue will pay $4.6 million to cover the costs of the five year internal monitoring program that is a part of the company's Corporate Integrity Agreement with the Health and Human Services Office of the Inspector General.

Eighth, Purdue will pay $3.4 million to the federal and state Medicaid programs for improperly calculated Medicaid rebates for years 1998 and 1999, and finally, Purdue and the three executives will pay $5 15,475 in criminal fines and special assessments to the court.

In addition to the guilty pleas and monetary penalties, the United States has directed Purdue, as part of the Corporate Integrity Agreement, to retain and pay for an Independent Monitor and staff to monitor Purdue's compliance with this agreement and federal law. The monitor and staff will be independent from Purdue's management and must file periodic reports with the government concerning Purdue's conduct and business practices. We believe this monitoring program, in conjunction with the Corporate Integrity Agreement, will ensure that in the future Purdue will market and promote its products in an honest and responsible manner. The public must be confident that we will keep close watch on how Purdue sells its most dangerous products.

I would now like to provide to you a brief summary of the investigation and some of our findings. The main violations of the law revealed by the government's criminal investigation are set forth in detail in the Statement of Facts released to you today.

The defendant The Purdue Frederick Company, a New York corporation headquartered in Connecticut, was created in 1892 and purchased by its current owners in 1952. Defendant Michael Friedman joined Purdue in 1985 and was appointed President and Chief Executive Officer in 2003. It is our understanding that Mr. Friedman has announced his intention to leave Purdue this year. Defendant Howard Udell joined Purdue in 1977 and is presently Purdue's Executive Vice President and Chief Legal Officer. Defendant Dr. Paul Goldenheim joined Purdue in 1985 as its Medical Director. Dr. Goldenheim left Purdue in 2004.

> Purdue put its desire to sell OxyContin above the interests of the public.

This case began in early 1995, when Purdue used focus groups of primary care physicians and surgeons to determine whether physicians would be willing to prescribe OxyContin for patients with non-cancer pain. According to Purdue's research, many of these physicians had great reservations about prescribing OxyContin because of the drug's addictive potential and side effect profile, and its abuse potential. It was clear from these focus groups that physicians were concerned about the safety and risks of OxyContin.

Purdue also learned from these focus groups that physicians wanted a long lasting pain reliever that was less addictive and less subject to abuse and diversion. Purdue understood that the company that marketed and sold that drug would dominate the pain management market. And that is exactly what Purdue tried to do.

Despite knowing that OxyContin contained high concentrations of oxycodone HCL, had an abuse potential similar to that of morphine, and was at least as addictive as other pain medications on the market, Purdue, beginning in January 1996, with the intent to defraud and mislead, falsely marketed and promoted OxyContin as less addictive, less subject to abuse and diversion, and less likely to cause tolerance and withdrawal than other pain medications. Purdue did so in the following ways:

First, Purdue trained its sales representatives to falsely inform health care providers that it was more difficult to extract the oxycodone from an OxyContin tablet for the purpose of intravenous abuse. Purdue ordered this training even though its own study showed that a drug abuser could extract approximately 68% of the oxycodone from a single 1 mg OxyContin tablet by simply crushing the tablet, stirring it in water, and drawing the solution through cotton into a syringe.

Second, Purdue falsely instructed its sales representatives to inform health care providers that OxyContin could create fewer chances for addiction than immediate-release opioids.

Third, Purdue sponsored training that falsely taught Purdue sales supervisors that OxyContin had fewer "peak and trough" blood level effects than immediate-release opioids resulting in less euphoria and less potential for abuse than short-acting opioids.

Fourth, Purdue falsely told certain health care providers that patients could stop therapy abruptly without experiencing withdrawal symptoms and that patients who took OxyContin would not develop tolerance to the drug.

And fifth, Purdue falsely told health care providers that OxyContin did not cause a "buzz" or euphoria, caused less euphoria, had less addiction potential, had less abuse potential, was less likely to be diverted than immediate-release opioids, and could be used to "weed out" addicts and drug seekers.

The results of Purdue's crimes were staggering. According to DEA, the number of oxycodone related deaths increased 400 percent between 1996 and 2001. During that same time period, the annual number of prescriptions for OxyContin increased from approximately 300,000 to nearly 6 million. Also, in February of 2002, the DEA released a report detailing the death rates caused by OxyContin abuse up to that time. According to the DEA, there were 146 deaths in which OxyContin was determined to be the direct "cause of or "a contributing factor to." DEA identified an additional 318 deaths that were "most likely" caused by OxyContin. In Virginia, our medical examiner reported that 228 people died in western Virginia from overdoses of oxycodone from 1996 to 2005.

For some communities, the danger went beyond just addiction and death. Beginning in 2000, localities began to report dramatically higher crime rates—some up as much as 75% from the year before. This sharp increase in crime was directly attributable to the abuse of OxyContin. Tazewell County estimated that OxyContin was behind 80–95% of all crimes that were committed there. From 1998 to 2003, burglaries, robberies, and larcenies jumped 131 % in Buchanan County and 102% in Russell County.

During the last 10 years, Virginia's law enforcement community has fought hard against the devastating effects OxyContin has had on our citizens and communities. During that time, we have convicted the OxyContin addicts who committed serious crimes to get money to buy more OxyContin, and we convicted street dealers who preyed upon the addicts' craving for this powerful narcotic. We also convicted pharmacists and physicians who illegally diverted OxyContin for personal gain and profit. With today's conviction of the maker of OxyContin, we have finally brought to justice the main component involved in this ring of abuse. The conviction of Purdue and its executives will end the misbranding and fraudulent marketing of OxyContin, deter other companies from committing like crimes, and provide desperately needed resources to fight addiction and abuse that threatens the health of millions of Virginians.

Thank you.

\* \* \*

NEWS RELEASE

UNITED STATES ATTORNEY'S OFFICE

WESTERN DISTRICT OF VIRGINIA

John L. Brownlee
United States Attorney

Heidi Coy
Public Affairs Specialist

May 10, 2007

THE PURDUE FREDERICK COMPANY, INC. AND TOP EXECUTIVES PLEAD GUILTY

John L. Brownlee, United States Attorney for the Western District of Virginia, and Virginia Attorney General Bob McDonnell announced today that The Purdue Frederick Company, Inc., along with its President, Chief Legal Officer, and former Chief Medical Officer have pleaded guilty to charges of misbranding Purdue's addictive and highly abusable drug OxyContin. Purdue and the three executives will pay a total of $634,515,475. OxyContin is a Schedule II prescription pain relief medication, classified as having the highest potential for abuse of legally available drugs. The Purdue Frederick Company, Inc., and the three executives have admitted that Purdue fraudulently marketed OxyContin by falsely claiming that OxyContin was less addictive, less subject to abuse, and less likely to cause withdrawal symptoms than other pain medications when there was no medical research to support these claims and without Food and Drug Administration approval of these claims.

"Even in the face of warnings from health care professionals, the media, and members of its own sales force that OxyContin was being widely abused and causing harm to our citizens, Purdue, under the leadership of its top executives, continued to push a fraudulent marketing campaign that promoted Oxycontin as less addictive, less subject to abuse, and less likely to cause withdrawal," said United States Attorney John Brownlee. "In the process, scores died as a result of OxyContin abuse and an even greater number of people became addicted to OxyContin; a drug that Purdue led many to believe was safer, less abusable, and less addictive than other pain medications on the market. Today's convictions are a testament to the outstanding work of the prosecutors and agents who spent years investigating this important case."

The Purdue Frederick Company, Inc. and Purdue Pharma, L.P. are part of a worldwide group of related and associated entities engaged in the pharmaceutical business. These entities manufacture, market, and distribute OxyContin, an extended-release form of oxycodone.

"Purdue put its desire to sell OxyContin above the interests of the public," said Assistant Attorney General Peter D. Keisler. "Purdue abused the drug approval process which relies on drug manufacturers to be forthright in reporting clinical data and, instead, misled physicians about the addiction and withdrawal issues involved with Oxycontin."

"The criminal behavior exhibited in this case damages the reputation of a critically important industry. Pharmaceutical companies have an obligation to patients, physicians, and those in the industry they serve to market prescription drugs in accordance with the law and FDA regulations." said Virginia Attorney General Bob McDonnell, "I applaud John Brownlee and his team for their leadership, as well as the Virginia Medicaid Fraud Control Unit, FDA and all of the other state and federal law enforcement agencies that worked so hard over the past four years to investigate this complex criminal scheme and bring the wrongdoers to justice."

"FDA will not tolerate practices that falsely promote drug products and place consumers at health risk," said Margaret O.K. Glavin, Associate Commissioner for Regulatory Affairs, FDA. "We will continue to do all we can to protect the public against drug companies and their representatives who are not truthful and bilk consumers of precious health care dollars."

The Purdue Frederick Company, Inc., pleaded guilty to felony misbranding OxyContin with the intent to defraud and mislead. President and Chief Operating Officer Michael Friedman, Executive Vice President and Chief Legal Officer Howard Udell, and former Executive Vice President of Worldwide Medical Affairs Paul D. Goldenheim, pleaded guilty to a misdemeanor charge of misbranding OxyContin. All the pleas were entered in United States District Court in Abingdon this morning.

"Purdue's illegal sales and marketing practices concealed information from patients and many health care providers regarding the potency and abuse potential of OxyContin for corporate profit," said Daniel R. Levinson, Inspector General for the U.S. Department of Health and Human Services. "We commend the highly qualified team of prosecutors and investigators from a variety of Federal and State agencies for developing a global resolution that addresses the criminal violations of the past, ensures strict compliance in the future, and serves as a strong warning to others who may consider illegally marketing pharmaceuticals."

"The falsification of drug product information is a very serious breach of the public's trust. IRS Criminal Investigation will continue to concentrate its resources on the tax and money laundering aspects of these types of investigations in cooperation with the United States Attorney's Office and other federal, state, and local authorities," said Charles R. Pine, Special Agent in Charge.

"Today's guilty pleas mark a significant milestone in the right against corruption by company officials who seek to illegally enrich corporate profits at taxpayers' expense," stated Gordon S. Heddell, Inspector General, U.S. Department of Labor. "These convictions demonstrate our steadfast resolve to investigate any individuals who would defraud Labor programs, such as the Office of Workers' Compensation Programs, by overcharging them. My office remains committed to working with other law enforcement agencies and the U.S. Attorney to fight this type of corruption."

Pursuant to written plea agreements, Purdue and the executives will pay a total of $634,515,475.00. Purdue's payments will include:

$276.1 million forfeited to the United States

$160 million paid to federal and state government agencies to resolve liability for false claims made to Medicaid and other government healthcare programs

$130 million set aside to resolve private civil claims (monies remaining after 36 months will be paid to the United States)

$5.3 million paid to the Virginia Attorney General's Medicaid Fraud Control Unit to fund future health care fraud investigations

$20 million paid to fund the Virginia Prescription Monitoring Program for the foreseeable future

In addition, Purdue will pay the maximum statutory criminal fine of $500,000.

Purdue's top executives will pay the following amounts to the Virginia Attorney General's Medicaid Fraud Control Unit:

$19 million paid by Michael Friedman
$8 million paid by Howard R. Udell
$7.5 million paid by Dr. Paul D. Goldenheim

Each executive will also pay a $5,000 criminal fine.

The Director of the Defense Criminal Investigative Service, Mr. Chuck Beardall, stated, "It is unthinkable that purely for greed, addictive drugs were fraudulently marketed to the public, and in so doing threatened the health and safety of our citizens. Among those endangered were soldiers, sailors, airmen, marines, and their families, all of whom avail themselves of the military health system. At a time when our military personnel and their loved ones are sacrificing so much, something like this is incomprehensible and grossly reprehensible."

According to the Statement of Facts filed with the Court, beginning in January 1996 and continuing through June 30, 2001, Purdue's market research found that "[t]he biggest negative of [OxyContin] was the abuse potential." Despite this finding, Purdue's supervisors and employees falsely and misleadingly marketed OxyContin as less addictive, less subject to abuse, and less likely to cause withdrawal than other pain medications. Purdue misbranded OxyContin in three specific ways:

1. Purdue sales representatives falsely told some health care providers that OxyContin had less euphoric effect and less abuse potential than short-acting opioids. This message was presented to some health care providers through the use of graphs that exaggerated the differences between blood plasma levels achieved by OxyContin compared to the levels of other pain relief medications. Purdue supervisors and employees participated in the misbranding in the following ways:
   A. Purdue supervisors and employees sponsored training that used graphs that exaggerated the differences between the blood plasma levels of OxyContin as compared to immediate-release opioids. These graphs were used to falsely teach Purdue sales supervisors that OxyContin had fewer "peak and trough" blood level effects than immediate-release opioids and that would

result in less euphoria and less potential for abuse than short-acting opioids.

B. Purdue supervisors and employees permitted new Purdue sales representatives to use similar exaggerated graphical depictions during role-play training at Purdue's headquarters in Stamford, Connecticut.

2. Purdue supervisors and employees drafted an article about a study of the use of OxyContin in osteoarthritis patients that was published in a medical journal on March 27, 2000. On June 26, 2000, each sales representative was provided a copy of the article together with a "marketing tip" that stated that the article was available for use in achieving sales success. Sales representatives distributed copies of the article to health care providers to falsely or misleadingly represent that patients taking OxyContin at doses below 60 milligrams per day can always be discontinued abruptly without withdrawal symptoms. The article also indicated that patients on such doses would not develop tolerance. The marketing tip that accompanied the article stated that one of the twelve key points was, "There were 2 reports of withdrawal symptoms after patients abruptly stopped taking CR [controlled release] oxycodone at doses of 60 or 70 mg/d. Withdrawal syndrome was not reported as an adverse event during scheduled respites indicating that CR oxycodone at doses below 60 mg/d [milligrams per day] can be discontinued without tapering the dose if the patient condition so warrants." These marketing claims were made even though Purdue representatives were well aware of the following information:

A. The year before the article was published and distributed to sales representatives, Purdue received an analysis of the osteoarthritis study and a second study from a United Kingdom company affiliated with Purdue that listed eight patients in the osteoarthritis study "who had symptoms recorded that may possibly have been related to opioid withdrawal," and stated that "[a] s expected, some patients did become physically dependent on OxyContin tablets but this is not expected to be a clinical problem so long as abrupt withdrawal of drug is avoided."

B. In May of 2000, Purdue received a report of a patient who said he or she was unable to stop taking OxyContin 10 mg every 12 hours without experiencing withdrawal symptoms. Executives also learned that "this type of question, patients not being able to stop OxyContin without withdrawal symptoms ha[d] come up quite a bit ... in Medical Services lately (at least 3 calls in the last 2 days)."

C. In February 2001, Purdue received a review of the accuracy of the withdrawal data in the osteoarthritis study that listed eleven study patients who reported adverse experience due to possible withdrawal symptoms during the study's respite periods and stated "[u]pon a review of all comments for all enrolled patients, it was noted that multiple had comments which directly stated or implied that an adverse experience was due to possible withdrawal symptoms." Even after receiving this information, on March

28, 2001, supervisors and employees decided not to write up the findings because of a concern that it might "add to the current negative press."

D. Supervisors and employees stated that while they were well aware of the incorrect view held by many physicians that oxycodone was weaker than morphine, they did not want to do anything "to make physicians think that oxycodone was stronger to or equal to morphine" or to "take any steps in the form of promotional materials, symposia, clinicals, publications, conventions, or communications with the field force that would affect the unique position that OxyContin ha[d] in many physicians['] mind[s]."

3. Purdue sales representatives, while promoting and marketing OxyContin, falsely told health care providers that the statement in the OxyContin package insert that "[d]elayed absorption, as provided by OxyContin tablets, is believed to reduce the abuse liability of a drug," meant that OxyContin did not cause a "buzz" or euphoria, caused less euphoria, had less addiction potential, had less abuse potential, was less likely to be diverted than immediate-release opioids, and could be used to "weed out" addicts and drug seekers.

The statement was later amended to read, "[d]elayed absorption, as provided by OxyContin tablets, when used properly for the management of pain, is believed to reduce the abuse liability of a drug." Nevertheless, Purdue continued to market OxyContin in the same manner as described above.

Purdue supervisors and employees took part in the misbranding in the following ways:

A. Supervisors instructed Purdue sales representatives to use the reduced abuse liability statement and the amended statement to market and promote OxyContin.

B. Supervisors told Purdue sales representatives they could tell health care providers that OxyContin potentially creates less chances for addiction than immediate-release opioids.

C. Supervisors trained Purdue sales representatives and told some health care providers that it was more difficult to extract the oxycodone from an OxyContin tablet for the purpose of intravenous abuse, although Purdue's own study showed that a drug abuser could extract approximately 68% of the oxycodone from a single 10 mg OxyContin tablet merely by crushing the tablet, stirring it in water, and drawing the solution through cotton into a syringe.

D. By March 2000, Purdue had received reports of OxyContin abuse and diversion occurring in different communities but allowed sales staff to continue promoting and marketing OxyContin in this manner.

The case was investigated by the Virginia Attorney General's Medicaid Fraud Control Unit; Food and Drug Administration, Office of Criminal Investigations; Internal Revenue Service Criminal Investigation; the Department of Health and Human Services Office of Inspector General; Department of Labor, Office of Inspector General; Defense Criminal Investigative Service; Virginia State Police; and West

Virginia State Police. The case was prosecuted by Assistant United States Attorneys Rick Mountcastle, Randy Ramseyer and Sharon Burnham and U.S. Department of Justice, Office of Consumer Litigation, Trial Attorneys Barbara Wells and Elizabeth Stein.

END

## GLOSSARY

**opioid:** any drug derived from the seeds of the opium poppy, or any synthetic drug based on this chemical formula

**oxycodone:** the active ingredient in OxyContin, one of several drugs derived from the opium poppy

**Schedule II drug:** under the federal Controlled Substances Act, this class of drugs is the most addictive among those that have some medicinal value

**withdrawal:** the process of stopping use of some drugs, during which the individual experiences strong mental (often anxiety) and physical symptoms

## Document Analysis

These two documents elucidated the settlement between the U.S. government and Purdue Fredrick Company/Purdue Pharma and three of its executives. The statement by Brownlee was a descriptive account of the legal process and arguments, while the joint press release by Brownlee and Coy was comparatively more sensational in its summary of what was achieved (and by whom). In both documents it is made clear that many individuals working at Purdue, including some of its top executives, had misled health professionals and members of the public as regards the addictive qualities of OxyContin. The case largely turned on the matter of dishonesty and misrepresentation: the company was not truthful in all its statements about the drug and mislead consumers in its marketing efforts.

Purdue lied about whether the drug could easily be misused and covered up the fact that the drug could quickly create dependency on the part of patients/users.

Brownlee clearly states that "Purdue's claims that OxyContin was less addictive and less subject to abuse and diversion were false." As he asserted, all the promises made about the drug's safety were fabrications for the purposes of increasing sales. Although this case addressed company malfeasance during the period 1996–2001 (by the end of which Purdue made some changes to its marketing/labeling materials), the problems created by the drug's widespread use did not end then. Having outlined Purdue's effort "to defraud and mislead," Brownlee cited some of the results of the company's distribution of the drug. He stated that the large fines (over $600 million) imposed on Purdue should help "deter other companies" from taking similar actions.

In the press release by Brownlee and Coy, which is more clearly geared toward the media, the two began by clearly affirming there had been no medical research supporting the company's claim that OxyContin was safe for individuals, or that it had fewer addictive qualities and was less likely to be abused than other opioids. While not criticizing the FDA, the writers made clear that the FDA's dependence on a company's research data, rather than data derived from independent sources, was part of the problem. Individuals at Purdue, including the top executives, had not been truthful during the approval process in order to reap the benefits of massive sales in the medical marketplace. The news release then went on to praise various individuals involved in creating the legal case against the company.

The three aspects of the case against Purdue were (1) false statements about the abuse/euphoric effects of the drug; (2) the creation of a false article for a medical journal to undergird the company's arguments; and (3) claims about OxyContin being safe due to delayed absorption.

## Essential Themes

The basic assertion in the statements about this 2007 settlement between the federal government and Purdue Pharma was that individuals within Purdue had lied on the application submitted to the FDA to gain approval for Oxy-Contin, and that they had continued to lie for at least the first several years in which the drug was on the market. Although some information was revised after 2001, the effects of this case redounded widely within the medical community after it was publicized. Nevertheless, sales of OxyContin continued to be strong. According to the FDA, the level of sales in 2007 was higher than in any previous year. Even with the negative publicity surrounding OxyContin, sales continued to climb over the next four years and only in 2017 dropped back to about the same level as sales in 2007.

In their guilty pleas, the defendants recognized that serious problems had resulted from the company's fraudulent marketing campaign. It was observed that, because warning signs from patients and physicians had not been heeded, the company and its executives had played a substantial role in the growing opioid crisis nationwide over the preceding years. The press releases served as warnings not only to drug distributors and health care providers to rethink their use of OxyContin, but also to pharmaceutical manufacturers and their marketing departments to be sincere and honest in their claims.

*—Donald A. Watt, PhD*

## Bibliography and Additional Reading

Jones, James P. "Opinion and Order: United States of America v. The Purdue Frederick Company, Inc., et al." *The United States District Court for the Western District of Virginia, Abingdon Division.*" Abingdon, VA: US District Court: Western District of Virginia, July 23, 2007.

McGreal, Chris. *American Overdose: The Opioid Tragedy in Three Acts.* New York: Public Affairs, 2018.

Meier, Barry. "In Guilty Plea, OxyContin Maker to Pay $600 Million." *The New York Times,* May 10, 2007.

Meier, Barry. "Origins of an Epidemic: Purdue Pharma Knew Its Opioids Were Widely Abused." *The New York Times,* May 29, 2018.

Purdue Pharma L.P. "Better Understanding the Opioid Addiction Crisis." Stamford, CT: Purdue Pharma L.P., 2019.

Zee, Art Van. MD. "The Promotion and Marketing of OxyContin: Commercial Triumph,

Public Health Tragedy." (from *American Journal of Public Health*, 2009) *PMC: US National Library of Medicine.* Bethesda, MD: National Center for Biotechnology Information, 2019.

# APPENDIXES

# ■ Chronological List

# ■ Web Resources

**Cholera Online: A Modern Pandemic in Texts and Images U.S. National Library of Medicine.**

http://www.nlm.nih.gov/exhibition/cholera/index.html

**Harvard University's Collection on Contagion: Historical Views of Diseases and Epidemics**

http://ocp.hul.harvard.edu/contagion/cholera.html

# ■ Bibliography

"1951 Annual Report of Trudeau Sanatorium." *Trudeau Sanatorium—Historic Saranac Lake*, localwiki.org/hsl/Trudeau_Sanatorium. Accessed 20 Aug. 2020.

"2009 H1N1 Pandemic (H1N1pdm09 virus)." *US Centers for Disease Control and Prevention*, www.cdc.gov/flu/pandemic-resources/2009-h1n1-pandemic.html. Accessed 18 Aug. 2020.

Aberth, John. The Black Death: The Great Mortality of 1348-1350: a Brief History with Documents. Boston, MA: Bedford/St. Martin's, 2005. Print.

"About Jacob Riis." *Victorian Richmond Hill*. New York: Richmond Hill Chapter, Queens Hist. Soc., 1980. Web. 8 Apr. 2014.

Addison, James Thayer. *The Story of the First Gas Regiment*. Boston: Houghton Mifflin, 1919. Print.

Allen, Arthur. Vaccine: The Controversial Story of Medicine's Greatest Lifesaver. New York: W.W. Norton, 2007.

Altschuler, Eric L., and Aesha Jobanputra, "What Was the Cause of the Epidemic in Savannah in 1733?" *Journal of the Royal Society of Medicine*, vol.107, no. 12, 2014, pp. 468–473, *NIH*, www.ncbi.nlm.nih.gov/pmc/articles/PMC4265100/. Accessed 19 Aug. 2020.

"The American Lung Association Crusade: Early Research and Treatment of Tuberculosis in the 19th Century." *Historical Collections at the Claude Moore Heath Sciences Library, University of Virginia*. 2007, exhibits.hsl.virginia.edu/alav/tuberculosis/. Accessed 18 Aug. 2020.

Anbinder, Tyler. Five Points: *The Nineteenth Century New York City Neighborhood that Invented Tap Dance, Stole Elections, and Became the World's Most Notorious Slum*. New York: Simon, 2001. Print.

Baba, Mary. "Irish Immigrant Families in Mid-Late Nineteenth Century America." *Yale-New Haven Teachers Institute*. Yale-New Haven Teachers Inst., 1990. Web. 8 Apr. 2014.

Babington, Anthony. *Shell Shock: A History of the Changing Attitude to War Neurosis*. Wiltshire: Redwood Books, 1990. Print.

Baker, G. P. *Justinian: The Last Roman Emperor*. Cooper Square P, 2002.

Barkan, I.D. 1985. "Industry Invites Regulation: The Passage of the Pure Food and Drug Act of 1906." *American Journal of Public Health*. Vol. 75, No. 1, pp. 18-26.

Barnett, Ross, Graham Moon, Jamie Pearce, Lee Thompson, and Liz Twigg. *Smoking Geographies: Space, Place and Tobacco*. Hoboken, NJ: Wiley, 2017.

Barry, John M., *The Great Influenza: The Story of the Deadliest Pandemic in History*. Penguin Books, 2004.

Basu, Zachary. "Pompeo Says There's 'Enormous Evidence' Coronavirus Originated in Wuhan Lab." *Axios*, May, 2020, www.axios.com/pompeo-coronavirus-wuhan-lab-5f305526-9ceb-49af-943a-fd8291a6d5d9.html. Accessed 18 Aug. 2020.

Battaglia Ricci, Lucia. Boccaccio. Rome: Salerno Editrice, 2000.

Beecher, Lyman, and Harriet Beecher Stowe. The American Woman's Home; or, Principles of Domestic Science: Being a Guide to the Formation and Maintenance of Economical, Healthful, Beautiful, and Christian Homes. Boston: Brown, 1869. Print.

Beecher, Lyman. Six Sermons on the Nature, Occasions, Signs, Evils, and Remedy of Intemperance. New York: Amer. Tract Soc., 1827. Print.

Bell, Dean Phillip, editor. Plague in the Early Modern World. Routledge, 2019.

Bennett, William J. "National Drug Control Strategy." U.S. Department of Justice National Institute of Justice. Washington, DC: The White House, 1990.

Bergin, Thomas G. Boccaccio. New York: Viking, 1981.

Bergquist, James M. Daily Life in Immigrant America, 1820–1870. Chicago: Dee, 2008. Print.

Bergreen, Laurence. *Capone: The Man and the Era*. Simon and Schuster, 2013.

Billings, Molly. "The Influenza Pandemic of 1918." *Human Virology at Stanford*. Stanford University, Feb. 2005. Web. 31 Jan. 2014.

"The Biological Weapons Convention." *United Nations Office for Disarmament Affairs*, 2015. Web. 11 Mar. 2016.

Blumenthal, Karen. *Bootleg: Murder, Moonshine, and the Lawless Years of Prohibition*. Flash Point, 2011.

Boccaccio, Giovanni. The Decameron. Trans. G. H. McWilliam. New York: Penguin Books, 2003. Print.

Bordin, Ruth. Frances Willard: A Biography. Chapel Hill: University of North Carolina Press, 1986.

Böhm, Thomas, Thomas Jürgasch, & Andreas Kirchner. *Boethius as a Paradigm of Late Ancient Thought*. Berlin: De Gruyter, 2014. Print.

Brandt, Allan. *The Cigarette Century: The Rise, Fall, and Deadly Persistence of the Product That Defined America*. New York: Basic Books, 2009.

Brent, Allen. *Cyprian and Roman Carthage*. Cambridge UP. 2010.

Brewster, Jack. "A Timeline of the COVID-19 Wuhan Lab Origin Theory." *Forbes*, 24 May 2020, www.forbes.com/sites/jackbrewster/2020/05/10/a-timeline-of-the-covid-19-wuhan-lab-origin-theory/. Accessed 18 Aug. 2020.

Brooks, Adrian. *The Right Side of History: 100 Years of LGBTQ Activism*. Berkeley, CA: Cleis P, 2015. Print.

Bush, George H.W. "Presidential Address on National Drug Policy." C-SPAN. Washington, DC: National Cable Satellite Corporation, 2019.

Bynum, William F. "In Retrospect: On the Mode of Communication of Cholera." *Nature*. Springer Nature Limited, 13 Mar. 2013, www.nature.com/articles/495169a. Accessed 19 Aug. 2020.

Carrell, Jennifer Lee. The Speckled Monster: A Historical Tale of Battling Smallpox. New York: Plume, 2004.

Chadwick, Henry. *Boethius: The Consolations of Music, Logic, Theology and Philosophy*. Oxford: Clarendon, 1990. Print.

Chan, Margaret. "Who Director-General Briefs Executive Board on Zika Situation." WHO, World Health Organization. 28 Jan. 2016, www.who.int/dg/speeches/2016/zika-situation/en/. Accessed 20 Aug. 2020.

Chase, Marilyn. *The Barbary Plague: The Black Death in Victorian San Francisco*. Random House, 2003.

Cheever, Susan. My Name Is Bill—Bill Wilson: His Life and the Creation of Alcoholics Anonymous. New York: Washington Square Press, 2004.

"Childhood Lost: Child Labor during the Industrial Revolution." *Teaching with Primary Sources*. Eastern Illinois University, n.d. Web. 10 Apr. 2014.

Choi, Matthew. "Trump Puts Pence in Charge of Coronavirus Response." *Politico*, 26 Feb. 2020, www.politico.com/news/2020/02/26/

trump-puts-pence-in-charge-of-coronavirus-response-117790. Accessed 18 Aug. 2020.

Cilliers, Louise. *Roman North Africa: Environment, Society, and Medical Contribution.* Amsterdam UP. 2019.

Clark, Krissy with Kevin Sullivan, ed. "America's Drug War, Revealed." Reveal: The Center for Investigative Reporting. (Broadcast on Minnesota Public Radio's "The Uncertain Hour".) Emeryville, CA: The Center for Investigative Reporting, 2020.

Clark, Norman H. *Deliver Us from Evil: An Interpretation of American Prohibition.* W.W. Norton and Company, 1976.

Clegg, Brian. *The First Scientist: A Life of Roger Bacon.* New York: Carroll, 2003. Print.

"Congress Profiles | US House of Representatives: History, Art & Archives." *Congressional Profiles.* N.p., n.d. Web. 25 July 2016.

Conis, Elena. Vaccine Nation: America's Changing Relationship with Immunization. Chicago: University of Chicago Press, 2015.

Copeland, Jeffrey S. *Plague in Paradise: The Black Death in Los Angeles, 1924.* Paragon House, 2018.

Cosby, Alfred W. *America's Forgotten Pandemic: The Influenza of 1918.* Cambridge UP, 1989.

Coss, Stephen. The Fever of 1721: The Epidemic That Revolutionized Medicine and American Politics. New York: Simon & Schuster, 2016.

Courtwright, David T. Dark Paradise: A History of Opiate Addiction in America. Cambridge, MA: Harvard University Press, 2012.

Crawford, Dorothy H. *Deadly Companions: How Microbes Shaped Our History.* Oxford UP, 2007.

Daniel, Peter, and David Markoff. "Dr. John Snow and Reverend Whitehead." *Cholera and the Thames.* City of Westminster Archives, 2020, www.choleraandthethames.

co.uk/cholera-in-london/origins-of-cholera/. Accessed 19 Aug. 2020.

Daniel, Peter. "The Work of the London City Mission." *Cholera and the Thames.* City of Westminster Archives, 2020, www.choleraandthethames.co.uk/cholera-in-london/origins-of-cholera/. Accessed 19 Aug. 2020.

Daniels, Roger. Coming to America: A History of Immigration and Ethnicity in American Life. Princeton: Perennial, 2002. Print.

David Rosner, Ronald H. Lauterstein, Jerold M. Michael, "The National Board of Health: 1879–1883," *Public Health Reports*, Vol.126, no 1 (2011), 123-29.

Davies, Pete. *The Devil's Flu: The World's Deadliest Influenza Epidemic and the Scientific Hunt for the Virus that Caused It.* Henry Holt, 2000.

Davis, Mike. *Late Victorian Holocausts: El Nino Famines and the Making of the Modern World.* Verso, 2001.

Defoe, Daniel. *A Journal of the Plague Year.* Gutenberg e-book. Dec. 1995, www.gutenberg.org/files/376/376-h/376-h.htm.

De Ste. Croix, G.E.M. *Christian Persecution, Martyrdom, and Orthodoxy*, edited by Michael Whitby and Joseph Streeter, Oxford UP, 2006.

Dinnerstein, Leonard, and David M. Reimers. Ethnic Americans: A History of Immigration. New York: Columbia UP, 1999. Print.

Dorsey, Bruce. Reforming Men and Women: Gender in the Antebellum City. Ithaca: Cornell UP, 2002. Print.

Duffy, John. *Epidemics in Colonial America.* Louisiana State UP, 1953.

"Dwight D. Eisenhower: Life in Brief." *Miller Center of Public Affairs.* University of Virginia, n.d. Web. 25 Jan. 2016.

Eamon, William. "Of Puppies and Toads: Marvelous Cures for the Plague." 30 Nov. 2010, williameamon.com/?p=329. Accessed 14 July 2020.

"The Early Years." The Drug Enforcement Administration, May 2018. www.dea.gov/sites/default/files/2018–05/Early Years p 12–29.pdf.

Ebel, Carol. "Samuel Nunes (ca. 1667–ca. 1741)." *New Georgia Encyclopedia*. 5 Jan. 2017, www.georgiaencyclopedia.org/articles/history-archaeology/samuel-nunes-ca-1667-ca-1741. Accessed 3 July 2020.

Ecarma, Caleb. "Trump's China Coronavirus Conspiracy Is Infiltrating Intelligence Agencies." *Vanity Fair*, 30 Apr. 2020, www.vanityfair.com/news/2020/04/donald-trump-china-coronavirus-lab-conspiracy. Accessed 18 Aug. 2020.

Edelman, Adam. "Trump Says Coronavirus Risk to Americans 'Very Low,' Puts Pence in Charge of Gov't Response." *NBC News*, 26 Feb. 2020, www.nbcnews.com/politics/donald-trump/trump-says-coronavirus-risk-americans-very-low-administration-effectively-handling-n1143756. Accessed 18 Aug. 2020.

Erlen, Jonathon, Joseph F. Spillane, and Rebecca Carroll. Federal Drug Control: The Evolution of Policy and Practice. New York: Pharmaceutical Products Press, 2004.

Faderman, Lillian. *The Gay Revolution: The Story of the Struggle.* New York: Simon & Schuster, 2015. Print.

Faupel, Charles E., and Alan M. Horowitz, and Greg S. Wever. The Sociology of American Drug Use. 2nd ed. New York: Oxford University Press, 2010.

Fenn, Elizabeth A. Pox Americana: The Great Smallpox Epidemic of 1775–82. New York: Hill and Wang, 2002.

Fitzhugh Mullan, *Plagues and Politics: The Story of the United States Public Health Service* (New York: Basic Books, 1989).

Fleming, Rebecca. "Galen and the Plague." *Galen's Treatise* Περὶ Ἀλυπίας (De indolentia) *in Context*, edited by Caroline Petit, Brill, 2019, pp. 219–44.

France, David. How to Survive a Plague: The Story of How Activists and Scientists Tamed AIDS. New York: Vintage, 2017. Print.

Frank, Jeffrey. "When Ike Trusted a New Vaccine." *New Yorker*. Condé Nast, 4 Feb. 2015. Web. 25 Jan. 2016.

Freeman, Henry. The Black Death: A History from Beginning to End. North Charleston, SC: CreateSpace Independent Publishing Platform, 2016. Print.

Fries, Amos A., and Jay West. *Chemical Warfare*. New York: McGraw-Hill, 1921. Print. Google eBook. Web. 3 June 2014.

Galen. *Method of Medicine, Volume II: Books 5-9.* Edited and translated by Ian Johnston, G. H. R. Horsley. Loeb Classical Library 517. Harvard UP, 2011.

Gately, Iain. *Tobacco: A Cultural History of How an Exotic Plant Seduced Civilization*. New York: Grove Press, 2003.

Gatherer, Derek, and Alain Kohl, "Zika Virus: A Previously Slow Pandemic Spreads Rapidly through the Americas," *Journal of General Virology*, 2016, vol. 97, no. 2, pp. 269–73, doi.org/10.1099/jgv.0.000381. Accessed 19 Aug. 2020.

Gerson, Stéphane. Nostradamus: How an Obscure Renaissance Astrologer Became the Modern Prophet of Doom. St. Martin's P, 2012.

Gerstein, Daniel M. *National Security and Arms Control in the Age of Biotechnology: The Biological and Toxin Weapons Convention*. Lanham: Rowman, 2013. Print.

Gholipour, Bahar. "2009 Swine-Flu Death Toll 10 Times Higher Than Thought." *LiveScience*, 26 Nov. 2013, www.livescience.

com/41539-2009-swine-flu-death-toll-higher.html. Accessed 18 Aug. 2020.

Gifford, Carolyn, and Amy R. Slagell, eds. Let Something Good Be Said: Speeches and Writings of Frances E. Willard. Champaign: University of Illinois Press, 2007.

Gifford, Carolyn, ed. Writing Out My Heart: Selections from the Journal of Frances E. Willard, 1855–96. Champaign: University of Illinois Press, 1995.

Gill, Christopher, et al., editors. *Galen and the World of Knowledge*. Cambridge UP, 2010.

Goldblat, Jozef. "The Biological Weapons Convention: An Overview." *International Review of the Red Cross. Intl. Committee of the Red Cross*, 30 June 1997. Web. 11 Mar. 2016.

Gonzenbach, William J. The Media, the President and Public Opinion: A Longitudinal Analysis of the Drug Issue, 1984–1991. (Routledge Communication Series.) Abingdon UK: Routledge, 2013.

Gottlieb, Anthony. *The Dream of Reason: A History of Philosophy from the Greeks to the Renaissance*. New York: Norton, 2000. Print.

Grant, Edward. *The Foundations of Modern Science in the Middle Ages: Their Religious, Institutional, and Intellectual Contexts*. New York: Cambridge UP, 1996. Print.

Gum, Samuel A. "Philadelphia Under Siege: The Yellow Fever of 1793." *The Pennsylvania Center for the Book*. Penn State U Libraries, 2010, www.pabook.libraries.psu.edu/literary-cultural-heritage-map-pa/feature-articles/philadelphia-under-siege-yellow-fever-1793. Accessed 18 Aug. 2020.

Gusfield, Joseph R. Symbolic Crusade: Status Politics and the American Temperance Movement. Champaign: University of Illinois Press, 1986.

Hackett, Jeremiah, ed. *Roger Bacon and the Sciences*. New York: Brill, 1997. Print.

Hamm, Richard F. Shaping the Eighteenth Amendment: Temperance Reform, Legal Culture, and the Polity, 1880–1920. Chapel Hill: U of North Carolina P, 1995. Print.

Handlin, Oscar. The Uprooted: The Epic Story of the Great Migrations That Made the American People. Philadelphia: U of Pennsylvania P, 2002. Print.

Hansler, Jennifer, and Nicole Gaouette. "Pompeo Admits the US Can't Be Certain Coronavirus Outbreak Originated in Wuhan Lab." *CNN*, 6 May 2020, www.cnn.com/2020/05/06/politics/pompeo-wuhan-lab/index.html. Accessed 18 Aug. 2020.

Hanson, Chad. "The Big Thames Clean Up." *Cholera and the Thames*. City of Westminster Archives, 2020, www.choleraandthethames.co.uk/cholera-in-london/origins-of-cholera/. Accessed 19 Aug. 2020.

Harper, Kyle. *The Fate of Rome: Climate, Disease, and the End of an Empire*. Princeton UP. 2017.

Haynes, Norrisa, et al. "At the Heart of the Matter: Unmasking and Addressing the Toll of COVID-19 on Diverse Populations," *Journal of American Heart Association*, vol. 42, no. 2, 14 July 2020, pp. 105–07, org/10.1161/CIRCULATIONAHA.120.048126. Accessed 18 Aug. 2020.

"Health Equity Considerations and Racial and Ethnic Minority Groups," *Centers for Disease Control and Prevention*, 24 July 2020, www.cdc.gov/coronavirus/2019-ncov/community/health-equity/race-ethnicity.html. Accessed 18 Aug. 2020.

Hempel, Sandra. *The Medical Detective: John Snow, Cholera and the Mystery of the Broad Street Pump*. Granta Books, 2007.

Hennessey, Morgan, et al. "Zika Virus Spreads to New Areas—Region of the Americas, May 2015–January 2016," Centers for Disease Control and Prevention, *Morbidity and Mortality Weekly Report*, 29 Jan. 2016, vol. 65, no. 3, pp. 55–58, www.cdc.gov/mmwr/volumes/65/wr/mm6503e1.htm. Accessed 19 Aug. 2020.

Henry, Stuart. Unvanquished Puritan: A Portrait of Lyman Beecher. Grand Rapids: Eerdmans, 1973. Print.

Hersey, John. *Hiroshima.* New York: Knopf, 1946. Print.

Hipp, Daniel. *The Poetry of Shell Shock: Wartime Trauma and Healing in Wilfred Owen, Ivor Gurney, and Siegfried Sassoon.* Jefferson, NC: McFarland, 2005. Print.

Hippocrates. Delphi *Complete Works of Hippocrates.* East Sussex, UK: Delphi Classics, 2015. Kindle file.

"History." *Trudeau Institute.* trudeauinstitute.org/history. Accessed 18 Aug. 2020.

*History Editors.* "Cholera." *History.com.* A&E Television Networks, 24 Mar. 2020, www.history.com/topics/inventions/history-of-cholera. Accessed 19 Aug. 2020.

Hoffman, Jan. "How Anti-Vaccine Sentiment Took Hold in the United States." New York Times, September 23, 2019.

Hogan, Michael J., ed. *Hiroshima in History and Memory.* New York: Cambridge UP, 1996. Print.

Holland, Steve, and David Brunnstrom. "Trump Says U.S. Investigating Whether Virus Came from Wuhan Lab." *U.S. News and World Report*, 15 Apr. 2020, www.usnews.com/news/world/articles/2020-04-15/trump-says-us-investigating-whether-virus-came-from-wuhan-lab. Accessed 18 Aug. 2020.

Honigsbaum, Mark. *The Pandemic Century: One Hundred Years of Panic, Hysteria, and Hubris.* W.W. Norton, 2019.

Horrox, Rosemary, ed. The Black Death. Manchester: Manchester University Press, 1994. Print.

Hotaling, Mary. *A Rare Romance in Medicine: The Life and Legacy of Edward Livingston Trudeau.* Utica, North Country Books, 2016.

Houston, Dr. W. R. "The Doctor Himself as a Therapeutic Agent." *The Annals of Internal Medicine* 11 (1938): 1416–1425.

Institute of Medicine (US) Committee for the Substance Abuse Coverage Study; Gerstein D.R., Harwood H.J., eds. Treating Drug Problems: Volume 2: Commissioned Papers on Historical, Institutional, and Economic Contexts of Drug Treatment. A Century of American Narcotic Policy. Washington, DC: National Academies Press, 1992.

Jepsen, Jorgen. Reviewed Work: "Drug Addiction—Crime or Disease? By the ABA and the AMA Joint Committee on Narcotic Drugs." The Journal of Criminal Law, Criminology, and Police Science 53. no. 1 (1962): 76–78.

John Hudak. Marijuana: A Short History. Washington, DC: Brookings Institute Press, 2016.

Johnson, Dennis R. 1982. "The History of the 1906 Pure Food and Drug Act and the Meat Inspection Act." *Food Drug Cosmetic Law Journal.* Vol. 37, pp. 5-9.

Jones, Edgar, and Simon Wessely. *Shell Shock to PTSD: Military Psychiatry from 1900 to the Gulf War.* East Sussex: Psychology Press, 2005. Print.

Jones, James P. "Opinion and Order: United States of America v. The Purdue Frederick Company, Inc., et al." The United States District Court for the Western District of Virginia, Abingdon Division." Abingdon, VA: US District Court: Western District of Virginia, July 23, 2007.

Jones, Maldwyn A. Destination America. London: Weidenfeld, 1976. Print.

Jonnes, Jill. Hep-Cats, Narcs, and Pipe Dreams: A History of America's Romance with Illegal Drugs. Baltimore: Johns Hopkins University Press, 1999.

Jouanna, Jacques. *Greek Medicine from Hippocrates to Galen: Selected Papers.* Boston: Brill, 2012. Print.

Kay, Gwen. Dying to Be Beautiful: The Fight for Safe Cosmetics. Columbus: Ohio State University Press, 2005.

Kaylor, Noel Harold, & Phillip Edward Phillips. *A Companion to Boethius in the Middle Ages.* Leiden: Brill, 2012. Print.

Kelaidis, Katherine. "What the Great Plague of Athens Can Teach Us Now." *The Atlantic,* 23 Mar. 2020, www.theatlantic.com/ideas/archive/2020/03/great-plague-athens-has-eerie-parallels-today/608545/. Accessed 18 Aug. 2020.

Kelly, John. The Great Mortality: An Intimate History of the Black Death, the Most Devastating Plague of All Time. New York: Harper Perennial, 2006. Print.

Kenneth B. Nunn. "Race, Crime and the Pool of Surplus Criminality: Or Why the War on Drugs Was a War on Blacks," Journal of Gender, Race and Justice 381 (2002). https://scholarship.law.ufl.edu/faculty-pub/107/.

Kent, Susan K. *The Influenza Pandemic of 1918–1919.* Boston: Bedford, 2012. Print.

Kingston, William. "Streptomycin, Schatz v. Waksman, and the Balance of Credit for Discovery." *Journal of the History of Medicine and Allied Sciences,* vol. 59, no. 3, 2004, pp. 441–62. JSTOR, www.jstor.org/stable/24632177. Accessed 19 Aug. 2020.

Kort, Michael. *Columbia Guide to Hiroshima and the Bomb.* New York: Columbia UP, 2007. Print.

Krishnakumar, Priya, and Soumya Karlamangla. "How Stricter Vaccine Laws Spared California from a Major Measles Outbreak." Los Angeles Times, May 6, 2019.

Kurtz, Ernest. Not God: A History of Alcoholics Anonymous. Center City, MN: Hazelden, 1991.

Lardieri, Alexa. "Trump to Hold Press Conference on Coronavirus." *US News and World Report.* 26 Feb. 2020, www.usnews.com/news/politics/articles/2020-02-26/donald-trump-to-hold-press-conference-on-coronavirus-threat-in-us. Accessed 18 Aug. 2020.

Lemon, Johanna, and Peter Daniel. "Milbank Prison." *Cholera and the Thames.* City of Westminster Archives, 2020, www.choleraandthethames.co.uk/cholera-in-london/origins-of-cholera/. Accessed 19 Aug. 2020.

Lerner, Adrienne. 2011. "Pure Food and Drug Act of 1906". *Food: In Context.* Vol. 2.

Little, Lester K. *Plague and the End of Antiquity: The Pandemic of 541–750.* Cambridge UP, 2008.

Littman, R. J., and M. L. Littman. "Galen and the Antonine Plague." *The American Journal of Philology,* vol. 94, no. 3, 1973, pp. 243–55. JSTOR, www.jstor.org/stable/293979. Accessed 19 Aug. 2020.

Lubove, Roy. *The Progressives and the Slums: Tenement House Reform in New York City, 1890–1917.* Pittsburgh: U of Pittsburgh P, 1963. Print.

Mallea, Paula. The War on Drugs: A Failed Experiment. Toronto: Dundurn Press, 2014.

Marciniak, Kristin. *The Flu Pandemic of 1918.* Minneapolis: ABDO, 2014. Print.

Markel, Howard. *Quarantine! East European Jewish Immigrants and the New York City Epidemics of 1892.* Baltimore: Johns Hopkins UP, 1999. Print.

"Mary van Kleeck Papers, 1849–1998: Biographical Note." *Sophia Smith Collection.* Smith College, n.d. Web. 10 Apr. 2014.

Mattern, Susan P. *The Prince of Medicine: Galen in the Roman Empire*. Oxford UP. 2013.

Mattingly, Carol. Well-Tempered Women: Nineteenth- Century Temperance Rhetoric. Carbondale: Southern Illinois UP, 2000. Print.

McAdoo, William G. *Crowded Years: The Reminiscences of William G. McAdoo*. Houghton Mifflin, 1931.

McGirr, Lisa. *The War on Alcohol: Prohibition and the Rise of the American State*. W.W. Norton and Company, 2015.

McGowan, Jeffrey. *Major Conflict: One Gay Man's Life in the Don't-Ask-Don't-Tell Military.* New York: Broadway Books, 2007. Print.

McGowan, Philip. "AA and the Redeployment of Temperance Literature." Journal of American Studies 48, no. 1 (2014): 51–78.

McGreal, Chris. American Overdose: The Opioid Tragedy in Three Acts. New York: Public Affairs, 2018.

McNeely, Ian F. *"Medicine on a Grand Scale." Rudolf Virchow, Liberalism and the Public Health*. Wellcome Trust Centre for the History of Medicine at U College, London, 2002.

McNeill, William H. *Plagues and Peoples*. Anchor, 1976.

Meacham, Jon. Destiny and Power: The American Odyssey of George Herbert Walker Bush. New York: Random House, 2015.

Meares, Hadley. "When the Plague Came to Los Angeles." Curbed- Los Angeles. 9 Apr. 9, 2020, la.curbed.com/2020/4/9/21211280/quarantine-plague-los-angeles-mexican-district. Accessed 18 Aug. 2020.

Meier, Barry. "In Guilty Plea, OxyContin Maker to Pay $600 Million." The New York Times, May 10, 2007.

Meier, Barry. "Origins of an Epidemic: Purdue Pharma Knew Its Opioids Were Widely Abused." The New York Times, May 29, 2018.

Mena, Ignacio, et al. "Origins of the 2009 H1N1 Influenza Pandemic in Swine in Mexico." *eLife*, vol. 5 e16777, 28 June 2016, www.ncbi.nlm.nih.gov/pmc/articles/PMC4957980/. Accessed 18 Aug. 2020.

Milov, Sarah. *The Cigarette: A Political History*. Cambridge, MA: Harvard University Press, 2019.

Mnookin, Seth. The Panic Virus: The True Story Behind the Vaccine-Autism Controversy. New York: Simon & Schuster, 2011.

Moote, Lloyd A. *The Great Plague: The Story of London's Most Deadly Year*. Johns Hopkins UP, 2006.

Mortimer, Ian. The Perfect King. New York: Vintage Books, 2008. Print.

Moses, Catherine. "The Making of Drug Policy in the George H.W. Bush and William J. Clinton Administrations: The Pursuit of Failure." Semanticscholar.org. Athens, GA: The University of Georgia, 2004.

Mullett, Charles F. *The Bubonic Plague and England: An Essay in the History of Preventive Medicine*. U of Kentucky P, 1956, pp. ix, 401.

Murch, Simon H. "Retraction of Lancet Paper on MMR Vaccine and Autism." The Lancet 363 (2004): 750.

Musto, David F. The American Disease: Origins of Narcotic Control. New York: Oxford University Press, 1999.

Myers, Martin G., and Pineda, Diego. Do Vaccines Cause That?!: A Guide for Evaluating Vaccine Safety Concerns. Galveston, TX: i4ph, 2008.

Nardinelli, Clark. *Child Labor and the Industrial Revolution*. Bloomington: Indiana UP, 1990. Print.

North, Robert L. "Benjamin Rush, MD: Assassin or Beloved Healer?" *NCBI Resources.* (Original in Proceedings: Baylor University Medical Center) US National Library of Medicine-National Institutes of Health, 2000, www.ncbi.nlm.nih.gov/pmc/articles/PMC1312212/. Accessed 18 Aug. 2020.

Offit, Paul A. Deadly Choices: How the Anti-Vaccine Movement Threatens Us All. New York: Basic Books, 2011.

Okrent, Daniel. *Last Call: The Rise and Fall of Prohibition.* Simon and Schuster, 2010.

Olorunnipa, Toluse, et al. "Trump Downplays Risk, Places Pence in Charge of Coronavirus Outbreak Response." *The Washington Post*, 26 Feb. 2020, www.washingtonpost.com/politics/trump-downplays-risk-places-pence-in-charge-of-coronavirus-outbreak-response/2020/02/26/ab246e94-58b1-11ea-9000-f3cffee23036_story.html. Accessed 18 Aug. 2020.

"Origins of Cholera." *Cholera and the Thames.* City of Westminster Archives, 2020, www.choleraandthethames.co.uk/cholera-in-london/origins-of-cholera/. Accessed 19 Aug. 2020.

Ormrod, W. Mark. Edward III. (The English Monarchs Series) New Haven: Yale University Press, 2013. Print.

Oshinsky, David M. *Polio: An American Story.* New York: Oxford UP, 2005. Print.

"Pandemic (H1N1) 2009." *World Health Organization.* www.who.int/csr/disease/swineflu/en/. Accessed 18 Aug. 2020.

Peckham, Robert. *Epidemics in Modern Asia.* Cambridge UP, 2016.

Peel, Mark, and Christina Twomey. *A History of Australia* 2nd ed. (Macmillan Essential Histories.) Palgrave, 2018.

Pembleton, Matthew R. Containing Addiction: The Federal Bureau of Narcotics and the Origins of America's Global Drug War. Amherst: University of Massachusetts Press, 2017.

Pepys, Samuel. *The Diary of Samuel Pepys: The Great Plague of London & The Great Fire of London, 1665–1666.* Benediction Classics, 2020.

Philip Jenkins. Decade of Nightmares: The End of the Sixties and the Making of Eighties America. New York: Oxford University Press, 2006.

Pinault, Jody Rubin. *Hippocratic Lives and Legends.* New York: Brill, 1992. Print.

Pompeo, Michael. "Secretary Pompeo Interview with Hugh Hewitt of the Hugh Hewitt Show." Interview by Hugh Hewitt. U.S. Dept. of State, 18 Apr. 2020, china.usembassy-china.org.cn/secretary-pompeo-interview-with-hugh-hewitt-of-the-hugh-hewitt-show/. Accessed 20 Aug. 2020

Porter, Stephen. *The Great Plague of London.* Amberley Publishing, 2012.

Porter, Stephen. *The Plagues of London.* The History P, 2008.

Powell, J. H. *Bring Out Your Dead: The Great Plague of Yellow Fever in Philadelphia in 1793.* Martino Publishing, 2016.

Power, Amanda. *Roger Bacon and the Defense of Christendom.* Cambridge: Cambridge UP, 2013. Print.

Price-Haygood, E.G. et al. "Hospitalization and Mortality among Black Patients and White Patients with Covid-19," *New England Journal of Medicine*, 2020, vol. 382, pp. 2534–43, doi:10.1056/NEJMsa2011686. Accessed 18 Aug. 2020.

Pringle, Peter. *Experiment Eleven: Dark Secrets Behind the Discovery of a Wonder Drug.* Walker & Company, 2012.

Procopius. *The Plague: History of the Wars II.xxii-xxxiii.* Medieval Sourcebook.

Fordham U, sourcebooks.fordham.edu/source/542procopius-plague.asp. Accessed 20 Aug. 2020.

Provine, Doris Marie. Unequal under Law: Race in the War on Drugs. Chicago: University of Chicago Press, 2007.

Purdue Pharma L.P. "Better Understanding the Opioid Addiction Crisis." Stamford, CT: Purdue Pharma L.P., 2019.

Putnam, Bertha Haven. The Enforcement of the Statutes of Labourers: During the First Decade after the Black Death: 1349-1359. New York: Columbia University, 1908. Web. 20 January 2017.

"Quarantine Act 1908." Federal Register of Legislation. Office of Parliamentary Council, 2020, www.legislation.gov.au/Series/C1908A00003. Accessed 18 Aug. 2020.

Raab, Selwyn. Five Families: The Rise, Decline, and Resurgence of America's Most Powerful Mafia Empires. Thomas Dunne Books, 2014.

Ralph Chester Williams, The United States Public Health Service, 1798-1950 (Washington, DC: Commissioned Officers Association of the United States Public Health Service, 1951).

Rasmussen, Cecilia. "In 1924 Los Angeles, a Scourge from the Middle Ages." The Los Angeles Times, 5 Mar. 2006, www.latimes.com/archives/la-xpm-2006-mar-05-me-then5-story.html. Accessed 20 Aug. 2020.

Ratia, Maura. "Investigating Genre through Title Pages: Plague Treatises of the Stuart Period in Focus." Studies in Variation, Contacts, and Change in English Varieng, vol. 14, Principles and Practices for the Digital Editing and Annotation of Diachronic Data. 2013, www.helsinki.fi/varieng/series/volumes/14/ratia/#sect3.4. Accessed 9 July 2020.

Reich, Jennifer A. Calling the Shots: Why Parents Reject Vaccines. New York: New York University Press, 2018.

Rimmerman, Craig A. Gay Rights, Military Wrongs: Political Perspectives on Lesbians and Gays in the Military. New York: Routledge, 2013. Print.

Rissanen, Jenni. "The Biological Weapons Convention." NTI. Nuclear Threat Initiative, 1 Mar. 2003. Web. 11 Mar. 2016.

Romo, Vanessa. "Trump Appoints Pence to Lead Government's Coronavirus Response." NPR, 26 Feb. 2020, www.npr.org/sections/health-shots/2020/02/26/809578063/trump-to-address-response-to-coronavirus. Accessed 18 Aug. 2020.

Rosen, William. Justinian's Flea: The First Great Plague and the End of the Roman Empire. Penguin, 2008.

Rothman, Sheila M. Living in the Shadow of Death: Tuberculosis and the Social Experience of Illness in American History. The Johns Hopkins UP, 1995.

Rush, Benjamin. "An Account of the Bilious Remitting Yellow Fever, as It Appeared in the City of Philadelphia, in the Year 1793." U.S. National Library of Medicine: Digital Collections. National Institutes of Health: National Library of Medicine, 2020, collections.nlm.nih.gov/bookviewer?PID=nlm:nlmuid-2569009R-bk#page/1/mode/2up. Accessed 18 Aug. 2020.

Rusten, J.S., editor Thucydides, The Peloponnesian War, Book II. Cambridge UP, 2008.

Sanger, David E. "Pompeo Ties Coronavirus to China Lab, Despite Spy Agencies' Uncertainty." The New York Times, 3 May 2020, www.nytimes.com/2020/05/03/us/politics/coronavirus-pompeo-wuhan-china-lab.html. Accessed 18 Aug. 2020.

Schaberg, William H. Writing the Big Book: The Creation of A.A. Las Vegas: Central Recovery Press, 2018.

Schaff, Philip, editor. "Treatise 7: On the Mortality." ANFO5. Fathers of the Third Century. www.ccel.org/ccel/schaff/anf05.iv.v.vii. html. Accessed 20 Aug. 2020.

Scherr, George H. *Why Millions Died: Before the War on Infectious Diseases.* UP of America, 2012.

Scourfield, J.H.D. "The *De Mortalitate* of *Cyprian*: Consolation and Context." *Vigiliae Christianae*, vol. 50, no. 1, 1996, pp. 12–41. *JSTOR*, www.jstor.org/stable/1584009. Accessed 19 Aug. 2020.

"Seasonal Influenza and Influenza A(H1N1)," *World Health Organization.* www.who.int/ith/diseases/si_iAh1n1/en/. Accessed 18 Aug. 2020.

Selinger, Reinhard. *The Mid-Third Century Persecutions of Decius and Valerian.* Peter Lang. 2004.

"Shell Shock and War Neuroses." *British Medical Journal* 2 (1918): 260.

Smith, William. An Emigrant's Narrative; or, A Voice from the Steerage. New York, 1850. Print.

Smoley, Richard. The Essential Nostradamus. Penguin, 2006.

Snow, John. *On the Mode of Communication of Cholera.* 2nd ed. John Churchill, 1855, *UCLA: Department of Epidemiology.* UCLA, Fielding School of Public Health, 2020, www.ph.ucla.edu/epi/snow/snowbook.html. Accessed 19 Aug. 2020.

Snowden, Frank M. *Epidemics and Society: From the Black Death to the Present.* Yale UP, 2019.

Special Correspondent. "From the Archives, 1919: First Flight from England to Australia." *The Sydney Morning Herald.* 2019, www.smh.com.au/national/from-the-archives-1919-first-flight-from-england-to-australia-20191107-p53895.html. Accessed 18 Aug. 2020.

Spinney, Laura, *Pale Rider: The Spanish Flu of 1918 and How it Changed the World.* Public Affairs Books, 2017.

State Library of South Australia. "Ross and Keith Smith Collection." *State Library of South Australia Digital Collections.* 2020, digital.collections.slsa.sa.gov.au/nodes/view/3613. Accessed 18 Aug. 2020.

Strassler, Robert, and Richard Crawley, editors. *The Landmark Thucydides: A Comprehensive Guide to the Peloponnesian War.* Simon and Schuster, 1998.

Surdich, Luigi. Boccaccio. Rome: Laterza, 2001.

Swift, Deborah. "Quackery and 17th Century Medicine." cryssabazos.com/2018/07/07/quackery-and-17th-century-medicine-by-deborah-swift-swiftstory-stuarts/. Accessed 14 July 2020.

Taylor, Rex, and Annelie Rieger. "Rudolf Virchow on the Typhus Epidemic in Upper Silesia: An Introduction and Translation." *Sociology of Health and Illness*, July 1984, Wiley Online Library, onlinelibrary.wiley.com/doi/full/10.1111/1467-9566.ep10778374. Accessed 18 Aug. 2020.

Tedlow, Richard S. "From Competitor to Consumer: The Changing Focus of Federal Regulation of Advertising, 1914–1938." The Business History Review 55, no. 1 (1981): 35–58.

Temin, Peter. "Government Actions in Times of Crisis: Lessons from the History of Drug Regulation." Journal of Social History 18, no. 3 (1985): 433–38.

Thompson, Hunter S. Fear and Loathing on the Campaign Trail '72. New York: Simon & Schuster, 2012.

Tieman, John Samuel. "The Origins of Twelve-Step Spirituality: Bill W. and Edward Dowling, S. J." U.S. Catholic Historian 13, no. 3 (1995): 121–35.

"A Timeline of COVID-19 Developments in 2020," *The American Journal of Managed Care*, 3 July 2020, www.ajmc.com/view/a-timeline-of-covid19-developments-in-2020. Accessed 18 Aug. 2020.

Tinker, Hugh. *South Asia: A Short History*. Frederick A Praeger, 1966.

Trudeau, Edward Livingston. *An Autobiography*. Doubleday, 1915.

Tucker, Jonathan B. *War of Nerves: Chemical Warfare from World War I to Al-Qaeda*. New York: Pantheon Books, 2006. Print.

Unger, Harlow Giles. *Dr. Benjamin Rush: The Founding Father Who Healed a Wounded Nation*. Da Capo P (Hachette Book Group), 2018.

United States. Bureau of the Census. Historical Statistics of the United States, 1785–1945. Washington: US Dept. of Commerce, 1949. Print.

"Update on the Zika Virus in the Americas," *Pan American Health Organization*, Provisional Agenda Item 7.6, CE158/INF/6, 20 May 2016, iris.paho.org/handle/10665.2/33749. Accessed 19 Aug. 2020.

Van Vugt, William E. Britain to America: Mid-Nineteenth- Century Immigrants to the United States. Chicago: U of Illinois P, 1999. Print.

Vilensky, Joel A., and Pandy R. Sinish. "Weaponry: Lewisite—America's World War I Chemical Weapon," *MHQ: The Quarterly Journal of Military History*. Weider History Network, 12 Jun. 2006. Web. 3 June 2014.

Vinten-Johansen, Peter, et al. *Cholera, Chloroform, and the Science of Medicine: A Life of John Snow*. Oxford UP, 2003.

Virchow, R.C., and L.J. Rather editors. *Collected Essays on Public Health and Epidemiology*, vol. 1. Science History Publications, 1985.

Virchow, Rudolf Carl. "Report on the Typhus Epidemic in Upper Silesia (1847–48)." *American Journal of Public Health*, vol. 96, no. 12, Dec. 2006, pp. 2102–105, doi: 10.2105/ajph.96.12.2102. Accessed 20 Aug. 2020.

Viseltear, A J. "The Pneumonic Plague Epidemic of 1924 in Los Angeles." *The Yale Journal of Biology and Medicine*, vol. 47, no.1 1974, pp. 40–54. *Semantics Scholar*, www.semanticscholar.org/paper/The-pneumonic-plague-epidemic-of-1924-in-Los-Viseltear/57de47cba187f116918ae452177b67507570d0b6. Accessed 18 Aug. 2020.

Wacker, Grant. Religion in Nineteenth Century America. New York: Oxford UP, 2000. Print.

Wadman, Meredith. The Vaccine Race: Science, Politics, and the Human Costs of Defeating Disease. New York: Penguin, 2017

Wainwright, Milton. "A Response to William Kingston, 'Streptomycin, Schatz v. Waksman, and the Balance of Credit for Discovery.'" *Journal of the History of Medicine and Allied Sciences*, vol. 60, no. 2, 2005, pp. 218–20. *PROJECT MUSE*, muse.jhu.edu/journals/jhm/summary/v060/60.2wainwright.html. Accessed 18 Aug. 2020.

Waitzkin, Howard. "One and a Half Centuries of Forgetting and Rediscovering: Virchow's Lasting Contributions to Social Medicine." *Classics in Social Medicine*. Albert Einstein College of Medicine, 2005, www.academia.dk/MedHist/Biblioteket/pdf/virchow_intro.pdf. Accessed 18 Aug. 2020.

Wakefield AJ, et al. "Ileal-lymphoid-nodular hyperplasia, non-specific colitis, and pervasive developmental disorder in children." Lancet. 1998; 351: 637–641.

Weisenberg, Elliot. "Rudolf Virchow, Pathologist, Anthropologist, and Social Thinker." *Hektoen International: A Journal of Medical Humanities*. Hektoen Institute of Medicine,

2009, hekint.org/2017/01/29/rudolf-virchow-pathologist-anthropologist-and-social-thinker/. Accessed 18 Aug. 2020.

"Whatever Happened to Polio?" *National Museum of American History.* Smithsonian Inst., n.d. Web. 25 Jan. 2016.

White, Christopher. The War on Drugs in the Americas. New York: Routledge, 2020.

Willard, Frances E. Women and Temperance; or, The Work and Workers of the Women's Christian Temperance Union. Hartford: Park, 1883. Print.

Williams, Gareth. Angel of Death: The Story of Smallpox. New York: Palgrave Macmillan, 2010.

Williams, Susan. Food in the United States, 1820s– 1890. Westport: Greenwood, 2006. Print.

Woodruff, H. Boyd. "Selman A. Waksman, Winner of the 1952 Nobel Prize for Physiology or Medicine." *Applied and Environmental Microbiology*, vol. 80, 2014, pp. 2–8, aem.asm.org/content/80/1/2. Accessed 18 Aug. 2020.

Young, James Harvey. "Food and Drug Regulation under the USDA, 1906–1940." Agricultural History 64, no. 2 (1990): 134–42.

Zee, Art Van. MD. "The Promotion and Marketing of OxyContin: Commercial Triumph, Public Health Tragedy." (from American Journal of Public Health, 2009) PMC: US National Library of Medicine. Bethesda, MD: National Center for Biotechnology Information, 2019.

Ziegler, Philip. The Black Death. New York: Harper Perennial Modern Classics, 2009. Print.

"Zika Virus Infection," *Pan American Health Organization*, Epidemiological Alert.7 May 2015, iris.paho.org/handle/10665.2/34232, Accessed 19 Aug. 2020.

Zinn, Howard. *A People's History of the United States: 1492 to Present.* New York: Harper, 2005. Print.

# ■ Index